Hi ~~XXXXXX~~ !

Don't Stu

Burgess

LIFE SCIENCE SERIES

Consulting Editors
ROBERT H. BURRIS, Biochemistry
HERMAN C. LICHSTEIN, Microbiology

MANOMETRIC TECHNIQUES

a manual describing methods
applicable to the study of
tissue metabolism

FOURTH EDITION, 1964

by

W. W. UMBREIT

R. H. BURRIS

J. F. STAUFFER

Chapters of Specialized Techniques by

M. J. JOHNSON, V. R. POTTER

AND W. C. SCHNEIDER

Contributions by

J. A. BAIN, H. BEINERT, P. P. COHEN,

H. F. DeLUCA, H. A. LARDY, G. A. LePAGE

AND G. A. PALMER

Burgess Publishing *Company*

426 South Sixth Street   Minneapolis 15, Minnesota

INTRODUCTION TO

Fourth Edition

It is now almost two decades since we first assembled the information on Manometry in a form usable to the beginner. These decades have seen an enormous expansion in metabolic studies, much beyond the two-fold increase traditionally expected per decade. Indeed, this expansion occurred in "related methods" rather than manometry, and has been reflected in the changing subjects treated in the various editions. The present edition thus reflects these changes, but it also begins the report of some new developments in manometry itself, that is, the first introduction of commercially available automatic recording devices for manometric measurements. As such, we expect changes in some of our approaches in this basic methodology. This edition, in spite of the intervening years, still has the same intent as the first edition: to place in the hands of the beginning graduate student the best methods suitable for his research, and to explain them to him in the clearest language we can employ.

We wish to thank all of the contributors sincerely, because this volume like those of the past is the result of a cooperative effort.

Permission to reproduce certain of the figures was kindly granted by: Dr. A. Lazarow and the C. V. Mosby Co. (figure 12); E. Machlett and Son (figures 16, 19, 29, 30 and 31); American Instrument Co. (figures 21, 26A and 32); Gilson Medical Electronics (figures 25, 26B, 35 and 40); The Mark Co. (figure 33); Roger Gilmont Instruments, Inc. (figure 34); Dr. M. Dixon and the Biochemical Journal (figure 42); Arthur H. Thomas Co. (figures 43, 44, 56 and 57); Central Scientific Co. (figure 45); Experimental Cell Research (figure 46); The Virtis Co. (figure 47); Ivan Sorvall, Inc. (figure 48); Gifford-Wood Co. (figure 49).

W. W. U.
R. H. B.
J. F. S.

CONTRIBUTORS

J. A. BAIN, Professor of Pharmacology, Emory University School of Medicine, Emory University, Atlanta, Ga.

H. BEINERT, Professor, Enzyme Institute

R. H. BURRIS, Professor of Biochemistry

P. P. COHEN, Professor of Physiological Chemistry

H. F. DeLUCA, Associate Professor of Biochemistry

M. J. JOHNSON, Professor of Biochemistry

H. A. LARDY, Professor of Biochemistry and Enzyme Institute

G. A. LePAGE, Professor of Biochemical Oncology, Stanford Research Institute, Menlo Park, Calif.

G. A. PALMER, Project Associate, Enzyme Institute

V. R. POTTER, Professor of Oncology

W. C. SCHNEIDER, Head, Nucleic Acids Section, Laboratory of Biochemistry, National Institutes of Health, National Cancer Institute, Bethesda, Md.

J. F. STAUFFER, Professor of Botany

W. W. UMBREIT, Professor of Bacteriology, Rutgers University, New Brunswick, N.J.

All contributors not designated otherwise are associated with the

University of Wisconsin, Madison, Wisconsin

TABLE OF CONTENTS

Chapter I
THE WARBURG
CONSTANT VOLUME RESPIROMETER

INTRODUCTION

Manometric methods for estimating exchange of gases have been used in the study of both chemical and biological reactions for generations. A wide variety of techniques have been employed and many types of apparatus have been developed. The type of respirometer which has met with widest use is commonly called the "Warburg" instrument, although, as pointed out by Warburg (1926), it was used before his adoption and modification of it. In essence the present instrument is derived from a "blood-gas manometer" described by Barcroft and Haldane (1902) or from that described by Brodie (1910). The respirometer is based on the principle that at constant temperature and constant gas volume any changes in the amount of a gas can be measured by changes in its pressure. As the apparatus is most commonly applied to measurements of oxygen uptake, we shall first describe its principles in terms of oxygen uptake and later consider other uses of the instrument.

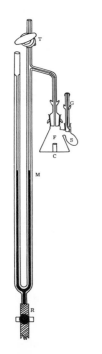

Figure 1
The Warburg constant
volume respirometer

APPARATUS

F = flask
S = sidearm
G = sidearm stopper with gas vent
C = center well (for alkali)
M = manometer proper
R = fluid reservoir; adjustment of the screw clamp alters the level of the fluid in the manometer
T = three-way stopcock

The scale of the manometer is graduated in centimeters (numbered) and in millimeters. Normally readings are recorded in millimeters to the nearest mm. or 0.5 mm.

The apparatus (fig. 1) consists of a detachable flask (F) sometimes equipped with one or more sidearms (S), attached to a manometer (M) containing a liquid of known density. The flask is immersed in a water bath at a constant temperature, and between readings the system is shaken to promote a rapid gas exchange between the fluid and the gas phase. It is assumed that the temperature of the manometer, which is not immersed, does not differ greatly from that of the flask. Details of the apparatus have been described by Burk and Milner (1932), Dixon (1951), Perkins (1943), Warburg (1923, 1924, 1926) and others. Further details of shaking apparatus will be found in Chapter 5.

The manometer shown in figure 1 has an open and a closed end. A reference point on the closed side of the manometer (usually 150 or 250 mm.) is chosen, and the liquid in the closed arm of the manometer is always adjusted to this point before recording pressure changes.

GENERAL PRINCIPLES

To measure an oxygen consuming reaction occurring in the flask, one turns the screw clamp on the fluid reservoir to adjust the manometer fluid to 250 mm. on the stopcock side of the manometer while the stopcock remains open. The stopcock then is closed, and the reading of the open arm of the manometer is recorded (assume that this is 249 mm. as in figure 2). After 10 minutes, the liquid has gone up in the closed arm and down in the open arm of the manometer as illustrated in the figure. One again adjusts the closed arm to 250 mm. and thus holds the volume of gas in the flask constant. The reading on the open arm now is 220 mm. For both the initial and 10 minute readings the fluid in the closed arm of the manometer was adjusted to 250 mm., but during the interval the reading on the open arm decreased from 249 to 220 mm. (29 mm.) as a result of oxygen consumption in the flask. If one knows the gas volume of the flask (V_g), the volume of fluid in the flask (V_f), the temperature of operation, the gas being exchanged, and the density of the fluid in the manometer, it is possible to calculate the amount of gas used up (or given off), providing only one gas is being changed. (There are methods to be described later for handling alterations in the amount of more than one gas.) (The essence of the method is to hold the gas and fluid volumes constant and to measure the decrease or increase in pressure when one gas alters in amount.)

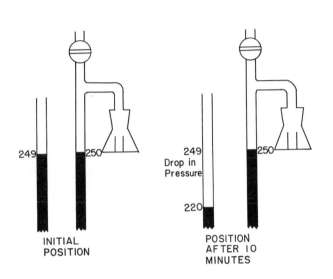

Figure 2
Diagram illustrating the determination
of pressure change

DERIVATION AND MEANING OF FLASK CONSTANT

Fundamentally this consists of so calibrating the system that from the observed pressure changes one can calculate the amount (in mm.^{3} or micro liters (μl) at 0°C. and 760 mm. pressure) of gas utilized or given off. The actual method for calibrating the apparatus will be described in Chapter 4.

The following symbols are employed:

Let h = the observed change in the manometer (open side) reading in mm.

$\quad\quad$ x = μl. gas (0°C., 760 mm. Hg pressure).

$\quad$ Vg = Volume of gas phase in flask including connecting tubes down to the reference point (150 or 250 mm. on closed arm of manometer).

$\quad$ Vf = Volume of fluid in vessel.

$\quad\quad$ P = Initial pressure in vessel of the gas involved in the determination. This is actually the partial pressure of the particular gas in a gas mixture. If this gas mixture contains water vapor, the partial pressure of gas involved in the determination will be less than its partial pressure in the dry condition. Hence if P is defined as dry gas, P - R should be used in equations involving moist gases.

$\quad$ P$_0$ = standard pressure, which is 760 mm. Hg or 10,000 mm. Krebs' or Brodie's fluid.

$\quad\quad$ T = Temperature of bath in absolute degrees (= 273+ temp. in °C.).

α = Solubility in reaction liquid of gas involved (expressed as ml.gas/ml. liquid when gas is at a pressure of 760 mm. Hg at the temperature T). Values for α are given on pages 5, 18 and 19.

R = Vapor pressure of water (or other fluid) at temperature T. The fluid in the flask will exert a vapor pressure (R) in the gas phase and some gas will dissolve in the fluid.

In the gas phase one has a volume of gas (V_g) at a temperature (T) and at a pressure P - R (P - R = partial pressure of gas involved less the vapor pressure of the fluid). This gas volume can be changed to standard conditions with the formula:

$$PV/T = P'V'/T'$$

(let prime symbols be standard conditions, i.e. V' = gas volume standard conditions, P' = P_0 = 760 mm. Hg, T' = 273 = 0°C.). Hence in the flask:

$$(P - R) \, V_g/T = P_0 V'/273$$

and gas at standard conditions = V' = $\dfrac{V_g \frac{273}{T}(P-R)}{P_0}$

Some gas is dissolved in the fluid initially. The amount of gas in the fluid is:

$$V_f \, \alpha (P - R)/P_0$$

Where α is the solubility of the gas (in ml. gas/ml. fluid) at a partial pressure of one atmosphere. The $(P - R)/P_0$ converts the solubility at one atmosphere to that actually existing in the flask.

This relationship holds, as Henry's law states, "The concentration of dissolved gas is directly proportional to the concentration (pressure) above the fluid." Hence if α is the solubility at P_0 (one atmosphere) the solubility at the actual pressure existing in the flask (P - R, atmospheric pressure less that due to water vapor) will be $\dfrac{\alpha (P - R)}{P_0}$.

Virtually nothing is known of the relationship between chemical structure and solubility of gases so that one has to determine the solubility empirically. There is thus a different solubility for each gas in each solution. (It is known, however, that the solubility of individual gases in a mixture is almost independent of the pressure of other gases,) i.e., the solubility of oxygen at a given pressure and at a given temperature will be the same whether N_2, CO_2 or other gases are present or not.

From the considerations above, the gas present at the start was that in the gas phase plus that in the fluid phase or:

$$\text{Gas at start} = V_g \, \frac{273}{T} \frac{(P - R)}{P_0} + V_f \, \alpha \, \frac{(P - R)}{P_0}$$

| Gas phase | | Fluid phase |

At the end of the observation period this gas has been changed by the amount x which has resulted in a pressure change of h mm. If gas is taken up, h is negative; if gas is given off, h is positive. We will here assume that it is taken up. The pressure is now $(P - R - h)$ rather than the initial value $(P - R)$.

$$\underline{\text{Gas phase is thus}}: \quad V_g \frac{273}{T} \frac{(P - R - h)}{P_o}$$

$$\underline{\text{Liquid phase}}: \quad V_f \, \alpha \, \frac{(P - R - h)}{P_o}$$

$$\underline{\text{Gas at end}} = V_g \frac{273}{T} \frac{(P - R - h)}{P_o} + V_f \, \alpha \, \frac{(P - R - h)}{P_o}$$

Gas taken up (x) is that which was present initially less that which appears at the end.

$$x = \text{initial gas} - \text{final gas}$$

$$x = \left[V_g \frac{273}{T} \frac{(P - R)}{P_o} + V_f \, \alpha \, \frac{(P - R)}{P_o} \right] - \left[V_g \frac{273}{T} \frac{(P - R - h)}{P_o} + V_f \, \alpha \, \frac{(P - R - h)}{P_o} \right]$$

$$= V_g \frac{273}{T} \frac{(P - R)}{P_o} + V_f \, \alpha \, \frac{(P - R)}{P_o} - V_g \frac{273}{T} \frac{(P - R - h)}{P_o} - V_f \, \alpha \, \frac{(P - R - h)}{P_o}$$

$$= V_g \frac{273}{T} \frac{h}{P_o} + V_f \, \alpha \, \frac{h}{P_o}$$

$$x = h \left[\frac{V_g \frac{273}{T} + V_f \, \alpha}{P_o} \right] = h \, k$$

Note that V_g, T, α, V_f and P_o are known and, for a given experiment, are constant; these values determine the flask constant k with which one can convert mm. pressure change into μl. gas taken up or evolved.

SUMMARY:

$$x = \text{amount of gas exchanged} = h \qquad\qquad k$$

                                                        alteration   flask constant
                                                        in reading
                                                        on open arm
                                                        of manometer

$$k = \text{flask constant} = \frac{V_g \frac{273}{T} + V_f \, \alpha}{P_o}$$

EXAMPLE: A Warburg flask has a total volume of 12.616 ml. up to the 250 mm. mark on the manometer. To measure oxygen uptake in this flask by yeast at 28° C., we add 1 ml. of yeast suspension, 1 ml. of 0.1 M glucose, 1 ml. of M/50 phosphate buffer. In the center cup of the flask we place 0.2 ml. 10% KOH to absorb the carbon dioxide the yeast may produce. What flask constant should be employed?

V_f = 3.2 ml. = 3,200 μl.

V_g = total volume - fluid volume = 12.616 ml. - 3.2 ml. = 9.416 ml. = 9,416 μl.

T = 273 + 28 = 301 α = 0.027 P_0 = 10,000

$$k_{O_2} = \frac{V_g \frac{273}{T} + V_f \, \alpha}{P_0} = \frac{9,416 \times \frac{273}{301} + 3,200 \times 0.027}{10,000} = \frac{8540 + 86.0}{10,000} = 0.863$$

Difference in pressure in mm. times 0.863 = μl. gas.

(Chapter 4 describes methods for determining the flask constants.)

Two points may be confusing. One, the choice of 0.027 for α, will be explained in the next section. The other is the use of P_0 = 10,000. The manometer in this case was filled with "Brodie's Solution" or a comparable manometer fluid (see p. 63). Such manometer fluids have a density of 1.033 compared to 13.60 for Hg so that:

$$P_0 = 760 \times \frac{13.60}{1.033} = 10,000$$

THE SOLUBILITY OF OXYGEN

The solubility of oxygen is expressed in Table 1 as ml. O_2/ml. fluid when the gas is at one atmosphere pressure. This term, α, is sometimes referred to as the "Bunsen Coefficient".

The α value of a particular gas is influenced by two factors. First, as is apparent from the values in Table 1, the solubility of gases decreases as the temperature rises. Second, the solubility of gases is appreciably diminished by the presence of dissolved solids (or liquids, but not gases) in the fluid. This is thought to be due to the hydration ("solvation") of the solute, which leaves less free solvent available for dissolving the gas. These effects are shown in Table 1 constructed from data in the International Critical Tables, Volume III, p. 271 (1928). Tables on the solubility of gases other than oxygen will be found in Chapter 4.

Table 1

The Solubility of Oxygen

Data as ml. gas dissolved per ml. fluid
when gas is at 1 atmosphere pressure, (α value).

Temperature °C.	Ringer's Solution	Water	2.0 N HCl	2.0 N H_2SO_4	2.0 M NaCl
0		0.04872			0.023
10	0.0480	0.03793			0.019
15	0.0340	0.03441	0.028		0.017
20	0.0310	0.03091			0.016
25	0.0285	0.02822	0.025	0.023	0.015
30	0.0260	0.02612			0.014
35	0.0245				
40	0.0230				
	Dixon (1943)	International Critical Tables (1928)			

Although the effect of salts on oxygen solubility appears large, it actually has little effect on flask constants for oxygen uptake. For example, a change from pure water to 2 M NaCl changes the α value from 0.028 to 0.016. This lowers the flask constant by $\dfrac{0.012 \times V_f}{10,000}$.

In the case described above, the k instead of being 0.863 would be, with 2 M NaCl, 0.859.

THE THERMOBAROMETER

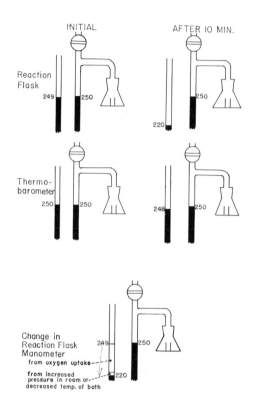

Figure 3
Diagrams illustrating the use
of the thermobarometer

In the development of the flask constant, k, a value P was employed which was assumed to remain constant from the beginning to the end of a given period. This "P" represented the initial atmospheric pressure. The pressure in the room and the temperature of the water bath are likely to change, however, and these changes are corrected for by a thermobarometer. The thermobarometer consists merely of a Warburg manometer with a flask containing water attached; the volume of the flask and the volume of water is not critical. However, a volume of water comparable to that in the reaction vessels usually is employed. Any change in the air pressure in the room will affect all manometers in the same way, even if the volumes of gas enclosed in the vessels differ. Likewise, any change in pressure resulting from a change in temperature will be the same for all vessels independent of their volumes.

Refer first to figure 3, initial, which represents the first reading; the reaction flask reads 249, the thermobarometer 250. At the end of a given period the reading on the reaction flask has dropped to 220, i.e., 29 mm. During the same time changes in the temperature of the bath or increased pressure in the room have caused the reading on the thermobarometer to drop to 248, i.e., 2 mm. The decrease in pressure observed in the reaction flask was due to two things: the use of some of the oxygen in the gas space inside the flask (27 mm.) and the external changes of temperature and pressure (2 mm.).

Correction of the readings obtained for changes registered by the thermobarometer are obvious after a brief study of Table 2 which illustrates actual experimental data.

If the level of liquid in the open arm of the thermobarometer has risen there has been a decrease in pressure in the room or an increase in temperature of the bath. For reaction flasks which have registered a drop in pressure the observed decrease is smaller than the actual decrease by the amount the thermobarometer fluid has risen; hence the rise in the thermobarometer reading is added to the observed pressure drop. If the reaction flasks have registered a rise in pressure, the increase in the thermobarometer reading is subtracted from this observed rise. Examples to illustrate these points are given in Tables 2 and 3.

Table 2

Corrections for Thermobarometer Changes

Time	Thermobarometer		Method 1 Respiring Flask #1			Method 2 Respiring Flask #1			
		Change (total)	Reading	Change	True Change	Reading	Chg. Interval	True Chg. Interval	Sum
0	250 mm.		249			249			
60	257 mm. (+7)	+7	248	-1	-8	248	-1	-8	-8
120 min.	259 mm. (+2)	+9	243	-6	-15	243	-5	-7	-15
0	250		249						
60	236	-14	111	-138	-124				

TEMPERATURE CONTROL

How accurately must the temperature of the bath be controlled? Two situations must be considered.

1. The whole bath is at a constant temperature but has dropped 1° below that accepted for calculation. The thermobarometer has responded to this drop in temperature so the main error involved arises from using the wrong flask constant. Suppose that in the case described in Table 3 the temperature throughout the bath dropped to 27°C. and the data were calculated for 28°C. At 28° the k_{O_2} is 0.942; at 27° it is 0.945. If the measurements are actually made at 27°C., but the factor for 28°C. is used, an error of about 0.3% is introduced.

2. If the bath is not uniform in temperature a flask at a point 1° C. higher in temperature than another flask would indicate a pressure corresponding to about 33 μl. of gas more per 10 ml. of gas volume (difference of 0.05° C. = 1.7 μl.)

Hence two factors are important; first, that the temperature be held at the point desired, and second and more important, that the temperature of the entire bath be held uniform to within 0.05° C. This latter factor necessitates vigorous stirring of the water in the bath.

THE USE OF THE WARBURG INSTRUMENT FOR THE MEASUREMENT OF RESPIRATION OF LIVING CELLS

Physiologically there are two meanings for the word "respiration". The older meaning confines the term to the actual uptake of gaseous oxygen. It was later realized that oxidations could occur (by the removal of hydrogen or electrons) without employing gaseous oxygen and so the term respiration was broadened to include any reaction by which the cell obtained energy, whether or not it involved gaseous oxygen as such. This has resulted in some confusion since the meaning of the term thus differs with various groups of investigators. For the purpose of this outline the following definitions are employed:

Respiration: The uptake of gaseous oxygen.
Fermentation: The transformations which occur in living cells (or enzymes therefrom) which do not employ gaseous oxygen.

In most cells, as contrasted to many enzyme preparations, the utilization of oxygen results in a release of carbon dioxide.(If these two gases (CO_2, O_2) are the only ones involved one can measure the respiration (O_2 uptake) by absorbing the liberated carbon dioxide in alkali. In the presence of alkali the carbon dioxide pressure in the air is zero within the limits of measurement. The gas exchange caused by the respiration is oxygen absorption plus carbon dioxide liberation. But the alkali keeps the carbon dioxide pressure zero, hence the change noted on the manometer is due solely to the oxygen utilization. The excess of carbon dioxide in solution, of course, continually distills over into the alkali, but it does not affect the observed pressure changes.)

SAMPLE CALCULATIONS

The data of Table 3 illustrate the method of calculating the μl. oxygen uptake from the observed changes in the level of the manometer fluid of the thermobarometer and of the reaction flask manometer. Two methods of calculation follow:

TOTAL UPTAKE METHOD:

The application of this method is illustrated in columns 4, 5, 6 and 7 of Table 3. The uptake in mm. is calculated by subtracting the initial reading (246) from all subsequent readings (column 4). The thermobarometer correction is obtained by subtracting the initial reading (265) from all subsequent readings (column 5). Since in the interval from 10^{55} to 11^{00} the total uptake of 19 mm. in the reaction flask was due in part (1 mm.) to thermal or barometric changes, the real uptake was 19 - 1 = 18 mm. (column 6). This value times the flask constant for the conditions employed gives the μl. oxygen taken up (column 7).

Table 3

Calculating Oxygen Uptake from Manometer Readings

Time	Reading, Thermo-barom-eter	Reading, flask	Total method				Interval method				
			Change, in mm.	Thermo-barometer correction	Actual change, in mm.	μl O_2 uptake	Change, in mm.	Thermo-barometer correction	Actual change, in mm.	μl. O_2 uptake	Sum
1	2	3	4	5	6	7	8	9	10	11	12
	mm.	mm.									
10^{55}	265	246	0	0	0	0	0	0	0	0	0
11^{00}	264	227	-19	-1	-18	17.0	-19	-1	-18	17.0	17.0
11^{05}	264	194	-52	-1	-51	48.1	-33	0	-33	31.1	48.1
11^{10}	264	159	-87	-1	-86	81.0	-35	0	-35	32.9	81.0
11^{15}	264	122	-124	-1	-123	115.9	-37	0	-37	34.9	115.9

Flask: 1 ml. yeast suspension, 1 ml. M/200 KH_2PO_4, pH 4.5, 0.5 ml. water, 0.5 ml. 0.032 M glucose; glucose in sidearm, tipped in at 10^{55}.

Volume flask = 13.5 ml.; k_{O_2} = 0.942   Temp. 28° C.; 0.2 ml. KOH in center cup.

INTERVAL UPTAKE METHOD:

This method is applied in the calculations shown in columns 8 to 12 of Table 3. Each reading is subtracted from the one following it (i.e., 246 from 227; 227 from 194, etc.) giving the change (column 8) over the interval. A similar calculation is made for the thermobarometer (column 9) from which the actual change (column 10) is readily apparent. These interval values are multiplied by the flask constant (column 11) to yield the uptake per interval and are added to yield the total uptake (column 12).

Although this method appears more laborious, it offers some advantages, especially when the rate of oxygen uptake is changing. In this case, for instance, the uptake during the first five minutes (17.0 μl.) is not the same as in the succeeding 5 minute intervals, for there is a tendency for the rate to increase throughout the determinations. This increase is not so readily apparent when calculated by the "total method" and may even be overlooked in graphing.

Many laboratories have found it convenient to employ mimeographed or printed tabular forms for recording manometric data. The data may be recorded there permanently or temporarily before transfer of pertinent information to a permanent notebook. Two examples of such data sheets are shown in Fig. 4. The upper section is a reproduction of a form which is printed on the back of 8-1/2 x 11 inch graph paper and spirally bound into a notebook. Data are recorded and calculated on the printed sheet, and the results are plotted on the opposite sheet of graph paper. The readings for any one flask are recorded horizontally across the page. In the lower portion of Fig. 4 is shown a mimeographed sheet on which data for each flask are recorded in vertical columns.

It is convenient to record flask constants on a card and to secure the card inside the front or back cover of the notebook by means of a Scotch tape hinge. The card can then be flipped over, so that it projects beyond the cover of the book, where it can be referred to readily during the calculation of results.

THE ABSORPTION OF OXYGEN

The absorption of oxygen by the respiring tissue takes place almost entirely from the oxygen in solution. This is the principle reason for shaking the fluids in the respirometer, i.e., to obtain a fluid phase saturated with the gas phase. But one must, under practical circumstances, take care that the rate of oxygen uptake by the tissue is not greater than can be replaced by the diffusion of oxygen from the atmosphere into the fluid. If the rate of oxygen uptake is so high that the oxygen is used up faster than it can diffuse into the liquid, then the rate of respiration observed is dependent upon the rate at which oxygen diffuses into the fluid and has little to do with the potential rate of the reaction itself.

The rate at which gas diffuses into a liquid is dependent upon the surface layer of the liquid. The gas may be thought of as moving across a film of surface, and the theory of such diffusion has been well worked out. Roughton (1941) has described methods for correcting for diffusion errors when they exist. However, for virtually all respiratory measurements it is sufficient to note that by shaking the flasks a continual new surface is exposed to the gas by virtue of the turbulence of the fluid in the flask. Hence, the greater the rate of shaking, the greater the rate of diffusion of the gas into the liquid, and the greater the rate of respiration one may measure without diffusion errors.

Dixon and Tunnicliffe (1923) and Dixon and Elliott (1930) have studied these effects in the Barcroft differential manometer (see Chapter 6) and have concluded that 600-700 μl. O_2

Title: Run No.:

Date: Temp.:   Contents of inner well: Gas phase:

No.	Flask Contents	Time; Reading in mm.; Change in mm.; Gas change in c. mm.
1		
2		
3		
4		
5		
6		
7		
8		
9		
10		
11		
12		
13		
14		
15		
16		
17		
18		
19		
20		

Signed ....

Prep: pH: Temp: Date: Noteb: Page:

Flask	T.B.						
In cup							
Side 1							
"2/well		/	/	/	/	/	/	/
K_____							

Time	Int.	A	△	A	B	C	D	A	B	C	D	A	B	C	D	A	B	C	D	A	B	C	D	A	B	C	D	A	B	C	D

10471M

Figure 4
Forms for recording manometric data

per hour can be safely measured without diffusion errors when a shaking rate of 100 oscillations per minute is employed (over 1500 µl. O_2/hr. at a rate of 138 oscillations per minute). Myers and Matsen (1955) have presented a detailed analysis of the kinetics of gas exchange in the Warburg respirometer.

In the Warburg respirometer the flasks used are usually smaller than those of the Barcroft respirometer, so the surface exposed to the gas is less; hence, limiting rates of oxygen uptake are reached sooner. The actual rates measurable without errors arising from gas diffusion in flasks of approximately 15 ml. volume containing 3 ml. of fluid have been determined in the experiment described below. This illustrates one method for determining whether the rate of oxygen diffusion is the limiting factor in any results one might obtain (Fig. 5).

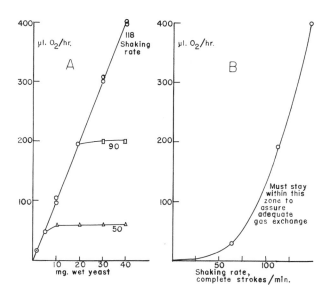

Figure 5
Influence of shaking on rate of oxygen uptake in flasks of about 15 ml. capacity. Section A - Each flask has amount of yeast indicated on abscissa made to 2 ml. with 0.02 M KH_2PO_4 (pH 4.8), 1 ml. of 3% glucose; 0.2 ml. 20% KOH in center well. Shaken at 50, 90 and 118 complete two-centimeter strokes per minute at 28°C. Section B - Data from Section A plotted to show adequate shaking rate for conditions described

The basis of the experiment described is as follows: the rate of oxygen diffusion from the gas phase into the fluid phase is dependent upon the surface boundary. This boundary is altered more rapidly with faster shaking allowing more rapid oxygen exchange. If more rapid shaking (and thus more rapid oxygen exchange) does not increase the rate of oxygen uptake, then the rate of oxygen diffusion is not the limiting factor in the system being studied.

Another principle which may be used (but only in certain circumstances) depends upon the fact that the higher the concentration of the gas the greater will be its rate of diffusion into a liquid. Hence, one can vary the percentage oxygen in the atmosphere above the liquid, use various quantities of tissue, and determine the maximum rate of oxygen uptake that can be achieved before diffusion factors become significant. This method is, however, not only more laborious but also more complex, for there are reports that some types of respiration are affected by the pressure of oxygen, per se. Therefore changing the shaking rate is the preferred method. Increasing the oxygen pressure is useful, however, when one finds it necessary to supply adequate concentrations of oxygen throughout a solid tissue. In this case the diffusion into the liquid is not the limiting factor, but diffusion into the respiring solid controls the oxygen level at its center. Obviously increased shaking will not alter these surfaces, so that the only practical solution is to increase the oxygen pressure. This is discussed under "tissue slices" in Chapter 8.

It sometimes happens that a reaction is dependent upon a contact between particles and that shaking disturbs this contact. One such example reported is the sulfur oxidation by bacteria (Vogler, LePage and Umbreit, 1942) in which a contact between the bacteria and the solid sulfur particles is necessary before oxidation can occur (Vogler and Umbreit, 1941, Umbreit, Vogel and Vogler, 1942). Shaking at rapid rates actually disturbs such contact and results in lowered oxidation. However, it is notable that if one employs rates of oxygen uptake lower than those at which limited diffusion becomes significant (i.e., at 100 strokes per minute, 300 µl. O_2/hr.) any variation in the rate of oxygen uptake with increase in shaking rate is not dependent upon the diffusion of oxygen since the fluid is already saturated. Therefore it is always desirable to determine the effect of alterations in the shaking rate to be certain that the results are independent of the rate of shaking. If they are not, one can readily determine whether the shaking rate is affecting the diffusion of oxygen or other factors (such as contact) by comparison with the rate of oxygen uptake which can be measured without diffusion effects under the conditions employed. Frequently important clues as to the nature of the reactions involved are obtained in this way.

THE ABSORPTION OF CARBON DIOXIDE

In the "direct method" of Warburg the oxygen uptake by living tissues, which also liberate CO_2, is measured by absorbing the CO_2 continuously in alkali during the determination. If the alkali employed fails to absorb the CO_2 completely and instantaneously, the CO_2 pressure in the gas phase will not be zero, and the readings on the manometer will not represent the true oxygen uptake. An example of circumstances of this type is given in the report of Brock, Druckrey, and Richter (1939); they observed that because of the large amounts of CO_2 liberated, readings on the manometer dropped only slightly or in some instances actually rose, yet oxygen was being consumed at a rapid rate. These workers found that the absorption of CO_2 was virtually instantaneous and that its pressure was held at approximately zero if the rate of CO_2 liberation was not more than 600 µl. per hour. Dixon and Elliott (1930) found that in the Barcroft apparatus (in the presence of adequate surface, see below) 1000 µl. of CO_2 per hour was almost instantaneously absorbed. Myers and Matsen (1955) also have examined the problem of CO_2 absorption in respirometers.

In absorbing CO_2 from the gas phase the same difficulties are encountered as in the absorption of oxygen. Here, however, because alkali is usually confined to the small center cup, an increased rate of shaking has little effect on increasing the surface. Hence some other method must be employed to increase the surface of the alkali. Usually small rolls or accordion folded pieces of filter paper are placed in the alkali cup. These should project above the side walls of the center cup into the open gas space. A desirable projection is about 5 mm. Such "KOH papers" are usually prepared in quantity by cutting filter paper into squares with 2 cm. sides (the exact dimensions will vary with the depth of the cup employed; this varies from instrument to instrument, but the size need be only approximate). These papers are then folded three or four times, accordion fashion, and inserted into the center cup with tweezers. When wet by the alkali, previously added to the cup, they provide a large surface for the absorption of CO_2.

Sufficient alkali should be added to moisten the entire paper and still leave a well of free liquid in the bottom of the cup. For the papers described 0.15 to 0.20 ml. is adequate. Sometimes difficulty is experienced with the alkali "creeping over" the cup into the outer compartment of the flask. This can be prevented by greasing the top of the cup before inserting the papers. A convenient way of doing this is to wind a small amount of cotton about the end of a glass rod so that when placed over the center cup it will completely cover its top. After the cotton is saturated with grease, it is rotated in contact with the top surface of the center cup to give it a light coat of grease. A tapered 15 ml. centrifuge tube also makes a convenient tool for greasing alkali cups; the bottom of the tube is greased and then rotated in the top of the alkali well. The relation of flask design to "creeping" of alkali is discussed in Chapter 4.

The concentration of alkali employed by various investigators differs widely, but KOH (because of the solubility of the potassium carbonate) is almost universally employed. Two things must be kept in mind in choosing the concentration. One is the capacity of the alkali employed to absorb CO_2; the other is the ease with which the alkali can be handled. Whereas the pressure of CO_2 above any solution of KOH approaches zero, very dilute solutions of KOH may be completely neutralized rather soon. Under most circumstances 1% KOH is undoubtedly sufficient. Most workers use 5, 10 or 20% KOH to be sure that an adequate supply is present to last throughout the experiment. 20% KOH offers no difficulty in handling. It is claimed by some that rather concentrated solutions of KOH (10-20%) react with the filter papers employed and that an oxygen uptake results from this reaction. While we have never experienced this, the recommendation that analytical grade filter papers be used for KOH papers should be followed whenever possible.

It is obvious that the conditions for obtaining adequate oxygen diffusion and CO_2 absorption are easily met. Usually the shaking rates employed are 100 to 120 two or three centimeter strokes per minute. Under these conditions (employing flasks of about 15 ml. capacity) one should use amounts of tissues that take up less than 300 μl. of O_2 per hour and give off less than 500 μl. CO_2. This usually means the use of about 100 mg. (wet weight) of animal tissues or somewhat less wet weight of yeast and bacteria. It is convenient to choose tissue concentrations which take up about 200 μl. O_2 per hour.

PROCEDURE EMPLOYED

The actual procedure in setting up systems for the measurement of respiration of living cells varies widely. A common procedure is listed as follows:

1. To clean, dry, Warburg flasks equipped with a center well, add materials (except cells) to the main compartment of flask.
2. Add materials (if any) to the sidearm.
3. Add 0.2 ml. alkali (usually 5, 10 or 20% KOH) to the center well, after greasing upper rim of well.
4. Grease attachment joint on manometer and grease and insert plug for sidearm.
5. Add cells.
6. Add filter paper strip to alkali in center cup (see absorption of carbon dioxide).
7. Attach flask to manometer.
8. Place in constant temperature bath.
9. Adjust and tighten flask after about 5 min. shaking in bath. (This is done since sometimes the grease becomes softer and the flask tends to creep slightly.)
10. Allow to equilibrate, with shaking, for 10-15 minutes.
11. Adjust manometer fluid to reference point on closed side of manometer with stopcock open.
12. Close stopcock.
13. Begin readings.

LIMITATIONS OF METHOD

The method described in the previous sections, in which any carbon dioxide formed is absorbed by alkali, is known as Warburg's "Direct Method". It is the method most widely used for determining respiration. As with any other method it has certain limitations; these are:

1. The gases exchanged must be only O_2 and CO_2. In most cases this condition is not difficult to meet since in the majority of tissues these are the only gases involved. Warburg (1926), however, points out that "the metabolism of bacteria is rarely so simple that it can be measured by this method". This is a somewhat pessimistic viewpoint, and many bacteria can be studied adequately by this method. However, one should always take care to check that the only gases involved are O_2 and CO_2 before relying upon data derived by this method.

2. The atmosphere in the flask must be free from carbon dioxide. For some tissues, this is of no consequence, i.e. they respire at the same rate, to the same extent, and follow the same pathways whether CO_2 be present or not. But for others, this is by no means true. Carbon dioxide may inhibit, may stimulate, or may alter the path of metabolism of a given cell, hence measurements in the absence of CO_2 may not give a reasonable estimate of the reactions occurring in its presence. For measurements in the presence of CO_2 the Warburg "Indirect Method" or the Pardee method may be used (see Chapter 3).

3. The rate of oxygen uptake, and the rate of carbon dioxide liberation and absorption must be within a particular range so that the assumptions of the method hold, i.e., that the fluid is always saturated with oxygen gas (or air) and that the pressure of carbon dioxide in the gas phase approximates zero.

In spite of the limitations of the "Direct Method" the conditions necessary for its adequate functioning can be met with ease in most cases.

EXPRESSING RESULTS OF DETERMINATIONS

The Warburg "Direct Method" is suitable for two general uses:

1. The determination of the rate of oxygen uptake.
2. The determination of the amount of oxygen uptake.

Both are usually measurable in the same determination. In expressing the rate of oxygen uptake, a quotient ("Q") is commonly employed. Several of these are in general use. These are defined as follows:

Q_{O_2} = μl. O_2 taken up per mg. dry weight of tissue per hour.

$Q_{O_2}(N)$ = μl. O_2 taken up per mg. tissue nitrogen per hour.

$Q_{O_2}(P)$ = μl. O_2 taken up per mg. tissue phosphorus per hour, or per mg. nucleic acid phosphorus per hour.

$Q_{O_2}(C)$ = μl. O_2 taken up per mg. tissue carbon per hour.

$Q_{O_2}(cell)$ = μl. O_2 taken up per cell per hour.

In short, one specifies in the Q term the conditions under which the rate was measured and the basis used to estimate the amount of tissue. In a general way:

$$\begin{array}{l} \text{(gas atmosphere)} \\ \text{Q} \qquad\qquad\qquad \text{(tissue basis)} \\ \text{(gas measured)} \end{array}$$

FOR EXAMPLE:

$Q_{O_2}^{O_2}(N)$ means $\mu l.O_2$ taken up per mg. nitrogen of tissue per hour in an atmosphere of pure oxygen.

$Q_{CO_2}^{N_2}(P)$ means $\mu l.CO_2$ given off in an atmosphere of nitrogen (or under anaerobic
conditions) per mg. of tissue phosphorus per hour.

Uptake of a gas is indicated by a minus (-) sign, release by a plus (+). Two conventions
are employed:

1. When the gas atmosphere is air, the condition indicator is omitted.
2. When the tissue basis is dry weight, this indicator is omitted.

Thus, the term Q_{O_2} is used rather than $Q_{O_2}^{air}$ (dry weight), and $Q_{O_2}(N)$ means oxygen
uptake in air per unit nitrogen per hour, while $Q_{O_2}^{O_2}(N)$ means oxygen uptake in pure
oxygen per unit nitrogen per hour.

The various values which are employed (Q_{O_2} and $Q_{O_2}(N)$ being the most common) represent an effort to estimate the "active" portion of the cell constituents. For example,
many bacteria produce a "gum", a carbohydrate material on the cell surface. This material is not "alive" (being usually a reserve carbohydrate that can be metabolized but
slowly), yet it contributes to the cell volume, the wet weight, the dry weight, and because
it frequently occludes mineral matter from the medium, it even contributes to the ash.
Because of this gum formation, the dry weight, etc. of such cells does not actually measure the active cell content. In such a case one then attempts to obtain a convenient measure of the amount of the active portion of the cell, usually nitrogen or phosphorus, or
some other component which is not influenced by the mere accumulation of an "inert"
storage product. The actual measure employed is dependent upon the tissue one is using,
and it should be one closely connected with cell activity. For a further discussion see
Burris and Wilson (1940) and Berenblum, Chain and Heatley (1939). Care must be taken
in comparing respiration rates (Q_{O_2} values) from tissues of different sorts, that inert
materials have not contributed to the basis used and thus influenced the rate obtained.

It is also possible to compare the effect of the treatments without knowing the exact
amount of tissue involved, as long as it is the same in all cases. Thus, one might use
1 ml. of a bacterial suspension (whose dry weight, nitrogen, etc. were not known) in
each of a series of buffers at different pH's. The effect of pH could be observed without
determining the exact amount of tissue.

The second use to which the "Direct Method" may be put is the determination of the
amount of oxygen taken up per unit of substrate added, i.e., how many moles of oxygen
are used in oxidizing x moles of substrate. For this purpose one usually employs flasks
with sidearms. A known quantity of the material to be studied is placed in the sidearm.
After equilibration, the rate of oxygen uptake is determined in the absence of substrate
(to be certain that it is constant), the substrate is then tipped in, and the oxygen uptake
determined until it again reaches the endogenous (respiration in the absence of substrate)
rate. An example of this type of data is given in an experiment shown in figure 6.

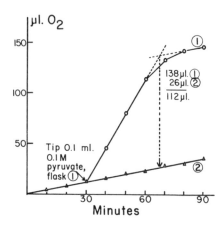

Figure 6

Example of the use of the Warburg "Direct Method" to determine total oxygen uptake per unit of substrate added. Flasks contain: 0.5 ml. (containing 1.0 mg. cell nitrogen) E. coli suspension, 1 ml. M/10 phosphate buffer pH 7.0, 0.1 ml. 4% KOH in center well. Flask 1: 0.1 ml. 0.1 M (0.01 mM.) pyruvate neutralized to pH 7.0 in side-arm, 1.4 ml. water added to main compartment. Flask 2: 1.5 ml. water added to main compartment. O_2 taken up due to pyruvate addition = 138 - 26 = 112 μl. or 0.005 mM. O_2 . As 0.01 mM. pyruvate was added, 0.5 O_2 was taken up per pyruvate molecule. This represents the removal of 2H from pyruvate or its oxidation to the acetate stage

It will be noted that from this type of experiment it is possible to obtain both the amount of oxygen used per mole of substrate and the rate of oxygen uptake. For example, in the experiment cited, the rate of oxygen uptake can be calculated from the period of 30 to 60 minutes; $Q_{O_2}(N) = 204$. The rate obtained under these conditions may not be the maximum rate, since to measure the stoichiometry of oxygen uptake in a reasonable length of time one may find it necessary to add substrate in quantities insufficient to saturate the enzyme systems. Normally the enzyme systems are considered saturated if one obtains a straight line function with time, but occasionally instances may be found in which the rate of oxygen uptake (or other functions of metabolism) may proceed in a linear manner, yet higher levels of the substrate will increase the rate.

In determining the amount of oxygen taken up per unit of substrate, it is frequently a problem to decide whether one should subtract from the oxygen uptake observed in the presence of substrate, the oxygen taken up over the same interval in the absence of substrate. That is, when a substrate is being oxidized at a rapid rate, does the endogenous respiration continue at its constant rate, or is it suppressed, or does it increase? These questions have not yet been answered. Undoubtedly the response depends upon the tissue involved, and no generalizations can be made. However, it is always good practice to determine the endogenous respiration and to report it, along with the oxidation in the presence of substrate, and to indicate whether or not the endogenous respiration was subtracted from the respiration in calculating the oxygen consumption per mole of substrate. By using cells labeled with C^{14} one should be able to follow the metabolism of endogenous substrates in the presence of added substrates. See Van Niel (1943) and Moses and Syrett (1955) for further discussion.

It is frequently convenient to express the amount of substrate employed in terms of gas produced or absorbed. Since 1 mole of any gas (at standard conditions) occupies 22.4 liters, it is possible to consider any substance in terms of liters with each mole equivalent to 22.4 liters. The following table (Table 4) makes this clear. One may thus speak of adding 11.2 μl. of glucose, which means that one has added 0.5 ml. of 0.001 M glucose solution or 5×10^{-7} moles of glucose. This terminology may not be clear when a reaction releases a fraction or more than 1 mole of gas per mole of substrate. For example, the complete oxidation of glucose releases 6 moles of CO_2, and to speak of 0.5 ml. of 0.001 M glucose as 11.2 μl. of glucose when 67.2 μl. of CO_2 actually are released is confusing.

Table 4

Relation between Concentration and Gas Volume

Unit	Contained in	0.1 M	0.01 M	Gas Volume in μl.
1 mole	1 liter of a 1 M soln.			2.24×10^7
1 millimole, 10^{-3} mole	1 ml. of a 1 M soln.	10 ml.	100 ml.	2.24×10^4
0.1 " , 10^{-4} mole	--	1 ml.	10 ml.	2,240
0.01 " , 10^{-5} mole	--	0.1 ml.	1 ml.	224
1 micromole, 10^{-6} mole	--	0.01 ml.	0.1 ml.	22.4

It is also possible to reverse this procedure and to determine μM of oxygen consumed rather than μl. One need only divide the μl. of O_2 consumed by 22.4 to obtain micromoles (10^{-3} millimoles) of the gas used. It is sometimes even convenient to employ a "Molar Flask Constant" rather than the usual flask constant such that the readings on the manometer may be directly converted into micromoles consumed. To obtain the "Molar Flask Constant" divide the usual flask constant by 22.4. It should be noted that what is measured on the manometer is O_2, not O, i.e., its molecular weight is 32.

W. W. UMBREIT

Chapter 2
CARBON DIOXIDE AND BICARBONATE

THE SOLUBILITY OF CARBON DIOXIDE

The solubility of carbon dioxide in pure water is in essence no different from the solubility of other gases. While it is true that the carbon dioxide forms carbonic acid which dissociates to form H^+ and HCO_3^- in accordance with the following equation,

$$CO_2 + H_2O \rightleftharpoons H_2CO_3 \rightleftharpoons H^+ + HCO_3^-$$

it is also true that over 99% of carbon dioxide in solution is in the form of dissolved carbon dioxide and less than 1% exists as H_2CO_3, H^+ or HCO_3^-. In the absence of materials which can combine with the acid, the solubility is comparable to that of any other gas. There are two factors which render the actual figures obtained on solubility in pure water somewhat more variable than those for other gases. One is the somewhat higher Van der Waals forces which exist in carbon dioxide, which is equivalent to saying that carbon dioxide deviates from the laws of an ideal gas somewhat more than other gases, but the error involved in manometric work is negligible. The other factor is that in dissolving in pure water, H^+ ions are generated so that the pH does not remain at 7, but gradually decreases as the pressure of carbon dioxide is increased. The α values for carbon dioxide are given in Table 5.

Table 5

The Solubility of Carbon Dioxide in Pure Water

Data in terms of $\alpha = ml.CO_2/ml.$ water or $\mu l.CO_2/\mu l.$ water at one atmosphere

Temp. °C.	(1)	(2)	(3)
0	1.713		
10	1.194	1.194	
15	1.019	1.019	1.014
20	0.878	0.878	
25	0.759		0.756
30	0.665	0.66	
35	0.592		
40	0.530	0.53	

(1) Handbook of Chemistry and Physics (1963) and earlier editions.
(2) Dixon (1951)
(3) International Critical Tables (1928)

THE INFLUENCE OF SALTS ON CO_2 SOLUBILITY

As was shown with oxygen, the presence of salts, etc., in solution has little effect upon the solubility of carbon dioxide, within physiological concentrations, providing that these do not combine with the carbonic acid. As is shown in Table 6 the effect of various salts, although greater than with oxygen, is negligible.

THE INFLUENCE OF CARBONATE AND BICARBONATE

If, however, there is anything in the solution which will combine with the carbonic acid (or bicarbonate ion), the observed solubility changes. Since from equation (1):

$$CO_2 \text{ (gas)} \rightleftharpoons CO_2 \text{ (dissolved)} \rightleftharpoons H_2CO_3 \rightleftharpoons H^+ + HCO_3^- \quad \boxed{1}$$

and since H_2CO_3 is essentially dependent upon CO_2 (dissolved) which is, in turn, directly dependent upon the pressure of carbon dioxide (pCO_2) in the gas phase, the equilibrium

Table 6

The Influence of Salts and Other Materials upon the
Solubility of Carbon Dioxide

Material	At 15°C (α values)			At 25°C (α values)		
	0.5 M	1.0 M	2.0 M	0.5 M	1.0 M	2.0 M
None	0.014	--	--	0.756	--	--
HCl	0.989	0.974	0.948	0.738	0.732	0.728
1/2 H_2SO_4	0.965	0.927	0.867	0.727	0.705	0.669
HNO_3	1.022	1.029	1.043	0.770	0.781	0.803
KCl	0.925	1.850	--	0.695	0.641	--
NH_4Cl	--	--	--	0.720	0.692	0.648
Glycerol	--	0.934	--	--	--	--

From International Critical Tables (1928)

constant of the dissociation of the carbonic acid, which would normally be written as equation (2a), becomes, in reality equation (2):

$$H_2CO_3 \rightleftharpoons H^+ + HCO_3^- \qquad K_1' = \frac{(H^+)\,(HCO_3^-)}{(H_2CO_3)} \qquad \begin{array}{l}K_1' \text{ indicates the first} \\ \text{dissociation constant} \\ \text{of carbonic acid.}\end{array} \quad \boxed{2a}$$

$$K_1 = \frac{(H^+)\,(HCO_3^-)}{(CO_2)} \qquad\qquad\qquad\qquad\qquad\qquad\qquad \boxed{2}$$

One may solve this equation (2) for H^+ as follows:

$$(H^+) = \frac{K_1(CO_2)}{(HCO_3^-)}$$

If one takes the logarithms of both sides:

$$\log (H^+) = \log \frac{K_1(CO_2)}{(HCO_3^-)}$$

But $-\log (H^+)$ is termed pH, so

$$pH = -\log \frac{K_1(CO_2)}{(HCO_3^-)}$$

But also, since log xy = log x + log y (from definition of logarithms):

$$pH = -\log K_1 - \log\left(\frac{(CO_2)}{(HCO_3^-)}\right)$$

In addition, since $\log\frac{x}{y} = -\log\frac{y}{x}$ the equation immediately above becomes:

$$pH = -\log K_1 + \log\frac{(HCO_3^-)}{(CO_2)} = -\log K_1 + \log\frac{bicarbonate}{carbon\ dioxide} \qquad \boxed{3}$$

One may note the similarity of the term pH to express $-\log(H^+)$, to the $-\log K_1$ occurring in equation (3). Hence the expression pK_1 is quite logical and a convenient way to express the value $-\log K_1$. We can therefore define the term:

$$pK_1 = -\log K_1$$

As long as such substitutions are being made, we can include in the pK_1 values employed another factor to account for the "activity" of the materials involved, which is not exactly the same as their concentration. We can thus define a pK' as follows:

$$pK' = pK_1 + \log \theta, \text{ where } \theta \text{ is the activity coefficient of the } HCO_3^-.$$

This will make the equation just a little more exact. Employing this value, then, equation (3) becomes:

$$pH = pK' + \log\frac{(HCO_3^-)}{(CO_2)} \qquad \boxed{4}$$

This equation (4) is sometimes called the "Henderson-Hasselbach equation" relating the CO_2 pressure, the bicarbonate ion concentration and the pH. Naturally, pK' must be known. This value is given by Hastings and Sendroy (1925) at infinite dilution $(pK'\infty)$ as 6.33 at 38°C., by MacInnes and Belcher (1933) as 6.343 at 25°C., 6.309 at 38°C., and by Shedlovsky and MacInnes (1935) as 6.317 at 38°C. The evidence cited by Shedlovsky and MacInnes (1935) points to 6.317 at 38°C. as the most probable value, and $pK'\infty$ will be taken as 6.317 at 38°C. in the subsequent discussion.

In concentrations of bicarbonate greater than infinite dilution the value of pK' will decrease, the decrease being theoretically $6.317 - 0.5\sqrt{\mu}$. Determinations show this decrease to be 0.08 to 0.15 μ (where μ = the ionic strength). In the case of manometric measurements the highest bicarbonate concentrations employed are of the order of 0.1 molar. Since this alters the pK' by less than 0.015, the correction is so small that it can be ignored for most measurements. However, there are circumstances in which this very real influence of ionic strength is of importance for precise work. This degree of accuracy is rarely required in manometric work.

At temperatures lower than 38°C. the pK' will increase. The increase due to temperature is given as 0.005 units per degree centigrade by Stadie and Hawes (1928). Shedlovsky and MacInnes (1935) found that the increase was not strictly linear, but from their data the following corrections may be applied: between 20 and 40°C. the increase due to temperature is 0.005 units/°C.; between 10 and 20°C., 0.006; between 0 and 10°C., 0.010. For virtually all manometric work the value 6.317 (38°C.) is sufficiently accurate, and this value will increase by 0.005 units per °C. as the temperature is lowered.

This equation (4) has very wide use, but it is subject to certain limitations. First, it neglects the second dissociation constant of carbonic acid (corresponding to the reaction $HCO_3^- = H^+ + CO_3^=$). However, E. J. Warburg (1922) has shown that if the pH is less than 8, the error arising from this neglect is unimportant. Second, the equation itself employs a term for bicarbonate concentration, (HCO_3^-), whose concentration one may not be able to determine exactly. For example, if $NaHCO_3$ is present, there will be HCO_3^- ion from the sodium bicarbonate and also bicarbonate ion from the dissociated carbonic acid (i.e., dissolved and dissociated CO_2). But again, E. J. Warburg (1922) showed that if the H^+ concentration was one one-hundredth (1,100) of the concentration of $NaHCO_3$ (or other metal bicarbonate), the bicarbonate concentration for use in equation (4) could be taken as equivalent to that of the bicarbonate added. Neglect of the bicarbonate from carbonic acid, under these conditions, would cause an error of less than 1 part in 1000. Thus at pH 5 ($H^+ = 10^{-5}$ M), the lowest bicarbonate concentration which could be employed would be 10^{-3} M (M/1000). At pH 7, the lowest bicarbonate concentration which could be employed would be 10^{-5} M (M/100,000). It is obvious that in the physiological range of pH 6-8 it would be difficult to supply sufficient bicarbonate to overcome any error arising from the neglect of the second dissociation constant of carbonic acid.

In actual practice, using contemporary Warburg instruments (overall accuracy of 5%), it is found that if bicarbonate salts are employed, one can use the concentration of the bicarbonate supplied as the (HCO_3^-) in the equation, providing the bicarbonate concentration supplied is at least ten times that of the H^+ concentration (pH 6, $H^+ = 10^{-6}$ M, bicarbonate must be at least 10^{-5} M; at pH 8, $H^+ = 10^{-8}$ M, bicarbonate must be at least 10^{-7} M). In addition, under most practical circumstances one may use the bicarbonate supplied as the total bicarbonate concentration providing it is at least ten times the concentration of other "carbon dioxide binding" materials.

The carbon dioxide concentration in equation (4) is expressed in the same units as the bicarbonate, i.e., in moles per liter. Since the value usually known is the percent carbon dioxide, the following equation (5) is used to convert percent of carbon dioxide in the gas into moles per liter in the solution.

$$\text{carbon dioxide in moles per liter of solution} = \frac{P \; \alpha \; CO_2 \cdot 1000}{760 \cdot 22,400 \cdot 100} \qquad \boxed{5}$$

where P = atmospheric pressure
CO_2 = percent of CO_2 at the atmospheric pressure, P
α = solubility of CO_2

Or simplifying:

$$\text{CO}_2 \text{ in moles per liter of solution} = P \; \alpha \; CO_2 \cdot 0.587 \cdot 10^{-6} \qquad \boxed{5}$$

The term P/760 converts the atmospheric pressure to standard conditions, α represents the solubility in the solution involved, 1000/22,400 is a factor to change α from liters/liter to moles/liter, and 100 in the denominator converts percent CO_2 to pCO_2.

Occasionally one will find equation (4) and (5) combined (as in equation 6).

$$pH = pK' + \log HCO_3^- - \log P (CO_2) - \log \frac{\alpha}{760 \times 2240} \qquad \boxed{6}$$

If carbon dioxide is expressed in terms of mm. Hg pressure (mm. CO_2) the equation may be written as equation (7):

$$pH = pK' + \log HCO_3^- - \log mm.\ CO_2 - \log \frac{\alpha}{760 \times 22.4}$$

7

The "Henderson-Hasselbach equation" shows that in order to measure CO_2 at pH 7 there must be CO_2 in the atmosphere, since if the CO_2 pressure is 0, or approaches 0, the factor $\log (HCO_3^-)/(CO_2)$, equation (4), becomes larger (hence the pH increases) or, if the pH is held low, the HCO_3^- becomes zero. At a pH of 5 or below, no appreciable amount of bicarbonate or carbonate ion can exist, hence any CO_2 released will escape to the air. Thus one can measure CO_2 evolution from urea under the action of urease (which can occur at pH 5) without supplying CO_2 to the atmosphere. But most physiological reactions occur at pH 7, hence because of low levels of CO_2 in the air, either the bicarbonate concentration must be kept low, or CO_2 must be supplied in the air (if the pH is to be maintained at 7). It is obviously impossible to keep the bicarbonate low because the reaction of carbonic acid with tissue buffers tends to increase bicarbonate. The error arising from this source is only negligible in practice when the bicarbonate concentration is at least 10 times higher than that of tissue buffers. Hence the practical solution is to add CO_2 to the gas phase. It should be emphasized that if one fixes the bicarbonate concentration, one can obtain any pH between the values of 6 and 8 by adjusting the pCO_2 and vice versa. We shall work out several examples, but it is obvious that the situation can be altered to fit many other cases.

PRACTICAL USE OF THE HENDERSON-HASSELBACH EQUATION

As described in the paragraph above, it is necessary to add CO_2 to the atmosphere under most operating conditions. It is convenient to fix the CO_2 level at 5% and to vary the bicarbonate concentration to obtain the pH desired. This concentration of CO_2 requires bicarbonate concentrations between 0.001 and 0.10 molar, and under these circumstances the amount of carbonate in solution is negligible. It is apparent that equation (4)

$$pH = pK' + \log \frac{(HCO_3^-)}{(CO_2)}$$

4

may be solved for $\log (HCO_3^-)$ and pH as follows:

$$pH = pK' + \log (HCO_3^-) - \log (CO_2) \qquad (\text{as } \log \frac{x}{y} = \log x - \log y)$$

$$- \log (HCO_3^-) = - pH + pK' - \log (CO_2)$$

$$\log (HCO_3^-) = pH - pK' + \log (CO_2)$$

8

In equation (8) $\log (CO_2)$ is expressed in moles/liter, thus substituting equation (5) into (8) one obtains (9):

$$\log (HCO_3^-) = pH - pK' + \log \frac{P\ \alpha\ CO_2}{760 \times 2,240}$$

9

If one fixes the CO_2 at 5% the last term becomes:

$$\log \frac{P\ \alpha\ 5.0}{760 \times 2,240} = \log P \alpha\ (2.94 \times 10^{-6})$$

At atmospheric pressure the P of course is dependent upon the exact pressure in the room; this pressure varies from day to day. However, the contribution of P to establishing the final concentration of bicarbonate is relatively small. For example, at 37°C. and pH 7.0 a change of P from 760 to 740 mm. Hg changes the bicarbonate required to obtain pH 7.0 from 0.00595 M (760 mm.) to 0.00588 (740 mm.). As the temperature is lowered this difference becomes slightly larger, e.g., at 20°C. 0.00786 M bicarbonate is required at 760 mm. and 0.00762 M at 740 mm. However, the change is still relatively small. In the following sections the data have been calculated for 740 mm. Hg pressure. Day to day alterations have relatively slight effect and only for the most precise work are any further corrections necessary. In the ordinary operation of the Warburg instrument the error introduced by working at pressures other than 740 mm. is so small that it can be ignored.

One may note that by specifying the conditions (5% CO_2, pressure between 760 and 720 mm. Hg calculated to 740 mm. Hg) equation (9) becomes:

$$\log (HCO_3^-) = pH - pK' + \log \alpha \ (2.17 \times 10^{-3})$$

The following table (Table 7) gives the bicarbonate concentration required at various temperatures to obtain the pH listed. The following two things may be noted:

First, at pH 7 the concentration of bicarbonate is some value (approximately 6) x 10^{-3} molar. At pH 6 it is this same value x 10^{-4} molar. At pH 8 it is the same value x 10^{-2} molar. Thus one need know only the concentration for one pH to know also the concentration required for 1 unit lower or 1 unit higher.

Second, the relationship between temperature and bicarbonate concentration is a linear one and at pH 7 for each degree below 37°C. the concentration of bicarbonate increases by 1 x 10^{-4} molar.

Table 7

Relation between Bicarbonate Concentration and pH.
(5% CO_2, atmospheric pressure of 740 mm. Hg.)

Temp. °C.	α CO_2	pK'	Molar Bicarbonate Concentration		
			pH 6	pH7	pH 8
20	0.878	6.392	7.6 x 10^{-4}	7.6 x 10^{-3}	7.6 x 10^{-2}
25	0.759	6.365	7.1	7.1	7.1
30	0.665	6.348	6.6	6.6	6.6
35	0.592	6.328	6.1	6.1	6.1
37	0.567	6.322	5.88	5.88	5.88
40	0.530	6.312	5.68	5.68	5.68

These facts make possible the construction of a chart (fig. 7) which facilitates the rapid determination of the bicarbonate concentration required. The line for 37°C. has been drawn in, since this is the temperature usually employed; however, concentrations required at any other temperature (between 20 and 40°C.) may be read by connecting the temperature scales at either end of the chart with a straightedge. A few examples given below will illustrate its use; with the chart the practical selection of the bicarbonate concentration for the pH desired becomes very simple. The chart itself is sufficiently accurate to furnish the degree of precision required for studies with the respirometer.

EXAMPLES:

1. At 37°C. what bicarbonate concentration is necessary to obtain a pH of 7.2, 7.6, 6.8?

    7.2 9.2×10^{-3} M = 0.0092 M

    7.6 23×10^{-3} M = 0.023 M

    6.8 36.7×10^{-4} M = 0.0036 M

2. At 25°C. what bicarbonate concentration is necessary to obtain a pH of 7.2, 6.8?

    7.2 11×10^{-3} M = 0.011 M

    6.8 45×10^{-4} M = 0.0045 M

3. At 37°C. and in 3 ml. liquid a reaction starting at pH 7.4 (14.5×10^{-3} M bicarbonate) evolves, from acid production, 200 μl. of CO_2 and then stops abruptly even though considerable substrate remains. At what pH did the reaction stop?

    200 μl. of CO_2 represents 200/22.4 or approximately 9 μM CO_2 = 9×10^{-6} moles. This amount was produced in 3 ml. of liquid. Each ml. of the bicarbonate solution at the start had $\dfrac{14.5 \times 10^{-3}}{10^3}$ = 14.5×10^{-6} moles of bicarbonate. As 9×10^{-6} moles total or 3×10^{-6} moles/ml. have been used, the amount remaining is $(14.5 - 3) \times 10^{-6}$ or 11.5×10^{-6} moles/ml. This is equivalent to 11.5×10^{-3} moles/liter and corresponds to a 11.5×10^{-3} molar concentration. By referring to the chart it is apparent that the pH corresponding to this concentration is 7.3. In general terms:

    $$\begin{matrix}\text{original molar} \\ \text{concentration} \\ \text{of bicarbonate}\end{matrix} - \frac{\mu\text{l.} \times 10^{-3}}{\text{fluid volume in ml.} \times 22.4} = \begin{matrix}\text{final molar} \\ \text{concentration} \\ \text{of bicarbonate}\end{matrix}$$

THE USE OF BICARBONATE BUFFERS FOR MEASURING ACID PRODUCTION UNDER ANAEROBIC CONDITIONS

In the absence of oxygen there can be no respiration (i.e., oxygen uptake). With a bicarbonate buffer and an atmosphere containing CO_2, as described in the previous section, CO_2 released by the cells will escape into the atmosphere and can be measured manometrically. If any additional acid is produced, the H^+ arising from its dissociation will combine with HCO_3^- and release CO_2 via H_2CO_3. Hence, in bicarbonate buffers and under anaerobic conditions both metabolic $\overline{CO_2}$ and CO_2 liberated through production of acid can be measured. Procedures for obtaining anaerobic conditions are described in Chapter 5.

If one employs a tissue which does not liberate CO_2 when metabolizing anaerobically, it is simple to determine the acid produced since one can take the CO_2 released from bicarbonate as a measure of the acid production. Another way which has been used to differentiate the "fermentation" CO_2 from CO_2 released by acid, is to determine the CO_2 production in the absence of bicarbonate and to subtract this from the CO_2 produced in its presence. However, the determination of the rate of CO_2 production in the absence of bicarbonate is unsatisfactory with most tissues, since to avoid any great effect of

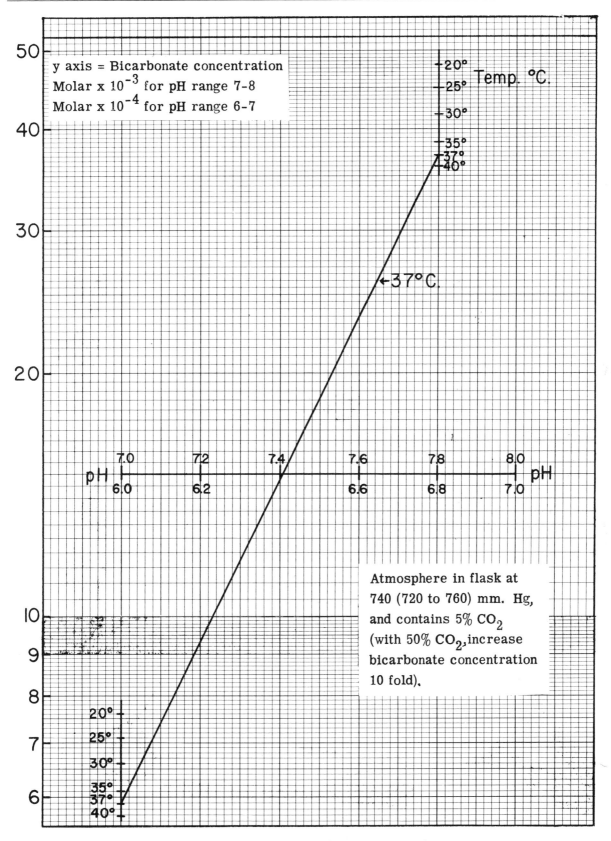

Figure 7
Chart for determining the proper bicarbonate concentration to use at a given
pH, pCO_2 and temperature

bicarbonate produced by interaction with buffers ("CO_2 retention") one must work in low concentrations of buffers. The CO_2 and acid liberated soon reduce the pH from the initial point and frequently stop metabolism.

A method which permits one to differentiate between the "metabolic CO_2" and CO_2 released by acid (both being measured as CO_2 liberated under anaerobic conditions) is the following:

Liberation of CO_2 will have little influence on the bicarbonate concentration, as the amount liberated is small relative to that in the gas phase and will not alter the pCO_2 appreciably. However, any acid which is liberated will produce CO_2 from bicarbonate and the amount of bicarbonate will decrease. By adding sufficient acid to measure the bicarbonate remaining one can estimate the acid and the metabolic CO_2. Two manometers (plus a thermobarometer) are required. Each flask has tissue, buffer, bicarbonate, and a known pCO_2, and the gaseous and liquid phases are in equilibrium. Each has acid (usually 0.1 - 0.5 ml. 3N H_2SO_4) in the sidearm or in "Keilin cups" (see Chapter 5). This quantity of acid is sufficient to stop the metabolism instantly and to reduce the pH below 5 (usually between pH 1 and 2) upon addition. In some rare cases the tissues are resistant to acid, so a poison is added along with the acid. After equilibration the acid is added in one of the flasks. The increase in manometer reading times k_{CO_2} gives the total initial bicarbonate available measured as CO_2. CO_2 output is measured for the experimental period in the other flask. Acid is then tipped in. In this case the amount of CO_2 released by the acid is a measure of the residual bicarbonate. The difference between this and the initial bicarbonate gives the amount of CO_2 produced by acid formation. Any other CO_2 released is that produced by the tissue as CO_2 and does not represent acid production (Warburg, 1914, 1926).

The usual Warburg instrument with 15 ml. flasks is capable of measuring over 300 $\mu l.$ of CO_2. Since 1 ml. of 0.001 molar $NaHCO_3$ will release 22.4 $\mu l.$ of CO_2, one may use as much as 1 ml. of 0.01 M $NaHCO_3$ (which in 3 ml. total volume at 37°C. and with 5% CO_2 gives a pH of 6.75) and release all the CO_2 as gas by tipping in acid. This will not extend the fluid in the manometer beyond its graduated range, providing one starts the experiment with the open end of the manometer at a low level (below 100 mm.).

Acid production under anaerobic conditions is usually spoken of as "glycolysis", and when animal tissues are employed the acid is largely lactic acid. In other cases, however, it is not valid to make the assumption that the product is lactic acid or that it is largely lactic acid. Hence, calculation of the acid produced as lactic is likely to result in error. Fortunately there is now available a very specific chemical method for the determination of lactic acid in the flasks (Barker and Summerson, 1941), so that one can actually determine how much of the acid produced is lactic acid.

THE INFLUENCE OF CARBONATE

It has been pointed out that the "Henderson-Hasselbach equation" neglects the second dissociation constant of carbonic acid. In the presence of bicarbonate and CO_2, most of the Na^+ and K^+ ions are associated with bicarbonate but some carbonate does always exist. The question is, is there enough of this to make any difference? The CO_2 or acid produced will combine with carbonate and convert it to bicarbonate. This reaction releases no gas, so the CO_2 or acid involved will escape manometric estimation. The equations involved are:

$$(H^+) \ (HCO_3^-)/H_2CO_3 = (H^+) \ (HCO_3^-)/(CO_2) = K_1 = 3 \times 10^{-7}$$

$$(H^+) \ (CO_3^{--})/HCO_3^- = K_2 = 6 \times 10^{-11}$$

$$K_1/K_2 = K' = \frac{(H^+)(HCO_3^-)}{CO_2} \bigg/ \frac{(H^+)(CO_3^=)}{HCO_3^-} = (HCO_3^-)^2/(CO_2)(CO_3^{--})$$

Thus $K' = K_1/K_2 = \dfrac{3 \times 10^{-7}}{6 \times 10^{-11}} = 0.5 \times 10^{+4} = 5 \times 10^{+3} = 5000$

Using 5% CO_2 with a bicarbonate concentration of 0.01 molar at 25°C., the concentration of carbonate is:

$$CO_3^{--} = \frac{(HCO_3^-)^2}{CO_2 \times K'} = \frac{(0.01)^2}{1.52 \times 10^{-3} \times 5 \times 10^{+3}} = \frac{1 \times 10^{-4}}{5 \times 1.52} =$$

$$1.32 \times 10^{-5} \text{ moles } CO_3^{--}/\text{liter}$$

In short, this is such a small quantity that it may be neglected.

W. W. UMBREIT

Chapter 3
DIRECT AND INDIRECT METHODS
FOR CARBON DIOXIDE

THEORY OF THE DIRECT METHOD

In the first chapter we noted that one could measure respiration even if carbon dioxide were given off, by absorbing all of the carbon dioxide in alkali. Therefore, if one had two flasks each respiring in exactly the same way, except that in one the carbon dioxide was absorbed whereas in the other it was not, one would have a measure of the carbon dioxide liberated (Dixon, 1951, Warburg, 1926). There is one point which should be especially noted; whereas one tissue (absence of alkali) respires in the presence of carbon dioxide, the other (with alkali) respires in its absence. If this should make a difference in the rate of oxygen uptake, or indeed in the course of the reactions followed, an error would be introduced. Generally carbon dioxide has little effect upon the rate of respiration, and methods will be described later which enable one to determine whether carbon dioxide influences the respiration rate and even to measure its effect under these conditions.

In terms of the symbols employed in Chapter 1, the change in the manometer fluid level (h) read on the flask without alkali, results from decreasing pressure due to the absorption of oxygen and increasing pressure due to the liberation of carbon dioxide.

Manometer change resulting from oxygen absorption $= h_{O_2} = x_{O_2}/k_{O_2}$ since $x_{O_2} = h_{O_2} k_{O_2}$

Manometer change resulting from carbon dioxide production $= h_{CO_2} = x_{CO_2}/k_{CO_2}$

The final observed reading h in the flask without KOH, would be the resultant of the two, i.e.,

$$h = h_{O_2} + h_{CO_2} = x_{O_2}/k_{O_2} + x_{CO_2}/k_{CO_2}$$

hence

$$x_{CO_2} = \left(h - \frac{x_{O_2}}{k_{O_2}} \right) k_{CO_2}$$

10

Now x_{O_2} is known from the flask which contained KOH, and k_{O_2} and k_{CO_2} are known for the flask without KOH, hence x_{CO_2} can be calculated.

EXAMPLE: 1 ml. of an algal cell suspension was placed in each of two flasks together with 2 ml. of water. Flask 1 ($k_{O_2} = 0.96$) contained 0.2 ml. KOH, flask 2 ($k_{O_2} = 1.04$, $k_{CO_2} = 1.25$) had no KOH. After equilibrating, respiration was permitted for 30 minutes. In flask 1, the change in reading (h) was 28 mm., hence 28 x 0.96 = 26.9 µl. O₂ taken up.

In flask 2, over the same interval, the manometer reading dropped 9.5 mm. hence,

$$x_{CO_2} = (-9.5 - (-26.9)/1.04)1.25 = (-9.5 + 25.8)1.25 = 16.3 \text{ x } 1.25 = 20.4 \text{ µl.CO}_2.$$

The R. Q. (Respiratory Quotient = CO₂ produced /O₂ consumed) is in this case, 20.4/26.9 = 0.76.

In essence this method determines the oxygen uptake in the absence of CO_2 in one flask, and one then calculates what the change in reading should have been in the other flask if no CO_2 were produced. The uptake observed is always less than this amount, hence the difference is due to CO_2 liberation.

A convenient way of recording data and making the calculations is to use a chart of approximately the following construction (Table 8).

Table 8

Method of Calculating Results

Time	Flask with KOH		Flask without KOH				R. Q.
	h	$\mu l.\ O_2$	h	$\dfrac{x_{O_2}}{k_{O_2}}$	diff.	$\mu l.\ CO_2$	
	mm. observed change corrected for thermobarometer	corrected h times k_{O_2} for flask	mm. observed change corrected for thermobarometer	column 3 divided by k_{O_2} of this flask	subtract column 5 from column 4	multiply column 6 by k_{CO_2}	divide column 7 by column 3
(1)	(2)	(3)	(4)	(5)	(6)	(7)	(8)
30 (from example cited)	-28	-26.9 $k_{O_2}=0.96$	-9.5	-25.8 $k_{O_2}=1.04$	+16.3	+20.4 $k_{CO_2}=1.25$	0.76

One may also substitute in equation (10) as follows. Equation (10) is:

$$x_{CO_2} = \left(h - \frac{x_{O_2}}{k_{O_2}} \right) k_{CO_2}, \text{ the constants referring to the flask without KOH} \qquad \boxed{10}$$

$$x_{O_2} = h'k'_{O_2} \text{ where } h' \text{ and } k'_{O_2} \text{ refer to the flask with KOH, hence}$$

$$x_{CO_2} = \left(h - \frac{h'k'_{O_2}}{k_{O_2}} \right) k_{CO_2} \qquad \boxed{11}$$

Therefore one may calculate the amount of CO_2 released or absorbed during a given interval by subtracting from the change in reading on the flask with no alkali, the change in reading on the flask with the alkali times the ratio of the two oxygen constants, the whole times the CO_2 constant.

CORRECTIONS FOR UNEQUAL AMOUNTS OF TISSUE

It sometimes happens, in using plant or animal tissues, that one does not add exactly the same amount of tissue to each of the flasks. If the differences in amount of tissue are not large, one may merely divide the readings (h) of each flask by the weight (or other measure of active tissue), to obtain the uptake per unit of tissue. The readings obtained with the two flasks are thus comparable. Suppose that in the example listed, the flask with KOH contained 0.97 mg. algae whereas the flask without KOH contained 1.15 mg.

algae. In flask 1, the change was 28 mm., or the change per mg. of tissue was $\frac{28}{0.97} = 28.9$; O_2 uptake was thus $28.9 \times 0.96 = 27.7 \mu l. O_2$ taken up per mg. tissue. In the flask without KOH the manometer reading dropped 9.5 mm.; $9.5/1.15 = 8.25$ mm. per mg. of tissue. The two changes are now comparable since both are based on the same quantity of tissue, hence

$$x_{CO_2} = \left(- 8.25 - \frac{(-27.7)}{1.04}\right) 1.25 = (- 8.25 + 26.6)\ 1.25 = 18.35 \times 1.25$$

$$= 22.9 \mu l. CO_2 \text{ produced; R. Q.} = 22.9/27.7 = 0.83$$

CORRECTIONS FOR RETENTION IN BUFFERS

When buffers are present they react with CO_2. For example:

$$Na_2 HPO_4 + CO_2 + H_2 O \rightleftharpoons NaH_2 PO_4 + NaHCO_3$$

Hence the CO_2 which escapes to the air (measured as x_{CO_2}) may be less than that actually produced in the intervals measured. As was shown in Chapter 2, at a pH of 5 or below no appreciable amount of HCO_3^- exists, hence if the solution is adjusted at the end of the reaction to a pH of 5 or below, all such "bound CO_2" will be released. Therefore in order to obtain the total CO_2 liberated in the presence of buffers, one tips in acid from the side-arm and releases the CO_2 from the buffer. Since the tissue or the buffer may have contained bound carbon dioxide initially, three manometers are used as follows:

(a) $+$ KOH to determine x_{O_2} (h)

(b) $-$ KOH $+$ acid added at end (h_2)

(c) $-$ KOH $+$ acid added at start (h_3)

The h_3 represents the initial bound CO_2, while h_2 represents that initially bound $+$ that released during the respiration. One can obtain the actual CO_2 evolved as follows:

Initial bound $CO_2 = h_3 k_3{}_{CO_2}$

Initial bound $CO_2 + CO_2$ evolved $= h_2 k_2{}_{CO_2}$

Hence, CO_2 evolved is $h_2 k_2{}_{CO_2} - h_3 k_3{}_{CO_2}$

Thus, if one takes the readings after the acid is added, the h of equation (10) is not h_2 but $h_2 - h_3 \dfrac{k_3{}_{CO_2}}{k_2{}_{CO_2}}$. Hence the equation (10) becomes $x_{CO_2} = \left[h_2 - h_3 \dfrac{k_3{}_{CO_2}}{k_2{}_{CO_2}} - \dfrac{x_{O_2}}{k_2{}_{O_2}} \right] k_2{}_{CO_2}$

A very useful method of correcting for CO_2 retention has been suggested by M. J. Johnson. Since at high pH values HCO_3^- is held in solution as well as CO_2, the effective value of α (which will be designated as α') will be larger than the true α value. Since pK'_a from the apparent first dissociation constant for carbonic acid is 6.317 at 38°C. (Shedlovsky and MacInnes, 1935),

$$\frac{\alpha'}{\alpha} = \frac{(HCO_3^-) + (CO_2)}{(CO_2)} = \left[\text{antilog } (pH - 6.317)\right] + 1$$

where the pH is that in the reaction flask during the experiment. If the flask constant used is calculated by the use of α' instead of α, retention of CO_2 will be corrected for automatically. As α' increases rapidly with pH, the retention correction becomes very large at pH values above 7, and the accuracy of the CO_2 measurement suffers accordingly. Values for α'/α at 30° and 37° C. may be obtained from figure 8.

RESPIRATORY QUOTIENTS

These quotients are defined as the ratio CO_2 produced/oxygen consumed, and they serve to indicate the nature of the metabolism. While an R. Q. of 1 would occur upon complete oxidation of carbohydrate (0.9 for most proteins, 0.8 for most fats) the finding of these values does not thereby prove that metabolism of carbohydrate, protein, etc., is the cause of the R. Q. Nevertheless, the R. Q. is an index of the processes occurring and should be measured if possible. Later sections (especially Chapter 7) will describe other methods for determining this value.

THE INDIRECT METHOD OF WARBURG

The one basic difficulty with the "direct" manometric methods described is the necessity for measuring oxygen uptake in an atmosphere free from CO_2. Yet there always is the possibility that such measurements are not valid, for the rate of respiration and decarboxylation reactions might be forced to completion if the CO_2 were all removed, and the influence of this situation upon the rate or course of oxygen uptake could not be estimated. By the direct method there is no way to determine whether or not the presence or absence of CO_2 has an effect.

This problem was solved, at least partially, by Warburg (1924, 1926) who described a method which has since been termed Warburg's "Indirect Method". The method is based upon the principle that changes in the volume of 2 gases of markedly different solubility can be measured simultaneously by following the manometric changes occurring over identical reaction mixtures in 2 flasks of markedly different gas or fluid volumes. A more recent solution (Pardee, 1949) to the problem of measuring oxygen uptake in the presence of CO_2 is described on page 43.

PRINCIPLES AND DERIVATIONS

We shall confine ourselves to the discussion of an example involving two flasks of approximately equal volume containing markedly different volumes of fluid. It will be apparent that exactly the same equations hold for other circumstances (see later). We shall also confine the discussion to the gases O_2 and CO_2 (whose solubilities are markedly different), but it will be apparent also that any other gases may be substituted providing their solubility in the fluid in the flasks is different.

Suppose that we have two flasks of approximately the same volume, but containing different volumes of fluid. The same amount of tissue is placed in each and the same reaction occurs in each. To distinguish the two flasks, we shall use small letter symbols for the flask containing less fluid: (h = change in reading on manometer, k_{O_2} = flask constant for O_2, k_{CO_2} = flask constant for CO_2, $- x_{O_2}$ = amount of O_2 taken up, $+x_{CO_2}$ = amount of CO_2

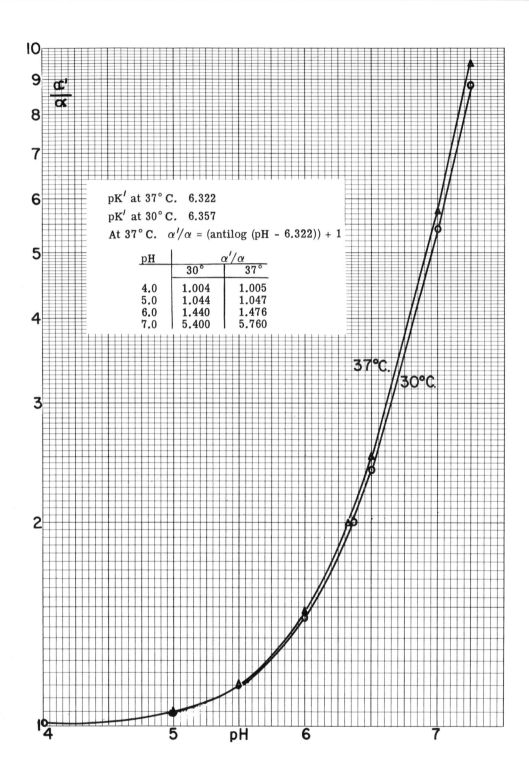

Figure 8
Ratios of apparent to real solubility of carbon dioxide

liberated, etc.) and capital letters (H, K_{O_2}, K_{CO_2}, X_{O_2}, X_{CO_2} etc.) represent the flask containing the larger amount of fluid. This is purely conventional and it is obvious that the symbols can be exchanged without influencing the derivation in the least. We also shall employ a different derivation than was used by Warburg (1924) because, to our minds, the derivation below is easier to understand and serves to emphasize that the derivation employed by Warburg is perfectly general; in short, that it is applicable to situations other than those described by him.

In the first flask with the smaller volume of fluid, the change observed on the manometer (h) is due to two things:

    (a) The uptake of oxygen (h_{O_2})

    (b) The release of CO_2 (h_{CO_2})

Thus:

$$h_{(observed)} = h_{O_2} + h_{CO_2}$$

but by definition:

$$h_{O_2} = x_{O_2}/k_{O_2} \text{ and } h_{CO_2} = x_{CO_2}/k_{CO_2} \quad (\text{since } x_{O_2} = h_{O_2} k_{O_2})$$

Therefore:

$$h_{(observed)} = x_{O_2}/k_{O_2} + x_{CO_2}/k_{CO_2} \qquad \boxed{12}$$

If the same reaction has occurred in the second flask containing the larger volume of fluid, the change observed on the manometer (H) similarly will be:

$$H = X_{O_2}/K_{O_2} + X_{CO_2}/K_{CO_2} \qquad \boxed{13}$$

However, if the identical reaction has occurred in each flask, the amount of oxygen taken up (x_{O_2}, X_{O_2}) in each case should be the same, and the amount of CO_2 released should be the same (X_{CO_2}, x_{CO_2}) hence:

$$x_{O_2} = X_{O_2}; \text{ and } x_{CO_2} = X_{CO_2} \qquad \boxed{13a}$$

Thus one may substitute (13a) in either equation (12) or (13) yielding:

    from equation (12) $h = X_{O_2}/k_{O_2} + X_{CO_2}/k_{CO_2}$ or $\boxed{14}$

    from equation (13) $H = x_{O_2}/K_{O_2} + x_{CO_2}/K_{CO_2}$ $\boxed{15}$

DETERMINATION OF OXYGEN EXCHANGE

Equations (12) and (13) can be combined in another way. Suppose that one solves equation (12) for x_{CO_2} in the following way:

equation (12) $h = x_{O_2}/k_{O_2} + x_{CO_2}/k_{CO_2}$ hence,

$$x_{CO_2}/k_{CO_2} = h - x_{O_2}/k_{O_2} \quad \text{or}$$

$$x_{CO_2} = k_{CO_2}(h - x_{O_2}/k_{O_2}) \qquad \boxed{16}$$

From equation (13), in the same way one obtains

$$X_{CO_2} = K_{CO_2}(H - X_{O_2}/K_{O_2}) \qquad \boxed{17}$$

But as was shown in equation (13a) $x_{CO_2} = X_{CO_2}$, hence equations (16) and (17) are equal to one another, or

$$k_{CO_2}(h - x_{O_2}/k_{O_2}) = K_{CO_2}(H - X_{O_2}/K_{O_2}) \qquad \boxed{18}$$

But equation (13a) also showed that $X_{O_2} = x_{O_2}$, hence this can be substituted to yield equation (19):

$$k_{CO_2}(h - X_{O_2}/k_{O_2}) = K_{CO_2}(H - X_{O_2}/K_{O_2}) \qquad \boxed{19}$$

The thing we are interested in determining is X_{O_2} (or x_{O_2}, since both are equal), hence solving for X_{O_2} as follows:

Multiply out equation (19):

$$hk_{CO_2} - X_{O_2}k_{CO_2}/k_{O_2} = HK_{CO_2} - X_{O_2}K_{CO_2}/K_{O_2}$$

Transpose terms:

$$X_{O_2}K_{CO_2}/K_{O_2} - X_{O_2}k_{CO_2}/k_{O_2} = HK_{CO_2} - hk_{CO_2}$$

Take out X_{O_2}:

$$X_{O_2}(K_{CO_2}/K_{O_2} - k_{CO_2}/k_{O_2}) = HK_{CO_2} - hk_{CO_2}$$

$$x_{O_2} = X_{O_2} = \frac{HK_{CO_2} - hk_{CO_2}}{\dfrac{K_{CO_2}}{K_{O_2}} - \dfrac{k_{CO_2}}{k_{O_2}}} \qquad \boxed{20}$$

Note: One will sometimes find this equation written with the capital and small letters interchanged (Dixon, 1951). It may be noted that this is exactly the same equation except that the sign of both numerator and denominator have been changed.

The oxygen taken up (x_{O_2} or X_{O_2}) depends on the reading of one flask (H) times its CO_2 constant (K_{CO_2}) less the reading of the other flask (h) times its CO_2 constant (k_{CO_2}) divided by a constant which is calculated from the ratio of the CO_2 and oxygen constants of the first flask less the ratio of the same constants for the second flask. Equation (20) may be modified to:

$$x_{O_2} = X_{O_2} = \frac{HK_{CO_2} - hk_{CO_2}}{C_{(O_2)}} \qquad \boxed{21}$$

where $C_{(O_2)} = $ constant $= K_{CO_2}/K_{O_2} - k_{CO_2}/k_{O_2}$

Once this constant ($C_{(O_2)}$) has been calculated from given experimental conditions, the calculation of the oxygen uptake becomes relatively simple. Normally one prepares a table of this sort:

(1)	(2)	(3)	(4)	(5)	(6)
H	HK_{CO_2}	h	hk_{CO_2}	Difference $HK_{CO_2} - hk_{CO_2}$	$\mu l.\ O_2$
Observed, corrected for thermobarometer changes.	Multiply column (1) by its flask constant for CO_2.	Observed, corrected for thermobarometer changes.	Multiply column (3) by its flask constant for CO_2.	Subtract column (4) from column (2).	Divide column (5) by $C_{(O_2)}$.

In making such calculations one must be careful to retain the algebraic sign of each measurement, i.e., if the level of fluid in the manometer drops, $-h$ is used. If it rises, $+h$. (See example below).

DETERMINATION OF CO_2 EXCHANGE

In an entirely similar manner one may use equations (12) and (13) to calculate the CO_2 exchange. Suppose that one solves equation (12) for x_{O_2} in the following way:

From equation (12) $h = x_{O_2}/k_{O_2} + x_{CO_2}/k_{CO_2}$ hence

$$x_{O_2} = (h - x_{CO_2}/k_{CO_2})k_{O_2} \qquad \boxed{22}$$

From equation (13) in the same way one obtains

$$X_{O_2} = (H - X_{CO_2}/K_{CO_2})K_{O_2} \qquad \boxed{23}$$

But $x_{O_2} = X_{O_2}$, from equation (13a), hence equations (22) and (23) are equal to one another, or:

$$(h - x_{CO_2}/k_{CO_2})k_{O_2} = (H - X_{CO_2}/K_{CO_2})K_{O_2} \qquad \boxed{24}$$

Equation (13a) also showed that $x_{CO_2} = X_{CO_2}$; hence for x_{CO_2} we can substitute X_{CO_2}

$$(h - X_{CO_2}/k_{CO_2})k_{O_2} = (H - X_{CO_2}/K_{CO_2})K_{O_2} \qquad \boxed{25}$$

Equation (25) may be solved for X_{CO_2} (the CO_2 liberation or uptake which we are trying to determine) as follows:

Multiply out (25): $hk_{O_2} - X_{CO_2}k_{O_2}/k_{CO_2} = HK_{O_2} - X_{CO_2}K_{O_2}/K_{CO_2}$

Transpose terms: $X_{CO_2}K_{O_2}/K_{CO_2} - X_{CO_2}k_{O_2}/k_{CO_2} = HK_{O_2} - hk_{O_2}$

Take out X_{CO_2}: $X_{CO_2}(K_{O_2}/K_{CO_2} - k_{O_2}/k_{CO_2}) = HK_{O_2} - hk_{O_2}$ hence,

$$x_{CO_2} = X_{CO_2} = (HK_{O_2} - hk_{O_2})/(\frac{K_{O_2}}{K_{CO_2}} - \frac{k_{O_2}}{k_{CO_2}}) = (HK_{O_2} - hk_{O_2})/C_{(CO_2)} \qquad \boxed{26}$$

The carbon dioxide taken up (if $X_{CO_2} = -$) or given off (if $X_{CO_2} = +$) is equal to the change in reading on one flask times the oxygen constant of that flask, less the change of reading on the other flask times its oxygen constant, divided by a constant.

Once this constant:

$$C_{(CO_2)} = K_{O_2}/K_{CO_2} - k_{O_2}/k_{CO_2}$$

has been calculated from given experimental conditions, the calculation of the CO_2 exchange becomes relatively simple. A table such as that used for oxygen may be used:

(1)	(2)	(3)	(4)	(5) Difference $HK_{O_2} - hk_{O_2}$	(6) $\mu l.CO_2$
H	HK_{O_2}	h	hk_{O_2}		
Observed, corrected for thermobarometer changes	Multiply column (1) by its flask constant for O_2.	Observed, corrected for thermobarometer changes.	Multiply column (3) by its flask constant for O_2.	Subtract column (4) from column (2).	Divide column (5) constant $C_{(CO_2)}$. If value in column is + CO_2 is liberated; if − CO_2 taken up.

SUMMARY

By using two flasks of approximately equal volume, one of which contains more fluid than the other, two equations were derived in the previous paragraphs which permit one to determine the oxygen uptake (or release) and the CO_2 production (or uptake). These equations are:

$$x_{O_2} = X_{O_2} = \frac{HK_{CO_2} - hk_{CO_2}}{C_{(O_2)}}$$

21

$$x_{CO_2} = X_{CO_2} = \frac{HK_{O_2} - hk_{O_2}}{C_{(CO_2)}}$$

26

Where the $C_{(O_2)}$ and $C_{(CO_2)}$ represent constants calculable from the experimental set-up employed.

This procedure permits one to determine O_2 uptake and CO_2 production in the presence of adequate supplies of CO_2, and thus enables one, by a comparison with the results of the "Direct Methods" described to determine whether or not CO_2 does influence the rate or the course of the process involved. An alternative method for measuring uptake of oxygen in the presence of CO_2 (Pardee, 1949) is described on page 43.

THE EQUATION CONSTANTS

The constants employed in equations (21) and (26) for calculating the oxygen and carbon dioxide exchange were defined as follows:

$$C_{(O_2)} = K_{CO_2}/K_{O_2} - k_{CO_2}/k_{O_2}$$

$$C_{(CO_2)} = K_{O_2}/K_{CO_2} - k_{O_2}/k_{CO_2}$$

In Chapter 4 methods for determining and calculating the flask constants (k or K) are described. Here it may be noted that:

$$K_{CO_2}/K_{O_2} = 1 \Big/ \frac{K_{O_2}}{K_{CO_2}}$$

It is therefore convenient to have not only the oxygen and carbon dioxide constants of each flask recorded for various volumes, but also their ratio. (It is not true, however, that $C_{(CO_2)}$ is the reciprocal of $C_{(O_2)}$.)

EXAMPLES OF THE USE OF
WARBURG'S INDIRECT METHOD

We will cite an experiment on algae to illustrate the use of the "Indirect Method". 1 ml. of a suspension of <u>Chlorella vulgaris</u> cells (containing 0.1 ml. packed wet cells) was placed in each of two Warburg flasks (No. 5, total volume = 13.9 ml.; No. 7, total volume 13.3 ml.). In the first flask was placed 1 ml. of M/1000 phosphate buffer (pH 4.5) (flask No. 5, $k_{O_2} = 1.08$, $k_{CO_2} = 1.22$); in the second, 5 ml. of the same phosphate solution was added (flask No. 7, $K_{O_2} = 0.67$, $K_{CO_2} = 1.09$). No added CO_2 was supplied to the air. After equilibration at 28°, readings were taken at 5 minute intervals. The readings obtained (corrected for thermobarometer changes) were as follows:

	Flask No. 5 (h)	Flask No. 7 (H)
First 5 minutes	0	-4.5
Second 5 minutes	-2	-5.5
Third 5 minutes	-1	-7.0
Fourth 5 minutes	0	-3.5

Oxygen uptake calculations are shown in Table 9; CO_2 exchange calculations are shown in Table 10.

Table 9
Oxygen Exchange

	Flask 7		Flask 5				
Time	H(mm.)	HK_{CO_2}	h(mm.)	hk_{CO_2}	Difference	$\mu l.O_2$	Sum
5	-4.5	-4.9	0	0	-4.9	-9.8*	-9.8
10	-5.5	-6.0	-2	-2.4	-3.6	-7.2	-17.0
15	-7.0	-7.6	-1	-1.2	-6.4	-12.8	-29.8
20	-3.5	-3.8	0	0	-3.8	-7.6	-37.4

$$K_{CO_2} = 1.09 \qquad k_{CO_2} = 1.22$$

$$* = -4.9/C_{(O_2)} = -4.9/.5 = -9.8$$

$$K_{CO_2}/K_{O_2} = 1.09/0.67 = 1.63 \qquad k_{CO_2}/k_{O_2} = 1.22/1.08 = 1.13$$

$$C_{(O_2)} = K_{CO_2}/K_{O_2} - k_{CO_2}/k_{O_2} = 1.63 - 1.13 = 0.50$$

Table 10
Carbon Dioxide Exchange

	Flask 7		Flask 5				
Time	H(mm.)	HK_{O_2}	h(mm.)	hk_{O_2}	Difference	$\mu l.CO_2$	Sum
5	-4.5	-3.0	0	0	-3.0	+11.1*	+11.1
10	-5.5	-3.7	-2	-2.2	-1.5	+ 5.6	+16.7
15	-7.0	-4.7	-1	-1.1	-3.6	+13.3	+30.0
20	-3.5	-2.3	0	0	-2.3	+ 8.5	+38.5

$$K_{O_2} = 0.67 \qquad k_{O_2} = 1.08$$

$$C_{(CO_2)} = K_{O_2}/K_{CO_2} - k_{O_2}/k_{CO_2} = 1/1.63 - 1/1.13 = 0.615 - 0.885 = -0.27 \text{ (see Table 9)}$$

*i.e. -3.0/-0.27 = +11.1

The data thus obtained have been plotted in figure 9 from which it is apparent that the R. Q. is very close to 1, i.e., for every molecule of oxygen consumed, one molecule of CO_2 is liberated. The example has been chosen to show that even relatively small changes in volume of either gas can be estimated quite accurately. It also has been chosen to illustrate, that under the conditions employed (i.e., pH 4.5) it is not necessary to add CO_2 to the gas phase in order to measure the respiration. In figure 9 we also have drawn in the oxygen uptake curve (broken line) obtained on the same algae when the CO_2 was absorbed by KOH (in the Warburg "Direct Method", Chapter 1). Comparison of the two curves shows that the presence of CO_2 does have an effect in this case, since respiration in the presence of CO_2 is less than respiration in its absence.

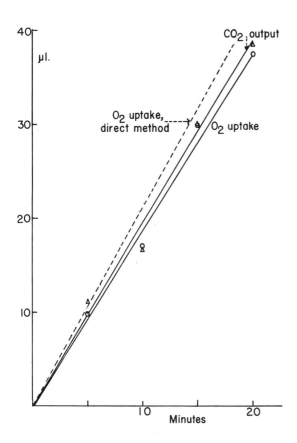

Figure 9
Solid lines are graphs of data illustrating use of the "Indirect Method" of Warburg. The broken line is for oxygen uptake measured by the "Direct Method". See text.

A second example employing a slightly different principle follows. In this case flasks of different volumes containing the same volume of fluid are employed. The example below deals with an unsupplemented isotonic brain homogenate which one does not wish to dilute, since soluble cofactors may diffuse out of the tissue. The reaction studied is the oxidation of glutamate in the presence of ammonia and adenylic acid, and for the sake of simplicity any effects of bound CO_2 and retention are ignored. In each of two flasks were placed the following materials: 0.2 ml. 0.1 M K_2HPO_4-KH_2PO_4, pH 7.3; 0.4 ml. 0.5 M KCl; 1.1 ml. isotonic (1.15%) KCl; 0.1 ml. 0.1 M $MgCO_3$; 0.2 ml. 0.1 M glutamate (pH 7); 0.1 ml. 0.1 M $(NH_4)_2HPO_4$; 0.3 ml. 0.01 M adenylic acid (pH 7); and 0.6 ml. isotonic KCl 10% rat brain homogenate. The larger flask (No. 12) had the constants K_{O_2} = 1.54, K_{CO_2} = 1.70, and the smaller flask (No. 1) had the constants k_{O_2} = 1.06, k_{CO_2} = 1.22. The readings obtained, corrected for thermobarometer changes, were as follows:

	Flask No. 1 (h)	Flask No. 12 (H)
1st 10 min.	−5	−2
2nd 10 min.	−10	−6
3rd 10 min.	−4	−2
next 20 min.	−7	−4

Calculations of oxygen uptake are shown in Table 11, and calculations of CO_2 exchange are shown in Table 12.

Table 11

Oxygen Exchange

Time, Min.	Flask 12		Flask 1		Difference	µl. O₂	Sum
	H(mm.)	HK_{CO_2}	h(mm.)	hk_{CO_2}			
10	-2	-3.4	-5	-6.1	+2.7	-54 *	-54
20	-6	-10.2	-10	-12.2	+2.0	-40	-94
30	-2	-3.4	-4	-4.9	+1.5	-30	-124
50	-4	-6.8	-7	-8.5	+1.7	-34	-158

$$C_{(O_2)} = \frac{1.70}{1.54} - \frac{1.22}{1.06} = 1.10 - 1.15 = -0.05$$

$$* \ \frac{2.7}{-0.05} = -54$$

Table 12

Carbon Dioxide Exchange

Time, Min.	Flask 12		Flask 1		Difference	µl. CO₂	Sum
	H(mm.)	HK_{O_2}	h(mm.)	hk_{O_2}			
10	-2	-3.1	-5	-5.3	+2.2	+55	55
20	-6	-9.3	-10	-10.6	+1.3	+33	88
30	-2	-3.1	-4	-4.2	+1.1	+27	115
50	-4	-6.2	-7	-7.4	+1.2	+30	145

$$C_{(CO_2)} = \frac{1.54}{1.70} - \frac{1.06}{1.22} = 0.91 - 0.87 = +0.04$$

The results have been plotted in figure 10 together with the oxygen uptake results obtained by means of the direct method (Chapter 1) and the carbon dioxide results obtained by the direct method (Chapter 3). Note first that while there are differences (the indirect method gave higher values) there is also relative agreement. This is striking if one considers that the actual readings in the case of the indirect method were from 2 to 5 mm. per interval. Yet the results obtained are a reasonably accurate estimate of the progress of the reaction.

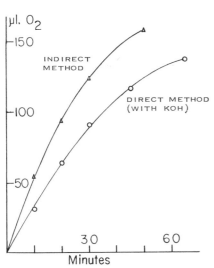

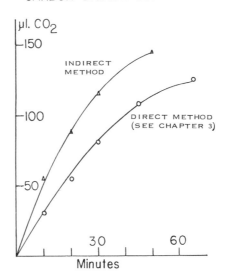

Figure 10
Graphs of data obtained for oxygen exchange and carbon dioxide
exchange by the direct and indirect methods

APPLICATIONS TO OTHER GASES

It should be pointed out that this type of system can be applied to gases other than CO_2
and O_2. For gases "a" and "b", equations (20) and (26) become:

$$x_a = X_a = \frac{HK_b - hk_b}{\dfrac{K_b}{K_a} - \dfrac{k_b}{k_a}} \quad \text{and } x_b = X_b = \frac{HK_a - hk_a}{\dfrac{K_a}{K_b} - \dfrac{k_a}{k_b}}$$

One may note that should gases "a" and "b" have the same solubility, then $K_a = K_b$ and
$k_a = k_b$ hence both equations equal infinity. Hence one can only apply this method to
gases whose solubilities differ appreciably.

PRACTICAL USE OF INDIRECT METHODS

To obtain data upon which a calculation may be based, one can do any of three things:

1. With flasks of approximately the same volume, employ markedly different
   volumes of fluid.

2. With the same volume of fluid, employ flasks of different volume. (See, for
   example, Emerson and Lewis, 1941 and Emerson and Chalmers, 1955.)

3. With flasks of the same volume, employ different amounts of fluid, and markedly different amounts of tissue such that the ratio of tissue to fluid medium

is the same in both cases. The derivations of this third type of use are somewhat different than previously described. We have not used this procedure,
and as it offers no advantages over the two procedures listed above, we omit
consideration of it here. Essentially one holds the tissue to fluid medium ratio
constant, divides the observed manometer changes by the amount of tissue, and
then calculates as described in the examples given. One must be certain that
the rate of reaction per unit tissue is the same in each case.

For a given situation, not all of these methods are equally suitable. For example, a reaction whose rate is dependent upon the concentration of a diffusible substance, such as a
coenzyme, will not proceed at the same rate in a flask containing a large amount of liquid
as in a flask containing a small amount of liquid. Hence, procedure 1 will give erroneous
results, whereas procedure 2 will give valid results. Under other circumstances procedure 1 might be preferable to procedure 2.

The derivations we have described above are somewhat different from those given by
Warburg (1924). They have been developed in this way to emphasize the broad applicability of this method. Warburg's treatment, while a perfectly general one, has been
more or less interpreted as a specific solution to the problem, and workers using the
method have usually attempted to duplicate the conditions used by Warburg, rather than
to employ the principles he emphasized in methods more suited to their conditions. It
is not necessary for the success of this method to use the modified flasks Warburg describes, to work in bicarbonate buffers at the concentration and at the pH that he employs,
nor is it necessary to work in an atmosphere of 5% CO_2. These conditions may be altered by the investigator at will and by the application of the laws of CO_2 – bicarbonate –
pH equilibria, outlined in Chapter 2, a wide range of conditions may be employed.

ADAPTATION TO MORE COMPLEX MEASUREMENTS

In the previous derivations and discussion we have described how it is possible to determine two gases simultaneously if their solubilities differ. One would have a very reasonable chance of determining oxygen and hydrogen, for example. Physiologically, however,
we are interested mostly in oxygen and carbon dioxide, and, as discussed in Chapter 2,
carbon dioxide while obeying the general laws of solubility, also forms carbonic acid
which can react with bases, and this alters the entire "solubility" picture.

If one is studying a reaction which produces no acid, but only CO_2, and can operate at a
pH below 5 (for example, urease acting on urea) one may employ a system with no CO_2
added to the atmosphere. Such reactions are, however, quite rare. An example of oxygen
uptake and CO_2 release under these circumstances is the respiration of acid tolerant sulfur bacteria (Vogler, LePage and Umbreit, 1941), but with few exceptions (Vogler, 1942)
such reactions are not sensitive to the presence of CO_2 and can thus be more readily
measured by more direct methods.

In the more normal physiological ranges, bicarbonate buffers may be employed; in this
case a CO_2 pressure in the atmosphere is required (see Chapter 2) to maintain a given
pH. If the concentration of bicarbonate ion is at least 10 times greater than any other
carbon dioxide retaining agent, the practical error involved from CO_2 retention by other
materials is usually negligible. Thus it is possible to use a Ringer's solution with bicarbonate at a definite CO_2 pressure and obtain adequate measurements of gas exchange. It
is under these circumstances that the method has been most widely used. As discussed
previously, another difficulty arises if acid is produced as well as CO_2, since both will
appear in the pressure changes as CO_2. What has usually been done is to assume a definite and constant R. Q. (usually taken as 0.9 or 1.0), i.e., for every oxygen taken up, one
(or 0.9) CO_2 is released. One then takes any extra CO_2 beyond this figure as being due

to acid production. But frequently, far from permitting assumptions of a definite and constant R. Q., this has been just the point which one wished to measure. Actually the problem of distinguishing between "respiratory CO_2" and acid production under these circumstances has never been critically solved although ingenious methods which approach a solution have been devised (Dixon, 1951).

If one wishes to work with media containing large amounts of CO_2-binding materials (protein, serum, etc.), the retention of CO_2 in the medium may become so large as to entirely invalidate the results of such measurements. The problem of "serum retention" (Warburg, 1925) has been approached and a reasonably satisfactory solution supplied for a few cases. But so complex do the conditions of operation become that most workers have studiously avoided such experiments. It is beyond the scope of this manual to describe these methods since they are admittedly too advanced for the beginner and are, in addition, of rather limited application. Before undertaking such studies a relatively long experience with manometric methods is probably necessary. Descriptions of the techniques employed and the theory upon which they are based will be found in papers by Warburg (1925), Warburg (1926), Warburg, Kubowitz, and Christian (1931), Dixon (1951), Dixon and Elliott (1930). The most general use of the "indirect" methods of Warburg has been in the determination of whether the presence of CO_2 (as bicarbonate) does indeed influence the reactions one is studying. If CO_2 is without effect, the "direct" methods are convenient and generally preferable. A short discussion of "retention" will be found in Chapter 7.

THE METHOD OF PARDEE

To this point two methods have been described for determining carbon dioxide (and/or acid production) simultaneously with oxygen consumption. These were the "Direct Method" which suffered from the difficulty that one tissue, respiring in the absence of CO_2, was compared to another tissue, respiring in the presence of CO_2. If the respiration rates of the tissues under the two conditions were not the same, the method yielded erroneous results. Except for this limitation, the method was simple and accurate. To determine whether the presence of CO_2 did or did not affect the rate of respiration (or CO_2 production) one had to employ the "Indirect Method" which was more difficult. If it could be demonstrated that the presence of CO_2 had no effect upon respiration, then oxygen uptake could be measured by the methods described in Chapter 1, and CO_2 or acid production by the direct method of Chapter 3. If it was demonstrated (by the indirect method) that CO_2 did influence the respiration, then one only could measure the respiration properly with the indirect system.

This situation now has been altered by a method introduced by Pardee (1949) and carefully checked and expanded by Krebs (1951b). This is a simple manometric method for measuring oxygen uptake of cells respiring in the presence of carbon dioxide. It is based on the use (in the center well of the manometric vessel) of a "CO_2-buffer" capable of maintaining a virtually constant pressure of CO_2 in the gas phase. A suitable "buffer" is an aqueous solution of diethanolamine which binds CO_2 reversibly, mostly as represented by the equation:

$$NH(CH_2CH_2OH)_2 + CO_2 + H_2O \rightleftharpoons HCO_3^- + \overset{+}{NH_2}(CH_2CH_2OH)_2$$

Any carbon dioxide formed by metabolism is removed by the reaction proceeding from left to right; any carbon dioxide used is replaced by the reverse reaction. Thus the tissue can be kept respiring in a known quantity of CO_2; CO_2 released is absorbed by the "buffer," and CO_2 taken up is replaced by the buffer.

This method does not measure CO_2, only oxygen uptake. It will serve to determine whether the system under study is altered by the presence of CO_2. If it is not, one may use the direct method for measurement of O_2 and CO_2 exchange. If, on comparison with oxygen uptake in the absence of CO_2, an effect of CO_2 is observed, then one may use the Pardee method to obtain rates of oxygen uptake, although the indirect method must be used to measure CO_2 formation.

The "CO_2–buffer" employed is diethanolamine containing 0.1% thiourea (Krebs, 1951b) to prevent auto-oxidation which occurs in some cases. Two methods of preparation follow:

1. Krebs (1951b) always employs a 4M diethanolamine buffer containing 0.1% thiourea; this buffer is prepared by passing a rapid stream of 100% CO_2 through 1/3 of the desired quantity of solution until it is saturated with CO_2. Saturation can be achieved in 30 minutes if a sintered aerator is used to give dispersion of the gas. The pH of the solution is about 8 after saturation with CO_2; the pH may be checked with phenolphthalein. The remaining 2/3 of the untreated solution is added to yield a stock solution. When it is to be employed, the stock solution is shaken (or aerated) with the gas mixture to be used in the respirometer at the temperature chosen for the subsequent determinations. The amount of buffer required depends on the amount of CO_2 to be exchanged, and thus depends upon the k_{CO_2} of the flask. The lower line of the large graph of figure 11 shows that at 40°C. and with 1% CO_2 in the gas phase, 0.5 ml. of the buffer (in equilibrium with 1% CO_2) is necessary if the k_{CO_2} is 1.5. This buffer is added to the center well. (If the flask constant k_{CO_2} = 2, then for the same conditions, 0.7 ml. of buffer would be necessary.) Further details are given by Krebs (1951b).

2. Pardee (1949) employs a slightly different system which we have also found satisfactory. We use 6 ml. diethanolamine (odorless and colorless; if it is otherwise refer to Pardee (1949)), 15 mg. thiourea, 3 grams of $KHCO_3$, the amount of 6 N HCl indicated in the inset of figure 11 for the conditions to be employed, and enough water to bring the volume to 15 ml. Thus, if 1% CO_2 is to be used, one adds 6 ml. diethanolamine, 15 mg. thiourea, 3 grams $KHCO_3$, 2.2 ml. 6 N HCl and 6.8 ml. H_2O. This mixture is shaken in a stoppered container and allowed to stand overnight. We generally use 0.6 ml. of this buffer per flask (in center well with filter paper) for flasks with k_{CO_2} from 1.0 to 2.0, 0.9 ml. (where possible) in flasks with k_{CO_2} of 2.0 to 3.0, to roughly follow the Krebs curve in figure 11.

In our hands, either of these methods seemed to work satisfactorily, and either seemed to be well within the range of accuracy desired.

W. W. UMBREIT

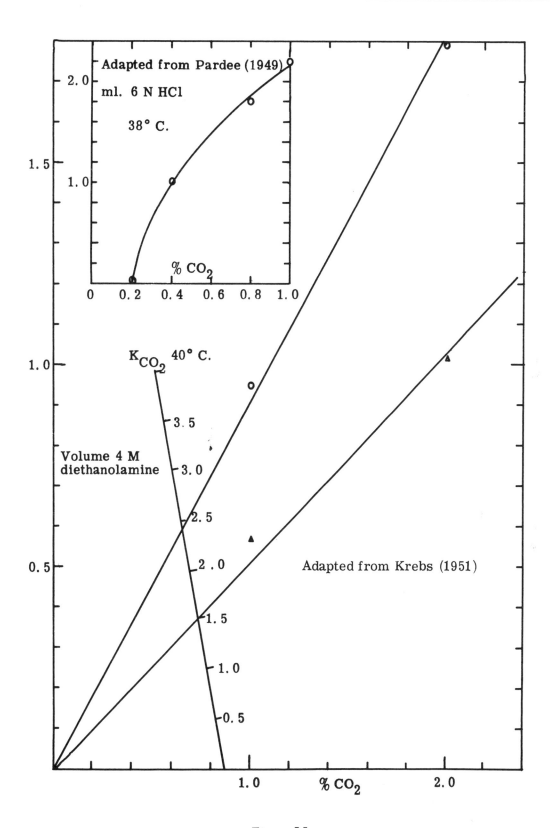

Figure 11
Graphs supplying information needed for the preparation of mixtures of diethanolamine
designed to maintain a constant pressure of CO_2. See text

Chapter 4
CALIBRATION OF RESPIROMETERS

Several methods for calibration of respirometers are described in this chapter. Although all the methods are valid and reasonably easy to employ, they vary in favor among individuals.

CALIBRATION WITH MERCURY

Although calibration with mercury may appear more laborious than other methods, it is the most accurate method available and is not particularly time consuming. If the weight of a flask and its mercury is 200 g., and this weight is determined within 200 mg. of its true weight, the error is only 1 part in 1,000 or 0.1%. As one normally is content with 1% accuracy in manometry, it is apparent that the mercury method furnishes a calibration whose errors are negligible in terms of the overall errors of manometric measurements. The method yields information from which flask constants can be calculated for any experimental condition.

With a diamond point scratch a permanent reference mark about 1 cm. above the flask-to-manometer ground joint. Weigh the Warburg flask empty. Fill the flask with clean mercury, and by using a capillary pipette with a bent tip tease any small air bubbles trapped at the sides and bottom of the flask to the surface. Place the flask on the dry manometer joint and seat the joint. If there is too much mercury or insufficient mercury to rise to the mark scratched on the capillary manometer, remove or add mercury with a capillary pipette until the mercury just reaches the mark when the joint is seated. Immediately plunge a thermometer into the flask of mercury and record the temperature. Weigh the flask and mercury.

Bore a hole in a rubber stopper to fit over the manometer ground joint, and put the stopper about half way onto the joint; this forms a well at the inlet to the manometer. Pour mercury quickly into this well with the manometer in an inverted position. This procedure minimizes the possibility of getting air bubbles in the mercury column. Tip the manometer to allow mercury to flow into the graduated arm of the manometer. Open the stopcock and allow the mercury to drop into contact with the stopcock. Remove the rubber stopper thus dumping the excess pool of mercury (it is convenient to work over a shallow box or tray lined with a sheet of paper to catch mercury). Tip the manometer until the mercury column coincides with the scratch mark and record the reading on the graduated manometer column. Weigh the mercury in a tared weighing bottle. Repeat the above procedure, this time introducing a shorter continuous column of mercury. Tip the entire column into the graduated manometer tube and record the mm. of tubing that it occupies. Weigh this mercury. Accept room temperature as a reasonably accurate measure of the temperature of the mercury.

Calculate the volume of the Warburg flask to the scratch mark by dividing the weight of mercury by its density at the recorded temperature. In the same manner find the volume of the manometer from the scratch mark to the recorded level, and the volume of the measured length of manometer tubing. Determine the volume of the manometer tubing per mm. length, and with this value correct the volume measured from the scratch mark to give the volume from the scratch mark to the 250 mm. mark. Calibration at the 250 mm. point is most convenient for studies of gas uptake. From the volume determined per mm. tubing length the calibration can be shifted to any other reference point that proves useful; the 50 mm. point is suitable when gas output is to be followed.

The sum of the flask volume and the manometer volume to the 250 mm. mark minus the liquid volume to be used in the flask is the V_g to be substituted in the equation to determine the flask constant. For density of mercury consult Table 14, page 59.

Schales' (1944) procedure has been modified by Loomis (1949), by Maxwell (1949) and by Santiago Grisolia. Grisolia's method, which permits separate calibration of flasks and manometers, is as follows:

1. Scratch a mark on the sidearm of the manometer above the ground glass joint.
2. Loosely clamp the manometer to a ringstand at an angle of about 30° with the horizontal, sidearm uppermost.
3. Close a short rubber tube with a screw clamp, fill it with mercury, and attach it to the inlet tube projecting below the manometer stopcock or to the "tail" of the stopcock. The stopcock should be open, and the rubber tube should be pushed on far enough so that the mercury approaches the sidearm scratch and the reference point (50, 150 or 250 mm.).
4. Tilt the manometer so that the mercury level is exactly at both the scratch mark and the reference point, or attach another screw clamp to compress the tubing to force mercury to these points.
5. Close the stopcock and pour out the mercury from the manometer into a tared receptacle. Weigh and calculate the gas volume of the manometer.
6. Place the manometer upright, fill the flask to be calibrated with mercury, and insert its ungreased sidearm plug. Remove any air bubbles with the aid of a wire.
7. Seat the flask on the ungreased ground joint of the manometer. If the mercury level is above or below the scratch mark on the manometer sidearm, remove or add small portions of mercury with the aid of a medicine dropper. Adjust until the level coincides with the mark when the flask is seated.
8. Measure the temperature of the mercury, pour it into a tared vessel, weight, and calculate the volume of the flask.
9. Add the values from steps 5 and 8 to obtain the total volume for a given flask and manometer.

This method has proved to be very efficient. After the manometer has been calibrated, further flasks may be calibrated with the manometer mounted and containing fluid.

MICROMETER TYPE CALIBRATOR

Calibration of manometers is particularly easy with the aid of the micrometer type calibrator (fig. 12) described by Lazarow (1949, 1951).

Calibration is achieved by displacing liquid (Lazarow suggested the use of H_2O, but we prefer Hg, as it does not wet glass) from the plastic standard taper reservoir so that it passes from the scratch mark on the manometer to 250 mm. (or any other point) on the manometer scale. The change in reading on the micrometer can be converted directly to volume, for the area of the piston is 1 sq. cm.; thus, each 0.001 cm. division on the micrometer scale is equivalent to 1 μl. A calibration accuracy of ± 0.2% is claimed. The calibration of flasks with mercury always has been a simple process, but the calibration of manometers has been more demanding. The micrometer device (sold by E. Machlett and Son, New York, and by other distributors) now makes manometer calibration distinctly more rapid and easy. Lazarow (1951) has described how the device also can be used to determine the volume of a Warburg vessel together with its manometer. Although

the apparatus was designed for Warburg manometers, it is even
more helpful for calibrating Barcroft manometers (see p. 52).

For speed, convenience and accuracy we calibrate flasks with
mercury and manometers with the micrometer type calibrator.

R. H. BURRIS

CALIBRATION WITH WATER AND MERCURY

The manometer is emptied, and cleaned; with the stopcock
closed, mercury is run into the ground joint while the manometer is inverted. By tilting the manometer it is easy to
adjust the mercury level so that it is exactly at the 250 mm.
point (or other reference point). The level of the mercury
in the ground joint arm is then marked; this can be done conveniently with a thin strip of gummed paper. The mercury is
emptied and weighed. This weight permits the calculation of
the volume of the manometer from the 250 mm. point to the
mark on the ground joint arm.

The clean dry flask with sidearm plugs in place is weighed. It
is then filled with distilled water which has been boiled to remove
dissolved gases and cooled. Water is added or removed until
the level just reaches the mark on the manometer arm when the
flask is firmly seated. It is well to add just enough water so
that the level rises about a mm. above the mark--the excess can
be removed by lowering the flask slightly and reseating; this
will force a small quantity of the water between the glass joint
and the flask whence it can be removed from the outside by absorption with a strip of filter paper. When the water has been
adjusted to the mark, the flask is removed and weighed. From the temperature of the
water its density can be ascertained, and the volume of the flask to the mark can be calculated. This added to the volume from the mark to the 250 mm. point gives the total
volume of the system.

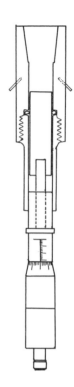

Figure 12
Micrometer type calibrator
described by Lazarow
(1949)

CALIBRATION BY RELEASE OF KNOWN VOLUME OF GAS

From the fact that the equation for the flask constant is x = hk, it is apparent that a knowledge of the values of h and x permits the calculation of k. Liberation or absorption of a
known quantity of gas (x) in a respirometer will give a measurable change on a manometer (h), and from this k can be obtained readily. Working back from the constant k,
the respirometer volume can be calculated, and from this information the respirometer
constants under different conditions can be determined. We use the "bicarbonate method"
routinely, for with this simple system many flasks can be calibrated rapidly and easily.

1. <u>Bicarbonate</u> <u>method</u>. With this method, the amount of CO_2 liberated by tipping
   acid into a solution of bicarbonate is determined in several flasks already
   standardized by other methods. The same procedure then is conducted in a
   series of unknown flasks. An example will clarify the procedure. Two flasks
   A (k_{CO_2} = 1.75) and B (k_{CO_2} = 1.84), standardized previously with mercury,
   are supplied with 2.5 ml. of approximately 0.005 M $KHCO_3$ solution in the main
   compartment. To each sidearm is added 0.5 ml. of approximately 2 N H_2SO_4.

After equilibration (37° C.) and reading, the acid is tipped in from the side-arms. In flask A, there is a rise of 121 mm. (corrected for thermobarometer); 2.5 ml. of $KHCO_3$ solution contain 121 x 1.75 = 212 µl. CO_2. Repeat: Flask A; h = 118, µl. CO_2 = 207. Flask B; first run, h = 116 x 1.84 = 213 µl. CO_2; second run, h = 112, µl. CO_2 = 206. Therefore, 2.5 ml. of the bicarbonate solution contains $\frac{212 + 207 + 213 + 206}{4}$ = 209.5 µl. CO_2.

Series of unknown and known flasks were treated simultaneously in the same manner and gave the following results:

| | Known flasks | | Unknown flasks | | | | | | |
	A	B	1	2	3	4	5	6	7
Run 1:	121	116	146	124	110	132	140	126	138
Run 2:	118	112	142	123	113	133	151	127	139
Average h			144	123	111	132	145	126	138
k_{CO_2}	1.75	1.84	1.45	1.70	1.88	1.58	1.44	1.66	1.52

Calculations to convert h to k_{CO_2} are as follows:

Since x = hk, $k = \frac{x}{h}$.

In this example, x (determined in the known flasks A and B) is 209.5, for flask 1, $k_{CO_2} = \frac{209.5}{144}$ = 1.45. Known flasks are used to standardize the solution of bicarbonate, as its composition may vary with conditions of storage, and as the composition of dry $KHCO_3$ is insufficiently reproducible to depend upon direct weighing for preparation of a primary standard. The above data are taken from a typical run and are not "doctored" in any way. Flask 5 should be re-run, since the factor determined in the first run was 1.495 and in the second 1.39. When variations greater than this have been encountered, they have resulted from blowing out pipettes or from having traces of residual alkaline detergent in the flasks.

2. Ferricyanide-Hydrazine method. This method was originally described by Michaelis and Rona (1930) and was brought to our attention by Dr. Bruno Rosenfeld who has used it extensively. It has the marked advantage that one can employ a weighed or a chemically standardized primary standard. The reaction is based on the following reaction, which occurs under alkaline conditions.

$$4 Fe^{+++}(CN)_6 + N_2H_4 \longrightarrow 4 Fe^{++}(CN)_6 + 4H^+ + N_2$$

The potassium ferricyanide is recrystallized when necessary from hot water, dried, and stored in a desiccator in the dark. It is used as 0.1 M solution, which will keep for several days in the dark. Note that each ml. of 0.1 M potassium ferricyanide liberates $\frac{2240}{4}$ = 560 µl. N_2, thus one would normally add 0.4 ml. (= 224 µl.) of 0.1 M solution. The other reagents required are 4 N NaOH and hydrazine; the latter is prepared by dissolving 5 gm. hydrazine sulfate $(N_2H_4 \cdot H_2SO_4)$ in 100 ml. of hot water. The excess separates on cooling, and the clear saturated solution is used:

A typical system employs the following:

Main compartment:

      0.4 ml. 0.1 M potassium ferricyanide ($= 224 \mu$l. N_2)
      0.4 ml. 4 N NaOH
      1.2 ml. water

Sidearm:

      0.5 ml. hydrazine sulfate solution
      0.5 ml. 4 N NaOH

After equilibration, the contents of the sidearm are tipped in, and h is determined. (The reaction is complete in about 30 min.)

$$k = \frac{x}{h} = \frac{224}{h}$$
(this is $k_{N_2} = k_{O_2}$)

If there is any doubt about the purity of the potassium ferricyanide, its solution can be standardized iodometrically as follows:

$$K_3Fe(CN)_6 + KI \longrightarrow K_4Fe(CN)_6 + \text{"I"}$$
$$K_4Fe(CN)_6 + 2 ZnSO_4 \longrightarrow Zn_2Fe(CN)_6 + 2K_2SO_4$$

In an Erlenmeyer flask containing 2 ml. 5% KI, 3 ml. of 0.5 M $ZnSO_4$, and 2 ml. N H_2SO_4, add 2 ml. of 0.15 or 0.1 M potassium ferricyanide solution. The iodine liberated is titrated with 0.05 N sodium thiosulfate with starch as an indicator.

W. W. UMBREIT

CALIBRATION FOR INTERCHANGEABILITY OF FLASKS

Allen (1948) has described a method whereby any flask can be used on any manometer without direct calibration for that manometer. This is particularly convenient when replacement is necessary. A flask is weighed and then filled with enough mercury to rise about 1 cm. into the manometer arm. It is then placed on the dry joint of the first manometer of a series and seated. A line is scratched with a diamond point at the top of the mercury column. One then repeats the procedure and marks the point to which the mercury rises on all other manometers of the series; care is taken to be sure that the temperature of the mercury does not change or that none is spilled. The manometer volumes are then calibrated to the mark as described under calibration with mercury. From this point on it is only necessary to calibrate any flask to the reference mark on any manometer, and the V_g for that flask in combination with any of the other manometers of the series can be calculated readily.

This method is simple and very satisfactory when all manometers of the set have relatively uniform standard taper joints. The ground joints, although standard in taper, seat to different depths in the flasks, and this variation may be so great that the mercury will not rise to a usable position in all manometers. This difficulty is not encountered with the method proposed by Dickens (1951).

For the method of Dickens, a standard taper inner joint with about an inch of capillary above the joint is obtained as a reference joint for calibration (calibration joint). Tare a flask plus the calibration joint, remove the joint, fill the flask with mercury, remove bubbles, insert the joint and seat it dry (never twist dry, ground glass joints!!). The excess mercury will flow out the top of the capillary. Reweigh the flask with calibration joint, record the temperature of the mercury, and from the weight of the mercury and its density at the observed temperature (see p. 59) calculate the volume of the flask to the top of the calibration joint. Repeat with all other flasks.

Choose a single flask (one without sidearms is most convenient), fill this calibration flask with mercury, and determine its volume on each manometer in the usual fashion (see p. 46), by adjusting the mercury until it rises to the scratch mark on the manometer. Determine the volume of the manometer from the scratch mark to 250 mm. (or other reference point) by any of the methods described earlier.

If a flask on the calibration joint has a volume of 14.50 ml. and on a given manometer has a volume of 14.00 ml., it is apparent that it seats farther on the manometer joint by an amount corresponding to 0.50 ml. It follows that any other flask will have 0.50 ml. less effective volume on this manometer than it has on the calibration joint. Thus the total volume of any flask on this manometer will be its volume on the calibration joint minus 0.50 ml. This factor (-0.50 ml. for the manometer discussed) is a constant for the manometer. Obviously the factor may be positive or negative for other manometers.

The following examples may aid in clarifying this concept: The tare of the calibration flask plus the calibration joint was 30.6 g., the gross weight of flask, joint and mercury was 190.2 g., so the net weight of the mercury was 159.6 g. The temperature of the mercury was 25° C. (density 13.534), so the volume of the calibration flask on the calibration joint equals 159.6/13.534 or 11.79 ml. Flask 1 had a volume of 12.03 ml. and flask 2 a volume of 11.27 ml. on the calibration joint.

Calibration with mercury indicated that the calibration flask on manometer 1 had a volume of 11.43 ml., a volume 0.36 ml. less than on the calibration joint; on manometer 2 the calibration flask had 0.05 ml. greater volume than on the calibration joint. The volume of either flask to the scratch mark on either manometer now can be calculated.

The volume of flask 1 on the calibration joint is 12.03 ml. The volume of any flask on manometer 1 is 0.36 ml. less than on the calibration joint, so the volume of flask 1 on manometer 1 is 12.03 - 0.36 = 11.67 ml. to the scratch mark.

The volume of flask 2 on the calibration joint is 11.27 ml. The volume of any flask on manometer 2 is 0.05 ml. greater than on the calibration joint, so the volume of flask 2 on manometer 2 is 11.27 + 0.05 = 11.32 ml. to the scratch mark.

Flask 2 on manometer 1 would have a volume of 11.27 - 0.36 = 10.91 ml. to the scratch mark.

The volume from the scratch mark to the 250 mm. or other reference point on the manometer is determined independently and is added to the flask volume to give the total volume of the system with an empty flask. The flask constant can be calculated from these data (see p. 4). The method is equally suitable for the calibration of Barcroft manometers.

W. W. UMBREIT and R. H. BURRIS

CALIBRATION OF THE BARCROFT DIFFERENTIAL RESPIROMETER

The constant of the Barcroft differential respirometer may be arrived at by three methods: (1) by calculation, using the simplified equation (equation 34, page 81), (2) by adding or removing a known volume of gas from the reaction side of the respirometer (Münzer and Neumann, 1917), and (3) by liberating or absorbing a known amount of gas in the reaction vessel in a chemical reaction (see page 48). Since the first method is preferred by most workers because of its simplicity and accuracy, it is the only one which will be described, despite the fact that the latter two methods may possess certain advantages under some circumstances.

DETERMINING THE CONSTANT BY CALCULATION: The usual case is to calculate the constant for O_2, i.e., K_{O_2} (NTP). 'A' is determined by running in sufficient mercury to form a 100-150 mm. column in the graduated portion of one side of the manometer. While holding the manometer by its ends to avoid a change in temperature, measure the length of the mercury colum in 3-4 positions. Run the mercury into the other side of the manometer and repeat the measurements. The length of the column in the several positions serves as a measure of the uniformity of the bore of the capillary tubing. The volume of the mercury column is calculated from the weight and density of the mercury at the temperature of the room. 'A' then equals the volume in μl. divided by the average length in mm. The A values for both sides of the manometer should agree to within 5% ; if not, it is desirable to check the K_{O_2} obtained by this method with one of the other two methods; method (2) is readily adaptable to determining the K_{O_2} value for different values of h, which covers this variation in cross-sectional area of the manometer tubes.

To determine the volumes of the manometer tubes: An index mark is made on each manometer limb about 1 cm. above the ground-glass vessel-joint. Attach a small funnel to the stopcock capillary with a 25-40 cm. length of rubber tubing. While manipulating the manometer in an inverted position, add mercury through the stopcock capillary until one meniscus coincides with the index mark and the other meniscus coincides with the "zero" on the graduated portion of the manometer (the 15 cm. graduation). Of course, there must not be any trapped bubbles of air. The stopcock is now closed and the mercury in the manometer limb shaken out and weighed. The volume of the mercury is determined from its weight and density, and it represents the volume of the manometer limb from the "zero" of the manometer to the "index mark". The same procedure is followed to determine the volume of the other manometer limb. Much of the labor involved in determining the A values and the volumes of the manometer tubes can be eliminated by employing the micrometer type calibrator shown in figure 12. Place Hg in the standard taper well of the calibrator, seat the calibrator on one of the standard taper joints of the manometer, attach the two with springs, and discharge any bubbles from the reservoir. Advance the micrometer screw to bring the Hg to the index mark above the ground joint of the manometer. Record the micrometer reading (reading 1). Advance the micrometer screw to displace Hg through the horizontal capillary, into the vertical capillary, and up to the stopcock (the opposite end of the manometer must be closed and the stopcock adjacent to the micrometer open while Hg is being raised to the stopcock; the stopcocks must be greased to prevent leakage). Close the adjacent stopcock, open the opposite stopcock, and advance the Hg to a readable position on the manometer (between 250 and 300 mm.). Record the micrometer reading (reading 2) and the point on the manometer to which the Hg has advanced. Advance the Hg to 150 mm. on the manometer and record the micrometer reading (reading 3). Advance the Hg to a point between 0 and 50 mm. and record the manometer and micrometer (reading 4) readings. By continuing this stepwise advance and measurement of the Hg until it reaches the index mark above the other flask, all the data necessary for calibrating the manometer can be obtained. The difference between micrometer readings 3 and 1 indicates the μl. volume from the index mark above the flask to the 150 mm. reference point (each 0.001 cm. advance of the micrometer screw displaces 1 μl. Hg). Readings 4 - 2, 4 - 3, and 3 - 2 indicate the volumes between the points recorded on one arm of the manometer and can be used to calculate the cross section of the capillary tubing and its uniformity of bore.

To determine the volumes of the flasks: The volumes of the flasks, which have been labeled R and L respectively, are determined at the temperature of the bath. Using a bit of filter paper held with curved forceps, or a pipe cleaner, to remove bubbles of trapped air, fill each flask with sufficient mercury so that the mercury is forced up to the "index mark" on the manometer limb when the flask is attched to its manometer limb. Ordinarily this requires time and patience. The mercury-filled vessel is placed in a shallow dish (a tea-glass coaster works very well) and the whole supported in the bath with the neck of the vessel projecting above the water. Allow time for temperature equilibration. Take hold of the coaster and neck of the flask, and carefully work the neck of the flask onto the ungreased joint of its capillary limb. When this operation is properly carried out no mercury is trapped in the ground-glass joint. Usually the meniscus of the mercury does not coincide with the "index mark" on the first trial. Return the coaster-supported flask to the bath, and add or remove mercury from the flask with a capillary-tipped eye-dropper. After allowing time for temperature equilibration, again attach the flask to its manometer limb for another check on the coincidence of the mercury meniscus and "index mark". This is obtained by repeating the above procedure. The mercury is then weighed and its volume determined at the temperature of the bath. The main sources of error in this determination are: Air is often trapped below the ground-glass joint. It can be removed by rocking the top of the respirometer from side to side. The temperature of the glass and mercury may change considerably while the vessel is being attached to the manometer unless this operation is carried out quickly. Avoid contact between flask and hands as much as possible. Finally, check the final coincidence of the mercury meniscus and "index mark" by submerging the end of the manometer limb with the attached flask filled with mercury in the bath.

By adding the volume of the vessel to the corresponding manometer limb volume, the total gas volume of one side of the respirometer is obtained. Determine the total gas volume of the other side in the same manner. These two gas volumes should be equal to within 0.1%. In most instances they will be unequal in volume. While it may help to switch the flasks, the quicker procedure is to pair flask and limb of manometer so that the volume of the reaction-vessel side of the respirometer is the smaller. Glass beads can then be added to the compensation-vessel side to obtain the same gas volume. The requisite volume of glass beads can be measured out by adding beads to water in a partially filled burette until the necessary volume is obtained. This "pairing" is unnecessary if it makes no difference which limb of the manometer carries the reaction vessel.

The gas volume of each side can now be obtained by subtracting the volume of the liquid (including that in the sidearms and center well, and the volume of the tissue) which will be used in the flasks from the total gas volume.

The density of the manometric liquid, e.g., iso-caproic acid, is determined at the temperature of the room by means of a pycnometer. P_O can then be defined in terms of mm. of manometric liquid.

The absorption coefficient, α, of oxygen in the liquid must be obtained from a table of "α values" (see Chapter 1), or determined by actual experiment. For most purposes the α for oxygen in water is sufficiently accurate. 'α' had best be determined or obtained from the literature for liquids other than water if the volume of liquid in the flask is more than 10 ml. It is possible to calculate the α of oxygen, carbon dioxide, and nitrogen from the data of Geffken (1904) for salt solutions.

Having obtained the above data, the K_{O_2} of the respirometer may be calculated with the use of equation (34). The example below may be of help. If all flasks and manometers are calibrated to be interchangeable (see p. 50), flasks of matching volumes can be selected readily for any manometer, when matched volumes appear desirable.

DETAILS OF CALIBRATION: (a) General considerations: Room and bath temperatures, 25°C; iso-caproic acid as manometer liquid; flasks of Warburg type with two sidearms; volume of liquid in each flask, 4.2 ml. (3.0 ml. of nutrient solution, 0.5 ml. 5% glucose in each sidearm, 0.2 ml. 20% KOH in center well). The reaction vessel is to contain 100 µl. (0.1 ml.) of algal cells suspended in 3,000 µl. of nutrient solution.

(b) Determination of A:

Average length of H_g column in left side of manometer = 105.8 mm.
Average length of H_g column in right side of manometer = 107.6 mm.
Weight of mercury   = 606.4 mg.

$$A = \frac{606.4}{106.7 \times 13.53} = 0.42 \text{ mm.}^2$$

(c) Determination of V_g and V'_g:

Wt. of H_g filling right flask and manometer limb = 251.3 gms.
Wt. of H_g filling left flask and manometer limb = 261.6 gms.

$$\text{Then } V_g = \frac{251.3 \times 1000}{13.53} - 4,200 = 14,372 \text{ µl.}$$

$$\text{And } V'_g = \frac{261.6 \times 1000}{13.53} - 4,200 = 15,134 \text{ µl.}$$

To reduce V'_g to the same volume as V_g, 760 µl. of glass beads are added to the left (compensation) vessel.

(d) Determination of P_0:

Wt. of 5.00 ml. of iso-caproic acid in a previously calibrated
    pycnometer   = 4.605 gms.
Density of the acid   = 0.921

$$\text{Then } P_0 = \frac{760 \times 13.53}{0.921} = 11,164 \text{ mm.}$$

(e) The absorption coefficient, α, of O_2 = 0.030

(f) Calculation of K_{O_2}:

$$K_{O_2} = h \left[\left(1 + \frac{0.42 \times 11,164}{2 \times 14,373}\right) \left(\frac{\frac{14,373 \times 273}{298} + 4,200 \times 0.030}{11,164} + \frac{0.42 \times 273}{2 \times 298}\right) \right]$$

and $X_{O_2} = h(1.61)$.

CALIBRATION OF THE WARBURG RESPIROMETER
BY REMOVING A KNOWN VOLUME OF GAS

A simplified apparatus operating on the same principle as the Münser and Neumann method (Münzer and Neumann, 1917) has been described by Scholander et al. (1950). The calibrator may be simply a gas-tight, graduated 1.0 ml. syringe, of an outside diameter the same as the glass capillary extending above the three-way stopcock of the respirometer, with the barrel cut off squarely at the 0.0 ml. mark. The tip of the plunger must also be cut off squarely. The calibrator is joined to the squared-off tip of the respirometer capillary that projects above the stopcock with a short piece of tygon tubing. The joint must be a void-free fit for any space here will lead to erroneous results. This may be accomplished by using a small amount of lanolin as a lubricant in butting the tip of the capillary and the syringe barrel, provided that any lanolin forced into the gas space of the capillary and syringe barrel is removed (a pipe cleaner works very well).

The respirometer, equipped with its empty vessel and the requisite amount of manometer fluid, with the calibrator attached is mounted on the shaker of the constant temperature water bath. With the three-way stopcock turned to open the respirometer to the air through the stopcock-plug vent, level the manometer fluid at the 150 mm. mark. After allowing sufficient time for temperature equilibration, push the plunger of the syringe down to the 0.0 mark on the barrel (this setting is automatically indexed because the plunger comes to rest on the tip of the manometer capillary). The stopcock is now turned to connect the gas space of the respirometer with that in the capillary above. After checking to see that the manometer fluid is level, the plunger of the syringe is now pulled upward to increase the unknown gas volume (volume of the respirometer plus that from the base of the stopcock to the point of union of capillary and syringe) by 100 μl. The manometer fluid is now returned to its former level in the closed side of the manometer and the difference in height of the fluid in the open side, i. e., $\underline{h}$, is recorded. On returning the plunger to its original position it should be possible to again level the fluid in both sides of the manometer at the 150 mm. mark.

The above procedure is carried out several times until the operator is assured by the constancy of the ratio of the increase in gas volume to $\underline{h}$, which should agree to within 1%, of the accuracy of the determinations of these two sets of values.

The total gas volume, $V_{uncorrected}$, of the system may now be calculated by substituting any of the acceptable corresponding values of V_c (volume of gas removed) and $\underline{h}$ in the following equation:

$$V_{uncorrected} = \frac{V_c}{h} \times P - 1$$

where P is atmospheric pressure (corrected) in mm. of manometer fluid.

The corrected gas volume, V, of the Warburg respirometer at the temperature of calibration may now be obtained by subtracting from the uncorrected gas volume the increase in volume, V_c, and the volume of the gas space in the capillary of the stopcock and in the length of glass capillary above the stopcock, V_y. V_y may be determined with Hg in the usual manner, or by filling the space with water from a graduated 1.0 syringe through a short piece of intravenous polyethylene tubing attached to the needle. Then,

$$V = V_{uncorrected} - V_c - V_y$$

The K_{O_2} and K_{CO_2} of the respirometer may now be obtained through the use of the equation given below under the heading of "Flask Constants".

J. F. STAUFFER

FLASK CONSTANTS

As derived and illustrated by an example in Chapter 1, the relation between the difference in reading observed on the Warburg manometer (h) and the gas change within the system (x) is:

$$x = h \left[\frac{V_g \frac{273}{T} + V_f \alpha}{P_o} \right] = hk \text{ where } k = \left[\frac{V_g \frac{273}{T} + V_f \alpha}{P_o} \right]$$

Since for any given experimental condition, the gas volume of the flask (V_g), the fluid volume of the flask (V_f), the temperature (T), the solubility of the gas in the fluid (α), and the pressure (in mm. of manometer fluid) of 1 atmosphere (P_o) are all constant, the value "k" (the "flask constant") is constant for any given set of experimental conditions and varies only as the experimental conditions vary.

FLASK CONSTANTS WITH DIFFERENT VOLUMES OF FLUID IN THE WARBURG FLASKS

One can, of course, calculate the constant to be employed for any set of experimental conditions from the equation above. However, there is a simple relationship between the constant for one set of conditions and the constant for the same conditions except for the presence of one more ml. fluid in the flask. We will definie this change in constant as $\triangle k$.

$$\triangle k = k' - k = \frac{(V_g - 1000) \frac{273}{T} + \alpha (V_f + 1000)}{P_o} - \frac{V_g \frac{273}{T} + \alpha V_f}{P_o}$$

(k' = constant for flask with 1 ml. more fluid in it)
(k = constant for original flask)

$$\triangle k = \frac{-1000 \frac{273}{T} + 1000 \alpha}{P_o}$$

Thus, $\triangle k$ is independent of V_g or V_f (i.e., factors governed by the size of the flask or the amount of fluid in it) and is dependent only upon α and T. For any temperature the $\triangle k$ is calculated easily.

For example, a flask has a k_{O_2} (37° C.) of 1.69 when it contains 3 ml. of fluid. If this flask were to contain 4 ml. of fluid its factor would be: k_{O_2} = 1.69 - 0.086 = 1.60. If it were to be run with 1.5 ml. of fluid its factor would be: k_{O_2} = 1.69 + (1.5 x 0.086) = 1.69 + 0.13 = 1.82.

CALCULATIONS OF FACTORS FROM k_e

Returning to the original equation for calculating the flask constant:

$$k = \frac{V_g \frac{273}{T} + \alpha V_f}{P_o}$$

it will be noted that if there is no fluid in the flask its constant (here labeled k_e) is:

$$k_e = \frac{V_g \frac{273}{T}}{P_0}$$

This constant is independent of the gas involved and depends only on the volume of the flask and the temperature. Further, the term $\frac{273}{T}$ is a constant (c) dependent only on the

temperature. The value of this constant (for Brodie's solution in the manometer, i.e., $P_0 = 10,000$) at different temperatures is given in Table 13.

CONSTANTS USED IN CORRECTING k WHEN THE FLASK CONTAINS A DIFFERENT VOLUME OF FLUID

Table 13

| Temperature | | $\triangle k$** | |
°C	(c)*	O_2***	CO_2
20	0.0932	-0.090	-0.005
25	0.0916	-0.089	-0.016
28	0.0907	-0.088	-0.020
30	0.0901	-0.087	-0.023
35	0.0886	-0.086	-0.029
37	0.0881	-0.086	-0.031
40	0.0872	-0.085	-0.034

* x 10^{-3}; $k_e = V_g(c)$

** For each additional ml. of fluid in the flask the factor changes by this amount.

*** The same values may be used for N_2 and H_2

Therefore, one may calculate readily any flask constant for any conditions as follows:

$$k = k_e + (\triangle k) \text{ (ml. fluid)}$$
$$= (V_g) (c) + (\triangle k) \text{ (ml. fluid)}$$

Thus at 37°C., flask volume 13,500 μl.:

$$k_e = 13,500 \times 0.0881 \times 10^{-3} = 1.19$$

$$k_{O_2} \left[3 \text{ ml. Fluid} \right] = 1.19 + (-0.086 \times 3) = 1.19 - 0.26 = 0.93$$

$$k_{O_2} \left[2 \text{ ml. Fluid} \right] = 1.19 + (-0.086 \times 2) = 1.19 - 0.17 = 1.02$$

$$k_{CO_2} \left[3 \text{ ml. fluid} \right] = 1.19 + (-0.031 \times 3) = 1.19 - 0.09 = 1.10$$

The MacLeod and Summerson (1940) graphical method of determining flask constants is based on the same principles as govern the calculations from k_e and $\triangle k$. If the k_e (0 ml.) and the k for any other volume (e.g., 3 ml.) are calculated and these constants are connected by a straight line on a graph with ml. fluid as the abscissa and flask constant as ordinate, the constant for any liquid volume can be taken from the line. The lines for a given temperature have the same slope, but a different intercept for each flask. With a series of lines for a given flask, at 10° temperature intervals, flask constants at any liquid volume and temperature can be obtained by inspection.

It should be noted also that the difference between the k_{O_2} and k_{CO_2} (or the constant for any other gas) is a constant under the same experimental conditions. In the equation:

$$k = \frac{V_g \dfrac{273}{T} + \alpha\, V_f}{P_o}$$

the nature of the gas influences only the factor α. Thus, at 37°C. and with 3,000 μl. fluid in the flask the term $\dfrac{\alpha\, V_f}{10,000}$ for O_2 is:

$$\frac{0.024 \times 3,000}{10,000} = 0.0072$$

and for CO_2 is:

$$\frac{0.57 \times 3,000}{10,000} = 0.171$$

and the difference is: 0.171 - 0.007 = 0.164.

The k_{CO_2} for any flask with 3 ml. of liquid at 37°C. is 0.164 higher than the k_{O_2} for the flask. If the k_{O_2} values are known for a set of flasks the k_{CO_2} values for the same conditions can be calculated merely by adding a constant.

CONSTANTS USED IN THE CALIBRATION OF FLASKS

Table 14

Temperature	Density* of Hg	Water	α O_2	α CO_2	α H_2	α CO	α N_2
20	13.5462	0.9982	0.0310	0.878	0.0182	0.0232	0.0154
25	13.5340	0.9971	0.0283	0.759	0.0175	0.0214	0.0143
30	13.5217	0.9957	0.0261	0.665	0.0170	0.0200	0.0134
35	13.5095	0.9941	0.0244	0.592	0.0167	0.0188	0.0126
37	13.5046	0.9934	0.0239	0.567	0.0166	0.0184	0.0123
40	13.4973	0.9922	0.0231	0.530	0.0164	0.0177	0.0118

*Density = grams/ml.

W W UMBREIT

NOMOGRAPHS FOR WARBURG FLASK CONSTANTS

Dixon (1945) published nomographs for the calculation of flask constants for both the constant volume and differential respirometers. Later, Dixon (1951a) published a very convenient set of improved nomographs; these were reproduced on a smaller scale by Dixon (1951). The use of either a nomograph or the rapid calculation from k_e and Δk simplify calculations. The nomograph (fig. 13), for the Warburg constant volume respirometer, given here, covers the usual flask volumes encountered.

To use the nomograph (fig. 13) to calculate the k_{O_2} for a flask, connect the volume of the fluid in ml. (scale A) with the temperature in °C. (scale B) and read the product where the straightedge intersects scale D. Then connect the gas volume in ml. (scale J) with temperature in °C. (scale I) and read the product at the point that the straightedge intersects scale H. Add these two products longhand or add them by connecting the products on scales D and H with a straightedge and reading the sum on scale G. This sum is the flask constant.

To calculate k_{CO_2} connect the volume of fluid in ml. (scale A) with the temperature (scale C) and read the product at the point the straightedge intersects scale E. Connect scales J and I and read on H as for determining k_{O_2}. Add the products longhand or connect the product on scale E with the product on scale H and read the sum on scale F. This sum is the flask constant.

R. H. BURRIS

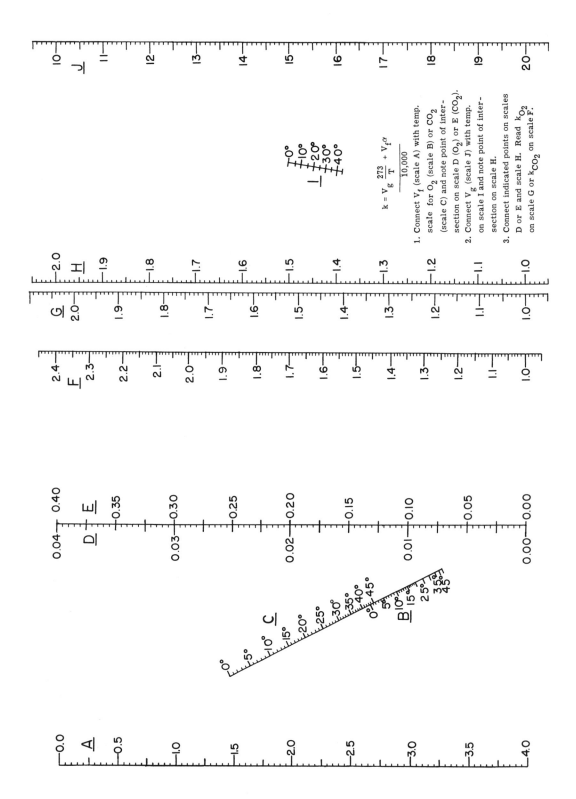

$$k = \frac{V_g \frac{273}{T} + V_f \alpha}{10,000}$$

1. Connect V_f (scale A) with temp. scale for O_2 (scale B) or CO_2 (scale C) and note point of intersection on scale D (O_2) or E (CO_2).

2. Connect V_g (scale J) with temp. on scale I and note point of intersection on scale H.

3. Connect indicated points on scales D or E and scale H. Read k_{O_2} on scale G or k_{CO_2} on scale F.

Figure 13
Nomograph for the calculation of Warburg flask constants

Chapter 5
USEFUL TECHNIQUES IN MANOMETRY

The practical operation of any instrument involves details which are not readily apparent from the description of the procedures or the theory of the instrument. We have collected below some of the techniques which are useful with manometric instruments.

CLEANING GLASSWARE

All reaction flasks must be cleaned thoroughly. There are many methods for cleaning manometric glassware, but only a few which are widely used will be described here. The most suitable method to employ may depend upon the reactions and types of enzyme preparations being studied. Often tissue homogenates are sensitive to metal contamination, whereas bacterial suspensions may be insensitive to small amounts of metals but markedly affected by traces of vitamins or other organic substances. When fatty preparations are used, thorough washing with an organic solvent is advisable, although under many conditions a hot water rinse is adequate for removing grease. Recently a number of ultrasonic cleaners, which will clean glassware very rapidly, have been placed on the market. Three other practical methods for cleaning reaction vessels follow:

1. Dichromate method:
   a. Place flasks in unleaded gasoline to remove grease, or remove with gasoline on a cotton swab.
   b. Wash with water.
   c. Place in cleaning solution for 12 - 24 hours. (Cleaning solution: dissolve 63 g. sodium (or potassium) dichromate by heating with 35 ml. water. Add conc. H_2SO_4 to 1 liter.)
   d. Remove, wash by rinsing in tap water at least 4 times and in distilled water twice. Some operators place the flask in dilute NaOH (5 g./liter) after removing the excess chromic acid before rinsing with distilled water. Others soak the flasks in distilled water for an hour after the initial rinsings and then give them a final rinse, for dichromatic residues adhere tenaciously to glass.
2. Nitric acid method:
   a. Place flasks in gasoline for 30 minutes to remove grease, or remove with gasoline on a cotton swab.
   b. Wash with water.
   c. Transfer to a mixture of equal parts of concentrated H_2SO_4 and HNO_3 in a Pyrex dish. Heat this mixture for 30 to 60 minutes in a hood. Cool.
   d. Remove, wash several times in tap water, and rinse twice with distilled water.
3. Detergent method:
   a. Remove grease with gasoline on a cotton swab. Rinse with water.
   b. Immerse in a pan containing 1 tablespoonful Kelvar per gallon of water. Kelvar (Wyandotte Chem. Corp., Wyandotte, Mich.) is recommended because it contains a substance to inhibit etching; many hot detergents etch glassware excessively. Boil gently for 15 minutes. Excessively long heating or boiling the pan dry will accelerate etching of the flasks. A cylindrical Pyrex jar with a coil of metal tubing immersed in the detergent solution provides a convenient cleaning bath; the bath is heated by passing steam through the coil.
   c. Rinse several times with tap water and twice with distilled water.

WATER

Discussion of water may appear prosaic, but a supply of suitable water is highly important, and Dr. R. W. McGilvery has furnished the following discussion. Building engineers and architects often have difficulty in appreciating the exacting requirement of biochemical research for pure distilled water, and the investigator should be alert for indications of improper design or malfunction of his own source. Although redistilled water is commonly used for reagents, most laboratories employ the building supply of distilled water for rinsing glassware, and this may leave a serious residue of contaminants.

General analyses of the water are seldom feasible for control purposes, but simple conductivity testers, which are commercially available, should be used to test the operation of the system at frequent intervals. This test will not detect the presence of contaminants such as aluminum dissolved from the piping. With pot type stills using the steam supply for heat, the main dangers arise from the development of leaks in the steam or condenser water supply or from the loss of the tin coating on the metal parts. Stills that condense raw steam after passing it through a charcoal bed have not given satisfactory service in our experience, for they pass organic materials, apparently derived from boiler additives, into the condensate.

With a hard water supply, satisfactory distilled water should have a conductivity no greater than that given by 1.5 ppm of NaCl, and preferably below that of 1.0 ppm. Water purified by passing it over ion exchange resins will have a very low conductivity, but this demineralized water commonly carries dissolved organic compounds derived from the resin.

Water for all reagents should be distilled from an all-glass apparatus fitted with a short length of wide-bore packed column or other efficient spray trap. The distillate should be discarded until its conductivity falls below that of CO_2-saturated water. No oxidizing agent should be employed unless a second distillation is to be made, because of the danger of producing volatile acids or aldehydes from organic contaminants. Apparatus combining a flask and distilling head in one piece, which frequently is sold for water distillation, may carry over considerable spray and accompanying contaminants from the boiling chamber. We find it helpful to demineralize distilled water with Amberlite MB-3 before redistillation. The rate of discharge of the resin also provides a convenient running check on the quality of the building supply. If the resin is not employed, the accumulated residual water from the glass still provides a check. If a sediment appears after distilling a few batches, its composition should be determined. In this way we have discovered gross contaminations by copper and by aluminum in our supply. In one case the aluminum concentration rose to about 10^{-4} M because of solution of the piping by contaminants from a faulty still.

OPERATIONAL TECHNIQUES

GREASE: The grease used in lubricating the ground glass joints of the flask-manometer connections or the plugs for the sidearms is usually either anhydrous lanolin or heavy vaseline. The grease used for the stopcock on the manometer is preferably a good stopcock grease such as is used for burettes.

At high temperatures, Celvacene light (Consolidated Vacuum Corp.) is useful because of its small change in consistency with changing temperature. Silicone greases also are desirable in this respect, but they are very difficult to remove from glassware.

BRODIE'S MANOMETER FLUID: Brodie's solution was long the standard manometer fluid, but now it generally has been replaced by Krebs' solution. The composition of Brodie's solution is:

> 23 grams NaCl
> 5 grams Sodium choleate (Merck)
> in 500 ml. water
> Density 1.033
> P_O = 10000

Evans Blue (200 mg./liter) or acid fuchsin are excellent dyes for the fluid; other dyes may be used, but some of these tend to decompose in the manometer. Determine the density of the solution with a pycnometer.

KREBS' MANOMETER FLUID: Krebs (1951a) described a manometer fluid with excellent properties, and Herbain (1951) suggested a fluid which also incorporated a synthetic surface active compound. Krebs' solution has the composition:

> 44 grams anhydrous NaBr
> 0.3 grams Triton X-100 (Rohm and Haas Co.), or 1.0 gram of the
>   syrupy commercially available solution of Lissapol N
>   (Imperial Chemical Industries Ltd.) or Stergene (Domestos
>   Ltd.); a comparable non-ionic detergent may be substituted.
> 0.3 grams Evans blue (or Acid Fuchsin - for red color)
> 1000 ml. water
> Density 1.033 at 20° C.

ORGANIC LIQUIDS AS MANOMETER FLUIDS: A possible objection to the use of Brodie's or Krebs' solution, although not a particularly serious one, is that the evaporation of water from the solution in the manometer increases the salt concentration and density of the manometer fluid. A single compound with a suitable density would provide a manometer fluid that would not change in density upon evaporation. An inspection of tables of organic compounds reveals a considerable number with densities close to 1.033 g./ml. (P_O=10,000). Many of these are of little utility because they are difficult to obtain, expensive, volatile, too viscous, or because they attack rubber. Ethyl lactate (1.031 g./ml. at 20°C.), plus crystal violet or malachite green for coloring, is the best of the compounds we have tried; it is somewhat more sluggish in its response than Brodie's solution or Krebs' solution.

It is customary to use a fraction of kerosene which boils in a narrow range as the fluid in Barcroft manometers. It is dyed with Sudan III, and its density is determined with a pycnometer. The low density of kerosene (P_O is around 13,000) gives a high sensitivity to the manometers. It is advisable to prepare a good volume of fluid (distill about 2 liters of kerosene), for manometer constants require recalculation if a fluid of different density must be substituted. Pure hydrocarbons with suitable properties may be used without distillation in place of kerosene. Schneider and Hogeboom have used, 2,2,4-trimethyl-pentane (iso-octane) as a manometer fluid; its boiling point is 99°C., and its density is 0.692 at 20°C. (P_O is approximately 15,000 mm.).

CLERICI SOLUTION:

> 7 grams thallium formate
> 7 grams thallium malonate
> 1 ml. water
> Density about 4; P_O value about 2500

MERCURY: It is convenient, when using mercury, to place a drop of water at the top of each column. This permits the mercury to flow freely. Density about 13.6 (dependent on temperature); $P_O = 760$.

REMOVING BUBBLES IN MANOMETER COLUMN: If the column of Brodie's fluid is broken in the manometer it may be readily joined again by rapidly compressing the rubber Brodie fluid reservoir with the finger and then releasing the pressure slowly. Repeating this soon raises the bubbles to the surface of the liquid.

ADDING MANOMETER FLUID: Draw the fluid into a hypodermic syringe. Jab the needle through the rubber tubing near the base of the reservoir and inject the desired quantity of fluid. The rubber tubing reservoir also may be filled before it is attached to the manometer and additions of fluid can be made through the open arm of the manometer (if the column of fluid is broken in the process it may be rejoined as described in the preceding paragraph).

ADDING FLUID TO BARCROFT MANOMETERS: This is easily accomplished by adding the fluid through a piece of polyethylene intravenous tubing forced over the tip of the needle of a hypodermic syringe. The plastic tubing is pushed down through the capillary of one side of the respirometer until it comes to a stop at the top of the restricted capillary of the manometer proper. Pressure on the tubing forms a liquid-tight union.

KEEPING TANKS CLEAN: Debris, algae, and sediment which often accumulate in a water bath can be trapped by keeping a fairly shallow, wide-mouthed jar in the bath. The collected sediment can be removed readily from the jar.

W. W. UMBREIT, R. H. BURRIS and J. F. STAUFFER

READING THE MANOMETER AFTER IT HAS PASSED THE GRADUATED RANGE

If gas uptake or release is more rapid than anticipated, the fluid level in the open arm of a Warburg manometer may come to rest below or above the graduated range when the fluid in the closed arm of the manometer is adjusted to its reference point. Volger (1942) described a method, which later was corrected by Cheng (1952), for estimating gas exchange under such conditions. The method follows:

Adjust the fluid in the closed arm until that in the open arm is on the scale. The distance one has moved the fluid in the closed arm from the zero point is called "e". Record the reading in the open arm. Adjust the closed arm so that the fluid is a distance 2e from the zero point. Record the reading in the open arm. The difference between the two readings of the open arm is the amount to be added to or subtracted from the first reading to give the actual reading if the closed arm had been at the zero point.

THEORETICAL: The corrections pointed out by Cheng (1952) have been included in this derivation. If the volume of gas (V_g) be decreased x by raising the level of manometer fluid in the closed arm by e cm., the corresponding pressure, P_O, will be increased by (y-e) so that:

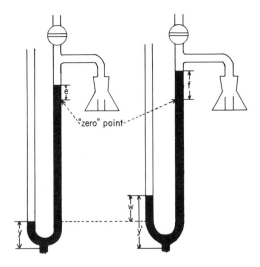

Figure 14
Diagram illustrating the method of reading the manometer after it has passed the graduated range

$$(V_g - x)(P_O + y-e) = V_g P_O \text{ or}$$

$$V_g(y-e) = x(y-e + P_O) \quad (\text{See fig. 14}).$$

Similarly if the fluid in the closed arm be raised f cm., the corresponding volume change (x') will cause an increased y' so that:

$$V_g(y'-f) = x'(y' - f + P_O)$$

Thus:

$$y/y' = x(y-e + P_O)/x'(y'-f + P_O)$$

Since $x = \pi r^2 e$ and $x' = \pi r^2 f$, where "r" is radius of the capillary tube of the manometer:

$$y/y' = \pi r^2 e(y-e+P_O)/\pi r^2 f(y' - f + P_O)$$
$$= e(y-e + P_O)/f(y'-f + P_O)$$

Since P_O is large (10,000 mm. of Brodie's solution), and (y-e) and (y'-f) are small, an accuracy of 1% is possible, if (y-e) and (y'-f) are not greater than 10 cm., by considering $y-e+P_O = y'-f + P_O$, from which $(y - e)/(y' - f) = e/f$. This reduces to $y/e = y'/f$.

If W were defined as the difference between the reading at y and y' (closed arm at e or f), then

$$y' - y = W \quad \text{or} \quad y' = W + y$$

Thus:

$$y = \frac{y'e}{f} = \frac{(W + y)e}{f} = \frac{We + ye}{f}$$

$$fy = We + ye$$

$$y(f - e) = We$$

$$y = \frac{We}{f-e}$$

If f were chosen to equal 2e, then y = W.

"y" is the distance off the scale (when closed arm is at zero point) from the first reading on the scale (when closed arm is at e).

ILLUSTRATION 1. Oxygen uptake is unexpectedly rapid and upon returning the closed arm to its zero point (250 mm.) the open end does not reach zero. By adjusting the closed arm to 260; the reading is 3; by adjusting to 270, the reading is 8. Hence e = 10; f = 20; W = 5; y = We/f - e = 5. Reading at zero point was 3 - 5 = -2.

ILLUSTRATION 2. In order to obtain a reading on the scale, it was necessary to adjust the closed arm to 280; (e = 30 from zero point of 250) hence 2e is impossible (310), since closed arm scale will not read to this point. Reading at 280 = 5. Reading at 300 = 16.

$$y = We/f - e = 11 \times 30/50 - 30 = 330/20 = 16.5$$

Reading at zero point = $5 - 16.5 = -11.5$

READING MANOMETERS WHILE THEY ARE IN MOTION

It often is desirable to read manometers while they are moving, so that gas-liquid mixing will not cease during the period of reading. Although this is not difficult with rocking or pivotal manometers shaken at normal speeds, it is difficult when shaking rates are high. Burk and Hobby (1954) (collaborating with V. Riley) described a method for such reading; the method employs an ordinary hand lens mounted on the manometer shaker, and the lens shakes with the manometers. When the lens is mounted at its focal distance from the manometer, even a rapidly shaken manometer appears stationary to the eye.

"FREE MANOMETER" METHOD OF READING

Goldstein (1949) reported that within the usual limits of accuracy accepted for Warburg respirometers ($\pm 1\%$) it is unnecessary to maintain a constant volume for reading. The method of reading without leveling the fluid in the closed arm of the manometer increases the capacity but decreases the sensitivity of the respirometer. Only the closed arm of the manometer is read, and the calculations described by Goldstein are relatively simple. The method probably will be applied chiefly when automatic photographic recording of manometer levels is advantageous, e. g., when very rapid readings or readings over a long period are required. Barcroft manometers also may be read photographically, for no leveling of the fluid is involved.

W. W. UMBREIT

ANAEROBIC MEASUREMENTS

An anaerobic condition is generally obtained in respirometer vessels by thoroughly flushing with nitrogen. Oxygen-free nitrogen is passed directly from a tank or other source into a manifold (often provided with a simple Hg pressure-relief valve) connected to the several flasks which are shaking in the bath. Ten minutes of slow flushing, or passage of a liter of nitrogen through each flask, should suffice to remove the oxygen. Dry nitrogen with a minimum purity of 99.96 % can be obtained from Linde Air Products Co. or Matheson Co. This gas is inexpensive and a tank of it supplies by far the most convenient source of nitrogen for use in connection with anaerobic measurements.

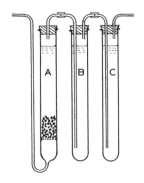

Figure 15
Gas train to remove residual O_2 from tank N_2: (A) Zn-Hg amalgam and 0.1 M vanadyl sulfate; (B) 0.1 M NaOH; (C) water

If a source of nitrogen of high purity is not available, ordinary tank nitrogen may be freed of oxygen with vanadous sulfate-amalgamated zinc reagent (Meites and Meites, 1948). A train of two washing bottles containing this reagent followed by a water wash may be used. A convenient, modified gas train of rugged units is diagrammed in figure 15, where the basic components, including the oxygen absorption tower with the sealed-in coarse fritted-glass disc and tubulature at the bottom, are constructed from 4.5 x 40 cm. pyrex test tubes. Gas from a cylinder is passed into (A) containing vanadous sulfate and

Hg- amalgamated zinc to absorb oxygen, through (B) containing 0.1 M NaOH to remove any hydrogen sulfide, and through (C) containing distilled water. The oxygen absorbing reagent is prepared by adding an excess (almost to the point of hydrogen evolution) of concentrated sulfuric acid to 200 ml. of 0.1 M sodium metavanadate in the presence of about 100 g. of slightly amalgamated zinc. The latter is prepared by letting a mixture of 100 g. of mossy zinc, 15 g. of $HgCl_2$ and 100 ml. of water stand with occasional shaking until the zinc acquires a shiny coating of mercury, decanting, and washing the zinc amalgam free of $HgCl_2$ with water. The reagent can be regenerated in situ by adding sulfuric acid.

Other oxygen absorbents that may be incorporated in various types of gas trains include chromous chloride-acetic acid and alkaline pyrogallol. The former may be objected to because it is likely to evolve some hydrogen gas, especially on standing idle; however, it is recommended by Stone and Skavinski (1945) for the quantitative removal of oxygen. The reagent is prepared as follows: The amount of chromic chloride ($CrCl_3 \cdot xH_2O$, where x is assumed to represent 6) required for the desired volume of 2 M solution is dissolved without heat and made up to final volume in 2 M acetic acid. The chromic ion is now reduced by passing the solution upward, at a rate of 100-150 ml./min., through a 0.1% mercury-zinc amalgam (prepared by shaking 240 gms. of 20-mesh zinc with 100 ml. of 3 M HCl for 30 seconds, dumping the mixture into 100 ml. of 0.013 M $HgCl_2$ solution, stirring rapidly for three minutes, and washing several times with water). The amalgam is immersed in water in a tubulated (top and bottom) reductor (a $CaCl_2$ drying tube works very well) provided with a glass-wool plug at the exit end (top) to trap any floating particles. Some of the chromous ion as formed is oxidized in scavenging the residual oxygen in the system while purging the water from the reductor, but soon the clear blue chromous solution begins to issue from the top. The flow of liquid through the reductor is maintained and the reagent now directed into the absorption vessel of the gas train, e.g., of the type shown in figure 15.

As mentioned above, alkaline pyrogallol is a good absorber of oxygen. This reagent is prepared by combining solutions of 25% pyrogallic acid and 40% KOH in the ratio of 1:10 to yield the volume desired. The high concentration of alkali is required to prevent the production of CO when the reagent reacts with oxygen, but this may occur nevertheless if the reagent is required to absorb oxygen at a rapid rate.

Commercial gas purifiers of different types are available in sizes (and gas output ratings) suited to laboratory use. As examples: Engelhard Industries, 113 Astor St., Newark, N. J., offers a compact catalytic unit (Deoxo) that utilizes hydrogen to remove oxygen from such gases as hydrogen, nitrogen, neon, argon, etc., and oxygen to remove hydrogen from oxygen, nitrogen, neon and argon. The Milton Roy Co., 1300 E. Mermaid Lane, Philadelphia, Pa., offers a table-top model purifier (Serfass) that produces at least 99.999% pure and dry hydrogen from impure sources containing 75% or more hydrogen. This unit operates on 115-v A. C. and utilizes a palladium-silver alloy to selectively separate, by diffusion, the hydrogen gas from all impurities.

The oxygen in tank nitrogen may be removed by passing the gas through bright copper turnings heated to 600-700 °C. in a combustion tube. A more thorough removal of oxygen is claimed when the gas is passed through a matrix of finely divided copper deposited on infusorial earth heated to 200-300 °C. (Meyer and Ronge, 1939). The matrix is formed by precipitating cupric hydroxide on the infusorial earth, drying, and reducing with hydrogen. The use of hot copper for removing oxygen may be undesirable in some instances, for example, Keilin and Hartree (1943) found that nitrous oxides formed in the reaction inhibited the action of catalase.

The evacuation procedure described under "Altering Gas Mixtures" may be used to obtain an anaerobic condition. Four evacuations to 75 mm. Hg residual pressure should leave only about 0.3 μl. of the original oxygen in a 15 ml. flask. Nitrogen may then be added directly from a tank or from a purification train.

J. F. STAUFFER

ALTERING GAS ATMOSPHERES

At times it is necessary to work with gas mixtures other than air. For this purpose side-arm flasks of the form shown in figure 16 are used; when the stopper of the sidearm is appropriately turned gas can be vented through the sidearm. Gas mixtures are supplied through the opened stopcock of the closable arm of the manometer.

It is necessary to run about a liter of gas through the flask to assure that all air has been displaced. By the use of a manifold arrangement an entire bank of flasks may be supplied with gas at one time. As an indication of the rate of gas flow a "U tube" is attached with rubber tubing to the sidearm stopper. The end of the glass "U" is pulled out into a capillary and dips just below the surface of the water in the constant temperature bath; bubbles from the tube show the passage of gas. It is desirable to have one outlet from the manifold connected to a glass tube of about 10 mm. bore which is immersed several inches in the water bath. This serves as a safety valve to release gas quickly if tank gases are admitted too rapidly to the manifold.

When a uniform gas mixture is to be used routinely, e.g., 5% CO_2 95% O_2, it is convenient to purchase such a mixture in steel cylinders. When small quantities of a number of mixtures are necessary they may be prepared in stoppered bottles by filling the bottles with water and displacing measured quantities of water with the gases comprising the mixture--the water is displaced directly into a graduated cylinder for estimation of volume. Alternatively, the stoppered bottle may be evacuated, flushed with one of the component gases and then filled with the various gases to the desired pressures as indicated by a mercury manometer. (More detail is given under "Methods for Preparing Gas Mixtures" page 69). The gas mixtures may be displaced from the bottles with water and passed through the Warburg flasks. (When the mixtures contain CO_2, the use of water as a displacing fluid will alter appreciably the composition of the gas mixtures unless the water is previously saturated with CO_2 at the CO_2 pressure used.)

Figure 16
Sidearm flask with gas-vent

Displacing air from respiration flasks by flushing with a flowing stream requires considerable amounts of gas. This procedure is costly with expensive gases and undesirable when carbon monoxide or other poisonous gases are being used. To decrease the amount of gas necessary to flush a flask we have employed an evacuation procedure. With the Gilson respirometer (page 75) it is particularly convenient to gas by evacuation; with the Warburg manometer the following method is applicable: Tubes in the form of a reversed h with a T at the top of the h are connected in series (a bank of 7 manometers is easily treated at one time), as illustrated in figure 17, and attached with rubber tubing to both arms of the Warburg manometer. The Brodie fluid is lowered to within a few cm. of the bottom of the manometer columns, as it will rise during the evacuation. After making sure that the manometer stopcocks are open, the screw clamp A is opened and the system is evacuated by means of a water aspirator until there is about 75 mm. Hg residual pressure, as indicated by mercury manometer C. Screw clamp A is now closed and clamp B opened; water in bottle D displaces gas from storage bottle E into the system until atmospheric pressure is reached. After two more evacuations and refillings the replacement of the original atmosphere is sufficiently complete, i.e., approximately 0.1% of the original gas remains.

On the last filling the pressure is allowed to build up until gas spills through the mercury manometer. The rubber tubing is then removed at F and the excess gas is lost from the flasks obviating the difficulties that would arise if a small vacuum were left to suck air into the flasks. The stopcocks on the manometers are closed immediately and the manometers placed on the bath; as the flasks warm up the stopcocks must be opened momentarily to release gas. If desired, the evacuation procedure may be performed in the constant temperature bath, though this generally presents no advantage.

When the system is under vacuum, the rubber tubing which serves as a reservoir for Brodie fluid will be compressed pushing the fluid up in the manometers. It is necessary to use tubing with reasonably heavy walls to minimize this effect, or to close off the fluid reservoir with a common laboratory screw clamp during the evacuation. Although a vacuum better than 75 mm. Hg residual pressure can be obtained readily,

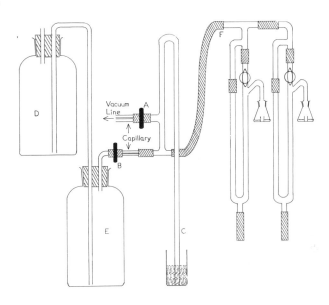

Figure 17
Apparatus for altering the gas atmosphere by the evacuation method

its use is not recommended routinely because of the bubbling of the Brodie fluid that may occur. It is helpful to de-gas the Brodie fluid under vacuum before filling the manometers. Capillaries are introduced in the vacuum and gas lines to limit the rate of gas flow; sudden changes in pressure are not registered uniformly on the two columns of the Warburg manometer, because the large volume of gas leaving or entering the Warburg flask must pass through the capillary tubing of the manometer. If the stopcock of the manometer is closed or plugged, vacuum is applied to one side of the manometer only, and fluid may be displaced into the evacuation line.

The method of adding gases by evacuation requires only a tenth to a twentieth as much gas as the flushing procedure, and one is always certain that every dead space in the most complicated flask has had its initial gas displaced by the desired gas mixture. Although the procedure was evolved originally to save valuable gases it has proved so convenient that we use it routinely.

R. H. BURRIS

METHODS FOR PREPARING GAS MIXTURES

Gas mixtures may be produced by evacuating respirometers on a manifold as described under "Altering Gas Atmospheres" and then adding measured pressures of various gases directly from gas cylinders. This apparently simple and direct procedure is undesirable because gases left in the manifold are swept into the flasks by succeeding gases. The method is reliable only when the respirometers are closed and the manifold evacuated.

between additions of various gases. It is usually much more convenient and reliable to premix gases in a reservoir and to add the mixture rather than the individual gases.

DISPLACEMENT PROCEDURES: A displacement procedure will give a gas mixture of somewhat inaccurate composition when the vapor pressure of the confining fluid is ignored; if the composition of the mixture is critical it is advisable to use mercury as the confining fluid. Fill flasks or bottles completely with the confining fluid, and allow each pure gas to enter until a given quantity of fluid has been displaced. The example following will clarify the actual procedure:

EXAMPLE: Procedure with water as the confining fluid. Gas mixture required: 100 ml. of 20 volume % O_2, 30% H_2, 50% N_2. Add pure N_2 to displace 50 ml. of water from a flask completely filled with water. Displace 20 ml. of water with O_2 and a further 30 ml. with H_2. An alternative procedure if pure N_2 were not available, would be: Add 50/0.8 = 62.5 ml. of air (of which 50 ml. is N_2, 12.5 ml. O_2), 7.5 ml. O_2 (20 ml. required in all less 12.5 ml. added with air equals 7.5 ml. still required), and 30 ml. H_2. The mixture made from air would be somewhat inaccurate, because the assumed composition of dry air may be inaccurate under laboratory conditions, and because the variable vapor pressure of water in air is not considered. Note also that no allowance is made for differential solubilities of the gases in the confining fluid remaining in the reservoir bottle.

EVACUATION PROCEDURE: Atmospheric pressure is observed on a barometer. The dry gas bottle of any size, in which the mixture is to be made, is attached to a manometer, as shown in figure 18. Connection A is closed (and kept closed throughout the operation), B is opened, and the flask is evacuated by attaching a water pump at C. Gases are added through D until the proper mixture is obtained. The procedure is best illustrated in the examples below.

EXAMPLE 1: Gas mixture required: 20% O_2, 30% H_2, 50% N_2, Atmos. pressure = 748 mm. Hg. Using air for the nitrogen source (assuming 80% N_2 and 20% O_2 in air), one needs 50% of 748 mm. = 374 mm. of N_2. To obtain this amount of N_2 from air, one needs 374/0.8 = 467.5 mm. of air. Hence one would evacuate with the water aspirator until the mercury in the manometer stood at (748 - 467.5 =) 280.5 mm. 20% oxygen requires 20% of 748 mm. = 149.6 mm. However 93.5 mm. have already been added with the air, hence 56.1 mm. of pure oxygen are to be added. One then attaches an oxygen source to D, and admits oxygen until the level of mercury in the manometer reaches (280.5 - 56.1 =) 224.4. 30% hydrogen requires 30% x 748 mm. = 224.4 mm., hence one attaches a hydrogen source to D, and permits hydrogen to enter until the manometer reaches zero (224.4 - 224.4 mm.).

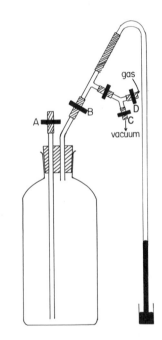

Figure 18
Apparatus for preparing gas mixtures by evacuation and refilling

To prepare gas mixtures which contain no oxygen, evacuate the gas bottle, refill with one of the components of the gas mixture, repeat this process twice, and proceed from this point. This is illustrated in the two examples given below:

EXAMPLE 2: Gas mixture required: 80% H_2, 5% CO_2, 15% N_2. Atmospheric pressure, 748 mm.; aspirator can evacuate to 720 mm. Evacuate to 720, return to zero with H_2; evacuate to 720, return to zero with H_2. Evacuate to 149.6 mm. (gas remaining in bottle is H_2); add CO_2 to 112.2 (from 149.6 - (0.05 x 748)), return to zero with pure N_2.

EXAMPLE 3: Gas mixture required: 20% H_2, 20% N_2, 60% He. Atmospheric pressure, 748; aspirator can evacuate to 720 mm. Evacuate to 720, return to zero with H_2 or N_2 (helium is more expensive and is not employed in the flushing out process). Repeat twice. Evacuate to 598.4 (gas remaining in bottle is H_2 or N_2), return to 448.8 with N_2 (or H_2); return to zero with Helium.

THE USE OF CYANIDE AS AN INHIBITOR

Cyanide is a useful inhibitor in the study of oxidations because it penetrates cells readily and strongly inhibits heavy metal (not necessarily iron) catalysts. HCN is a weak acid and its salts in solution consist largely of undissociated HCN. Further, in spite of its ready solubility, HCN is volatile and is absorbed, along with CO_2, by the alkali. Similar properties have been reported for azide (Machlis, 1944). In the first edition of this book a theoretical analysis of HCN volatility was given together with tables of KOH-KCN mixtures for CO_2 absorption in the center alkali cup. The composition of these mixtures, essentially as described by Krebs (1935a), was intended to be such that HCN would be in equilibrium between the alkali well and the reaction chamber so no interchange of HCN would occur. However, Riggs (1945) has demonstrated that the assumptions made are not valid and that experimentally a much more complex situation is involved. He suggests, therefore, that the cyanide concentration in the experimental vessels should be determined empirically. Laties (1949) found that the concentrations of KOH in center well mixtures in equilibrium with external concentrations of cyanide in excess of 10^{-4} M had so little capacity for CO_2 absorption, that 1.0 M KCN served almost as well as KCN-KOH. He suggested that for most measurements of cyanide inhibition, 1.0 M KCN was quite suitable as a CO_2 absorbent.

Robbie (1946, 1948) and Robbie and Leinfelder (1945) have developed methods for maintaining the cyanide concentration in the experimental fluid at known levels. The best of these methods involves the use of mixtures of calcium cyanide and calcium hydroxide. These mixtures are applicable to a wide range of concentrations and provide a constant tension of HCN (and a virtually constant pH in the center well) even though gas is given off or CO_2 absorbed. Since $Ca(OH)_2$ is only slightly soluble and a large excess is kept in suspension in the center well, a reserve is constantly available to replace that lost by precipitation of $CaCO_3$. In addition the very large reserve of HCN in the center well permits the adjustment of the center well concentrations so that they will provide the HCN necessary for the experimental fluid; thus this fluid will differ from a control only by the presence of HCN.

Table 15
Composition of Center Well Fluid at 37.5°C.*

HCN	Ca(CN)$_2$	KCN
10^{-2} M	1.45 M	-
10^{-3} M	0.32 M	-
10^{-4} M	0.38 M	0.83 M
10^{-5} M	0.0046 M	0.078 M
10^{-6} M	0.0005 M	-

* Adapted from Robbie (1948). Calcium cyanide solutions contain 10% $Ca(OH)_2$ suspension. KCN solutions contain 0.5 M KOH. For intermediate concentrations and for other temperatures refer to Robbie (1948).

The methods of preparing the calcium cyanide and its use are described in detail by Robbie. For convenience a few of the data are collected in Table 14, but before precise work is done on cyanide inhibition the publications of Robbie, particularly Robbie (1948), should be consulted.

ADDITION OF MATERIALS DURING THE COURSE OF THE REACTION

It frequently is desirable to add substances to reaction flasks during the course of the reaction. This usually is accomplished by using Warburg flasks equipped with one or more sidearms (fig. 19). After tipping in material from a sidearm, rinse the sidearm with some of the fluid from the main compartment of the flask, and then tip this back into the main compartment. Without such a rinse, quantitative transfer of the material from the sidearm is not obtained. When removing manometers and attached flasks from baths for such operations, place a finger over the open end of the manometer; this prevents expansion or contraction arising from temperature changes from pushing out or sucking back the fluid from the manometers. Do not fill sidearms to full capacity. If the sidearm is capable of holding 1 ml., it is best employed for contents of 0.5 ml. or less. This not only prevents any material from spilling over into the main compartment prematurely, but also allows more rapid attainment of equilibrium between the gas phase and the liquid in the sidearm. Unless the two phases are at equilibrium, gas may suddenly be taken up or evolved when the material from the sidearm is tipped into the main compartment.

Figure 19
Double sidearm
Warburg flask

It also is well to adjust the composition of the materials in the sidearm so that only one factor is altered upon the addition of its contents to the main compartment. For example, addition of 0.5 ml. M/10 glucose to a bacterial suspension in M/50 phosphate buffer alters not only the glucose concentration but the phosphate concentration as well.

"Keilin cups" provide a means for adding materials to flasks with insufficient sidearms. "Keilin cups" are small tubes (Keilin, 1929) provided with a small hook, of platinum wire or glass, by which they may be hung from the edge of the center well. They can be dislodged by a careful jarring of the apparatus. It is possible (as pointed out by Dixon, 1951) to add more than one material by use of two "Keilin cups" with hooks of different lengths; one cup is released by a less vigorous jar of the apparatus than the other. Usually, however, the addition from sidearms is preferable. Among the most useful "all purpose" flasks are the two sidearm flasks equipped with a gas venting plug (fig. 19).

Small glass cups with an iron rod sealed into one side can be held against the wall of a respirometer vessel by a magnet placed outside the vessel. Removal of the outside magnet allows the cup to drop into the reaction mixture. These devices, which are commercially available, permit the addition of materials without the temperature change which accompanies the removal of vessels from the constant temperature bath. Addition of materials without removing flasks from the bath also may be accomplished from sidearms which rotate in standard taper joints (fig. 22).

If a sidearm plug of a respirometer vessel is replaced with a rubber serum bottle stopper, measured quantities of materials can be injected into the vessel through the stopper with a hypodermic needle and syringe. It is necessary to allow for the change in pressure which will accompany such an addition.

Laser (1955) has described an ingenious flask which permits dialysis during the course of a manometric run. Laser employed such flasks for the slow addition of peroxide to his reaction mixture, and the flasks also should prove useful for the slow addition of other substrates.

DESIGN OF RESPIROMETER FLASKS

Two shapes of flasks are in common use. These are illustrated in figure 20. Flasks of type A (with sharply angled bottom edges) tip less easily when detached from the manometer and are suitable for use on manometric instruments which employ a reciprocating motion. When used on the type of instrument in which the manometer is rocked back and forth, tissue tends to collect at the edge of the flask. Type B flasks (with rounded bottom edges) may be used equally well with either type of shaking device, but they tend to tip more easily. Type A flasks are preferred for irradiation work.

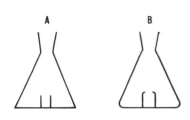

Figure 20
Different shapes of Warburg flasks

An additional modification has been suggested by P. P. Cohen. If the center well is slightly constricted at the top (as shown in "B", fig. 20), splashing or "creeping" of alkali into the main compartment is largely prevented.

Warburg (1962) devised the modified vessel shown in figure 21. The large area of KOH solution in the alkali well absorbs CO_2 more rapidly than in the conventional vessel, the entire floor area of the vessel is open for reactants, and the center well communicates with one side sac so that acid (or other materials) can be added into the KOH well to release CO_2.

When there is a very limited supply of the enzyme under study, it may be desirable to employ unusually small reaction vessels. The most frequently used vessels have a volume of about 15 ml., but flasks of 7 to 8 ml. volume also are available commercially.

A reaction in these vessels with half the usual amount of materials will cause a shift in the manometric fluid equivalent to that observed with the usual flasks and the usual amount of reactants; the precision of measurement in the two cases will be essentially the same.

Figure 21
Double sidearm flask with centrally located KOH cup

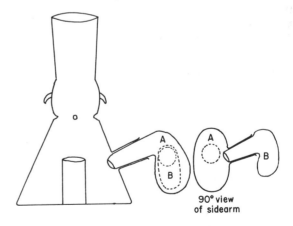

90° view
of sidearm

Figure 22
Flask with rotating sidearms

A flask (figure 22) with a standard taper sidearm opening has been used on stationary manifolds which do not allow tipping of the flasks, or on shaken manometers which must remain in the respirometer bath to avoid shifts of temperature. When sidearm B is inserted directly into the outer joint on the flask, its contents can be added directly to the main chamber of the flask by rotating the sidearm (rotating sidearms have been used for many years on Dixon-Keilin flasks). If it is necessary to mix materials in the sidearm, sidearm A is inserted into the flask and sidearm B is inserted into A; rotation of B adds material to A. A standard taper plug is inserted into the main flask sidearm outlet when no sidearm is required. For work under aseptic conditions a cotton plug is placed below the top ground joint and is retained by the indents at the base of the bulged section.

Figure 23
Adapter for preventing entry or escape of bacteria from reaction vessel

In the isolation of intermediates of a reaction it often is helpful to increase the amounts of the reactants and to carry on the reaction and measurements in flasks of 75 to 125 ml. volume. Flasks very similar to the one shown in figure 30 are useful. When a cotton plug is inserted the flask can be sterilized and kept aseptic during a run. The sidearm opening is plugged with cotton during sterilization; when a run is set up, the cotton plug is discarded and replaced by a sterile glass plug which is lubricated with sterile grease.

The use of aseptic technique may be dictated by the desire to keep contaminants from the system or to prevent the spread of pathogens. If standard flasks only are available, an adapter (suggested by J. B. Wilson) is useful for work with pathogens. This adapter (figure 23) consists of an outer joint to fit the manometer, an inner joint to fit the flask, and an intervening space carrying a cotton plug. The adapter, the sidearm plugs, and the cotton plugged flask are sterilized separately, the flask is filled using normal bacteriological precautions, the cotton plug from the flask is discarded, and the cotton plugged adapter lubricated with sterile grease is connected to the flask and manometer. The sterile sidearm plugs are lubricated with sterile grease before inserting them. After the run, the flask together with adapter is removed and sterilized (by autoclaving or preferably by immersion in a disinfectant) as a unit before opening.

R. H. BURRIS and W. W. UMBREIT

REFERENCE POINTS

The reference point should be chosen to make maximum use of the graduated scale of the manometer. When gas uptakes are measured 250 mm. is a convenient point; when gas evolution is measured 50 mm. is convenient. 250 mm. also may be used as a reference point for gas release if one attaches a length of rubber tubing to the open arm of the manometer and gently blows the manometer fluid to a level of about 50 mm. in the open arm and 250 mm. in the closed arm before closing the stopcock.

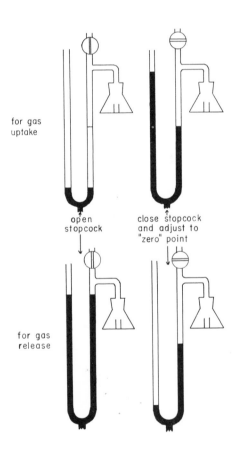

for gas uptake

open stopcock

close stopcock and adjust to "zero" point

for gas release

Figure 24
Diagram illustrating the manometer setting to obtain maximum range

The following method using 150 mm. as the reference point is suggested by P. P. Cohen: In measuring gas uptake the manometer fluid is set, with the stopcock open, near the bottom of the scale as shown in figure 24. The stopcock is closed. Adjusting the fluid to the reference point of 150 mm. in the closed arm raises the fluid in the open arm near the top of the graduated scale. In measuring gas release, the opposite type of setting is employed as indicated in figure 24. This permits the use of the same reference point for both uptake and release of gas and makes maximum use of the graduated scale.

W. W. UMBREIT

CONSTANT TEMPERATURE
BATHS AND SHAKING APPARATUS

The basic requirements for the bath which holds the microrespirometers are that it be capable of maintaining a uniform constant temperature throughout and of providing adequate shaking of the flasks. Wide latitude in shape and size of the bath is permissible, but for many years the most common design was a rectangular bath carrying 7 manometers on each of 2 sides. Shaking was provided by a rocking or a reciprocating motion. The new Gilson manometers described below are accommodated in a rectangular bath, figure 25, but all manometers are read from one side. In this apparatus, the vessels are shaken, but the manometers are stationary.

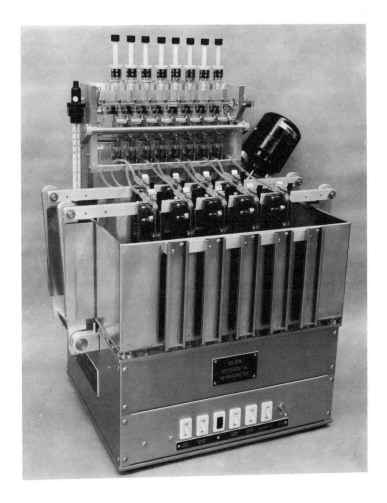

Figure 25
Gilson differential respirometer

Lardy et al. (1948) described a circular bath and a modified shaking mechanism possessing distinct advantages over the earlier apparatus. (American Instrument Co., Silver Spring, Md., figure 26A, and G. M. E. Co., Middleton, Wis., figure 26B produce apparatus essentially following the original design of Lardy et al., and somewhat modified apparatus is produced by Precision Scientific Co., Chicago; Hospital and Laboratory Supplies Ltd., London; Townson and Mercer Ltd., Croydon, England; and by a German company whose products are sold in the United States under the trade name "Bronwill" and are sold in England by Shandon Scientific Co. Ltd., London.) Manometers may be placed around the entire periphery of a circular bath, so the unit is more compact than a conventional rectangular bath of equal capacity. A bath 22 inches in diameter will accommodate 18 manometers. The extra manometers available substantially improve the productivity of the apparatus. The instrument is arranged so that the entire shaking mechanism may be rotated, thus each manometer may be brought directly in front of the operator without his changing position. This feature permits the apparatus to be installed in a corner or along a wall with only one side of the bath accessible, whereas the usual rectangular bath must occupy a space-consuming, open position in the room to provide accessibility from 3 sides. A uniform temperature is easily maintained in the circular bath, for it contains no "dead spots" to hinder circulation. The water is circulated either with a centrifugal pump or with a stirring motor.

A. Aminco circular Warburg apparatus   B. GME circular Warburg apparatus

Figure 26

The first circular models were provided with the conventional rocking type of shaking device. This was chosen because the manometers can be read without stopping them, whereas a reciprocating shaker must be stopped for accurate reading because the manometer fluid bounces excessively. Later circular models have employed a pivotal shaker; the flask describes a considerable arc while the manometer scales move very little. The slight movement of the manometer scales is toward and away from the observer, and the scales may be read while moving with virtually the same ease as when they are stationary. Comparisons of the rocking, reciprocating and pivotal types of shaker have shown them all to be very effective in providing agitation of the contents of the flasks.

H. A. LARDY and *R. H. BURRIS*

Chapter 6
THE DIFFERENTIAL RESPIROMETER AND ITS APPLICATION TO STUDIES OF RESPIRATION, FERMENTATION, AND PHOTOSYNTHESIS

The differential respirometer was introduced by Barcroft (1908), and it is often called the "Barcroft respirometer" or "Barcroft manometer". The term respirometer is somewhat misleading however, since this type of apparatus is used in measuring the rate of photosynthesis (O_2 evolution alone, or O_2 evolution and CO_2 uptake simultaneously) as well as determining the rates of respiration and fermentation. It will suffice to point out that any type of apparatus designed to measure the uptake of a gas in terms of the change in the reading of a manometer can serve equally well to measure the evolution of the gas. Of course, in either case all conditions affecting the gas exchange must be taken into consideration.

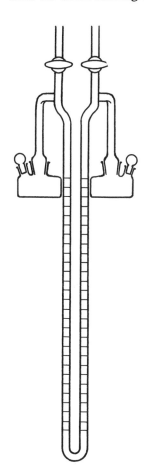

Figure 27
The differential
respirometer

One model of the differential respirometer, which illustrates its basic design, is shown in figure 27. Models are now available, or can be built to specifications, incorporating a double-capillary, consisting of a single straight piece of glass containing two parallel capillaries of equal bore separated by about 2 mm. and joined at the bottom, instead of the usual U-shaped manometer portion of the instrument. This relative new feature in design is an improvement in that it is easier to read the levels of fluid in the two capillaries and shaking of the vessels does not have to be interrupted.

It is evident from an examination of figure 27 that the differential respirometer is essentially a closed system formed of two flasks connected by a manometer. In practice the volumes of liquid and gas on both sides of the manometer are the same. One flask contains the cells or tissue and is called the reaction vessel (on the right, R). The other flask (on the left, L), free from cells or tissue, is called the compensation vessel, i.e., it serves to compensate for changes in temperature and barometric pressure during the course of an experiment. It is readily understood that a change in temperature will have the same effect (on the volume and pressure, and on the solubility of the gas being measured) in each flask and thus will produce no change in the height of the manometer liquid. Also, the use of the compensation vessel to form a closed system makes the manometer readings independent of any changes in barometric pressure which may occur during an experiment. Therefore, a thermobarometer is unnecessary. Obviation of this instrument represents a refinement in technique that possibly cannot be appreciated until one has compared the differential respirometer alongside a Warburg respirometer and its thermobarometer. The smoothness in operation of the former is especially impressive in a laboratory where atmospheric pressure is erratic due to the "chimney effect" of the whole building or to variation in pressure in the ventilating system. Of course, it is possible to use the Warburg respirometer with its open limb instead of the differential respirometer, if this is desirable, in any situation where a reaction is to be measured by the uptake or evolution of a gas.

CONSTRUCTION AND MOUNTING

Differential respirometers can be purchased directly from, or can be built to specifications by a number of glass fabricating companies. Institutional glass-blowers and others interested in constructing this type of respirometer may obtain precision bore, thick-walled capillary tubing from the Fischer and Porter Co., Hatboro, Pa. Interchangeable standard taper ground-glass fittings are generally used for the stopcocks, and for the connection between each flask and limb of the manometer. The upright portion of the respirometer is about 45 cm. in length. Each side of the manometer is graduated in millimeters, with numbered centimeter graduations, over a 30 cm. portion. The two symmetrical halves of the respirometer are constructed as nearly alike as possible in respect to the internal diameter of the capillary manometer tubes, limbs and stopcock connections, and gas volume. There is no restriction on the design of the flasks provided the gas exchange of the cells or tissue is not hindered. Many laboratories use the standard Warburg flasks with side arm and center well; also, when both Warburg and differential respirometers are in use in a laboratory it is convenient to have the standard taper ground-glass flask connectors of both types of the same size. For photosynthesis measurements, flasks similar to those represented in figure 28 are used. Generally, the flasks do not have a volume of more than 20 ml.

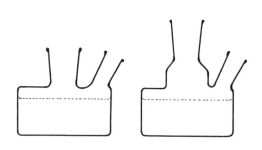

Figure 28
Flasks for use in measuring
photosynthesis

The respirometer is mounted on an inverted L-shaped wood or metal support which in turn is attached to a suitable shaking device. As mounted, the graduated portions of the manometer tubes are vertical. The flasks are side-by-side and submerged at least 2 cm. beyond their necks in a constant temperature bath.

Four types of shaking devices have been or are being used in various laboratories. These are: (1) the older method of rocking the vessels from side to side with the base of the mount as a horizontal pivot; the more recent methods of (2) swinging the flasks through an arc with the base of the mount serving as a vertical pivot, and (3) horizontal oscillation; a special type (4) whereby the flasks are rotated a few millimeters off-center (Warburg and Negelein, 1922a). The second and third types of shaking devices are common in most tissue-metabolism laboratories. At present the third method is preferred to the others in measuring photosynthesis because it minimizes frothing, more nearly maintains equal thickness throughout the vessel of the light-absorbing layer of cell suspension, and, especially when using the "two-respirometer method" (see below), its use facilitates equal shaking of the two pairs of vessels and supplying measured quantities of light to each of the two reaction vessels. Regardless of the type, all of these shaking devices are constructed to allow considerable variation in rate of shaking and in the amplitude of the arc, swing, oscillation, or rotation of the flasks.

THEORY

The theory of the apparatus has been described and elaborated a number of times since the original account by Barcroft (1908). The most complete description of the theory for use in measurements of photosynthesis and respiration is given by Warburg and Negelein (1922a).. Dixon (1951) has also published a very complete description together with several extensions and modifications. The following account is based on those of Dixon and Warburg and Negelein.

Let: R = Reaction vessel.
        L = Compensation vessel.
        V_g = μl. of gas in the reaction-vessel side of the manometer.
        V'_g = μl. of gas in the compensation-vessel side of the manometer.
        V_f = μl. of liquid in the reaction vessel (including the tissue).
        V'_f = μl. of liquid in the compensation vessel.
        A = Cross-sectional area of the manometer capillary, in mm².
        h = Manometer reading in mm. (the difference in height of the manometer liquid in the limbs of the manometer).
        P_0 = Normal pressure (760 mm. Hg), in mm. manometer liquid.
        P = Atmospheric pressure (corrected), in mm. of manometer liquid.
        $\triangle P$ = Increase in pressure of the confined gas in the reaction vessel.
        $\triangle P'$ = Increase in pressure of the confined gas in the compensation vessel.
        p = Pressure of water vapor in the gas spaces, in mm. manometer liquid.
        T_0 = 273° Absolute.
        T = Temperature of the gas and liquid in the vessels in absolute degrees.
        α = Solubility coefficient of the gas produced or absorbed (μl. per μl. of liquid).

Suppose the apparatus contains the same volumes of gas and water on both sides of the manometer, and that the manometer liquid is at the same height in the two limbs of the manometer. The amount of gas (at 0°C., 273° Abs., and 760 mm. Hg; or NTP) in each gas space is:

$$\text{For } R = V_g \frac{273}{T} \frac{P - p}{P_0} \qquad\qquad \text{For } L = V'_g \frac{273}{T} \frac{P - p}{P_0}$$

27 **27'**

If x amount of gas is evolved in R, the manometer reading will be h. The increase in volume of the gas space in R is then $\frac{h}{2}$ A; the decrease in volume of the gas space in L is also $\frac{h}{2}$ A. But h does not indicate the true value of $\triangle$ P of the gas in R because of the compensatory effect of the rise of pressure in L. In other words, both pressure and volume increase in R while the pressure increases and the volume decreases in L. Taking these changes into consideration, the final volumes of the gas spaces will be:

$$\text{for } R = (V_g + \frac{h}{2} A) (\frac{P + \triangle P - p}{P_0}) \quad \text{for } L = (V'_g - \frac{h}{2} A) (\frac{P + \triangle P' - p}{P_0})$$

28 **28'**

Since the pressure has increased in each vessel, the increase in the amount of gas dissolved in the liquid must be taken into account. It is:

$$\text{for } R = V_f \, \alpha \, \frac{\triangle P}{P_0} \qquad\qquad \text{for } L = V'_f \, \alpha \, \frac{\triangle P'}{P_0}$$

29 **29'**

Summarizing: The amount of gas, x, produced in R is equal to the sum of the final volume of the gas space and the increase in the amount of the gas dissolved in the water less the original volume of the gas space; or,

$$x = (V_g + \frac{h}{2} A) (\frac{273}{T} \frac{P + \triangle P - p}{P_0}) + (V_f \alpha \frac{\triangle P}{P_0}) - (V_g \frac{273}{T} \frac{P - p}{P_0})$$

$$\text{and } x = V_g \frac{273}{T} \frac{\triangle P}{P_0} + \frac{h}{2} A \frac{273}{T} \frac{P + \triangle P - p}{P_0} + V_f \alpha \frac{\triangle P}{P_0}.$$

$$\text{and } x = \triangle P \left[\frac{V_g \frac{273}{T} + V_f \, \underline{\alpha}}{P_o} + \frac{A}{2} \frac{273}{T} \frac{(P-p)\frac{h}{\triangle P} + h}{P_o} \right] \qquad \boxed{30}$$

On the other hand, no gas was produced in L; but the changes in volume and pressure must be accounted for in arriving at a value for P in order to solve equation (30).

Thus,

$$0 = (V'_g - \frac{h}{2}A) \left[\frac{273}{T} \frac{P + \triangle P' - p}{P_o} \right] + \left[V'_f \underline{\alpha} \frac{\triangle P'}{P_o} \right] - \left[V'_g \frac{273}{T} \frac{P-p}{P_o} \right]$$

$$\text{or } 0 = V'_g \frac{273}{T} \frac{\triangle P'}{P_o} - \frac{h}{2} A \frac{273}{T} \frac{P + \triangle P' - p}{P_o} + V'_f \underline{\alpha} \frac{\triangle P'}{P_o}$$

$$\text{or, } 0 = \triangle P' \left[\frac{V'_g \frac{273}{T} + V'_f \, \underline{\alpha}}{P_o} - \frac{A}{2} \frac{273}{T} \frac{(P-p)\frac{h}{\triangle P'} + h}{P_o} \right]$$

$$\text{and } \triangle P' = h \left[\frac{\frac{A}{2} \frac{273}{T} (P + \triangle P' - p)}{V'_g \frac{273}{T} + V'_f \, \underline{\alpha}} \right] \qquad \boxed{31}$$

As the pressure was originally the same on both sides of the manometer and as the pressure has increased by $\triangle P$ and $\triangle P'$ in R and L respectively, the difference in pressure as measured on the manometer is,

$$h = \triangle P - \triangle P'$$

$$\text{Or,}^* \triangle P = h + \triangle P' \qquad \boxed{32}$$

Substituting $\triangle P'$ of equation (31) in equation (32),

$$\triangle P = h + h \left[\frac{\frac{A}{2} \frac{273}{T} (P + \triangle P' - p)}{V'_g \frac{273}{T} + V'_f \, \underline{\alpha}} \right]$$

$$\text{or, } \triangle P = h \left[1 + \frac{\frac{A}{2} \frac{273}{T} (P + \triangle P' - p)}{V'_g \frac{273}{T} + V'_f \, \underline{\alpha}} \right]$$

And substituting this value of $\triangle P$ in equation (30) results in the complete expression for the differential respirometer:

$$x = h \left[1 + \frac{\frac{A}{2} \frac{273}{T} (P + \triangle P' - p)}{V'_g \frac{273}{T} + V'_f \underline{\alpha}} \right] \left[\frac{V_g \frac{273}{T} + V_f \, \underline{\alpha}}{P_o} + \frac{A}{2} \frac{273}{T} \frac{(P-p)\frac{h}{\triangle P} + h}{P_o} \right] \qquad \boxed{33}$$

For the usual type of differential respirometer V_g (and V'_g) is about 30,000 μl., V_f (and V'_f) is about 3,000 μl., and A is always less than 0.5 mm^2; $\triangle P$ (and $\triangle P'$) will probably

---

*This equation is for respirometers with vertical manometers. If the manometer is tilted, then $\triangle P = h \cos \theta + \triangle P'$ where θ is the angle of tilt.

never differ from h by more than 50% ; the maximum value of h is 300 mm; P will rarely be less than 95% of P_0; T will rarely be greater than 37.5°C.; p will be less than 5% of P; also, $V_f \alpha$ (and $V'_f \alpha$) is not more than 5% of the value of V_g (and V'_g), even for the very soluble CO_2 gas.

If it is assumed that these various quantities have their maximum values as stated above, by substituting in equation (33) it is found that,

$$x = h (1 + 0.07) \ (2.9 + 0.13)$$

This shows that the second term is about 1/14 of the first and the fourth term is about 1/20 of the third. Such a trial calculation proves that it is permissible to substitute P for $(P + \triangle P' - p)$, to omit $V'_f \alpha$ in the second term, and to omit the last half of the fourth term of equation (36) without introducing an error of more than 1%. Thus, we obtain the simplified equation,

$$x = h \left[\left(1 + \frac{A\,P_0}{2\,V'_g}\right) \ \left(\frac{V_g \frac{273}{T} + V_f\,\alpha}{P_0} + \frac{A}{2}\frac{273}{T}\right) \right]$$

34

where the product of the terms within the brackets is the "constant" of the respirometer. To obtain the volume, x, of the gas evolved at NTP it is necessary only to multiply the value of the constant by the manometer reading, h.

Dixon (1951) has pointed out that a description of the theory, such as that given above, which assumes that the whole apparatus is at the temperature T actually reduces the error of the constant as determined by equation (34); furthermore, the use of p at T instead of at room temperature (as should be the case) introduces an error of less than 0.5% in the constant. It was also assumed that the gas spaces were filled with the same kind of gas as that evolved. It might be supposed that the pressure of a second gas would affect the constant due to the fact that with the increase in volume, $\frac{h}{2}$ A, the partial pressure of the second gas would be reduced and some of the gas would pass from the liquid into the gas space. However, the reduction in partial pressure of a contained gas due to the increase in volume is very small. Even for a relatively high concentration of a very soluble gas, i.e., 10% CO_2, the error introduced is less than 0.1% ; the presence of 80% N_2 has even less effect.

Details and examples of calibration of the Barcroft differential respirometer by calculation, using the simplified equation (equation 34), are presented in Chapter 4 (pages 52 to 54).

APPLICATIONS OF THE DIFFERENTIAL RESPIROMETER

PHOTOSYNTHESIS

The discussion in this section is based on a consideration of photosynthesis as: carbon dioxide uptake and oxygen production by green cells in light.

In measuring photosynthesis the experiment usually involves a determination of the rate of gas exchange during each of three sequential periods, as follows: (1) a dark period, to determine the rate of respiration; (2) a period during which the cells are illuminated; (3) a second dark period. It is readily understood that the gas exchange between a chlorophyll -containing cell and its environment during the period of illumination results from both photosynthesis and respiration, i.e., the observed rate of photosynthesis is less than the true rate because of the evolution of carbon dioxide and the uptake of oxygen in respiration which continues during the time the cells are illuminated. Hence, in order to obtain the rate of photosynthesis, the rate of respiration is usually measured immediately before and immediately after the illumination and the average of these two rates added to the observed rate of photosynthesis. This method of correcting for respiration during photosynthesis, of course, is open to criticism. Its validity has been challenged often, and in the course of the study of photosynthesis (using manometric or other types of instruments) many different procedures and experimental conditions have been applied in attempts to substantiate or refute it, to circumvent it, or to minimize the effect of possible errors introduced by it in calculating the rate of photosynthesis. Regardless, the problem of correcting for respiration still remains and, rather than enter into a general discussion of this, the reader is referred to Kok (1948), Moore and Duggar (1949), Burk et al. (1949), Warburg et al. (1949), Burk and Warburg (1951), Brackett et al. (1953), Yuan et al. (1955), Bassham et al. (1955) and Kok (1960). In practice, one or another of the following three techniques is followed in arriving at the rate of respiration during the period the cells are illuminated: (1) relatively short periods of light and darkness to minimize the chance of the rate of respiration changing during the light period (but see Burk, 1953); (2) relatively long periods of light and darkness to assure steady-state conditions during the rate measurements, and relying on equal rates of respiration before and after a light period to represent the rate of respiration during the light period; (3) maintaining the cells at, or above or below, the compensation point (rate of photosynthesis = rate of respiration) and supplying additional light during the "light" period to obviate any correction for respiration alone. The choice of which technique to use is determined by the viewpoint of the operator regarding the correction for respiration, what feature of photosynthesis is being determined, and, to some extent, by the apparatus and facilities at hand.

The following discussion will serve to distinguish two variations of the technique described above in obtaining the rate of photosynthesis (corrected for concomitantly occurring respiration).

A. "Steady-state of gas exchange" method. The following chart indicates the general relationships:

Conditions	Dark	Light Constant intensity	Dark
Processes	Respiration	Photo. & Resp.	Respiration
Time (minutes)	→ 0 5 10 15 20 25	30 35 40 45 50 55	60 65 70 75 80
Manometer readings taken.	Equilibration period ↑ ↑ R_1	↑ ↑ P & R	↑ ↑ R_2

The duration of the light and dark periods may be varied, although 20-60 minute periods appear to be satisfactory. The R_1 and R_2 periods, which may differ in duration, are the same as or some proportion of the P & R period.

In this method, time is allowed for attainment of equilibrium in the "plant cell - suspending liquid - gas phase" system before R_1, and R_2 and P & R are measured, i.e., these quantities are measured during the steady state.

It is apparent that the true rate of photosynthesis (as $\mu l.$ O_2 produced per minute) is obtained as follows:

$$\text{Photo.} = \frac{O_2\,_{P\,\&\,R}}{\text{Minutes}_{P\,\&\,R}} + \tfrac{1}{2}\left(\frac{O_2\,_{R_1}}{\text{Minutes}_{R_1}} + \frac{O_2\,_{R_2}}{\text{Minutes}_{R_2}}\right)$$

This calculation may be considerably simplified by substituting the h values obtained for the different periods in the following equation:

$$h_{\text{Photo.}} = -\left[\tfrac{1}{2}\left(\frac{h_{R_1}}{\text{Minutes}_{R_1}} + \frac{h_{R_2}}{\text{Minutes}_{R_2}}\right) - \frac{h_{P\,\&\,R}}{\text{Minutes}_{P\,\&\,R}}\right]$$

where the negative sign before the bracket allows for the correct substitution of either negative or positive values of $h_{P\,\&\,R}$

Then:

$$X_{O_2\,\text{Photo.}} = K_{O_2}(h_{\text{Photo.}})$$

As an example: In a determination of photosynthesis in light of low intensity:

$h_{R_1(10\ minutes)} = -4.0\,mm.;\ h_{R_2(10\ minutes)} = -3.8\,mm.;\ h_{P\,\&\,R(10\ minutes)} = -2.0\,mm.$

(i.e., during the illumination period the rate of respiration was greater than the rate of photosynthesis).

$$h_{\text{Photo.}} = -\left[\tfrac{1}{2}\left((-0.4) + (-0.38)\right) - (-0.2)\right] = 0.19\ mm.$$

In another case, where high light intensity was used:

$h_{R_1(10\ minutes)} = 2.0\ mm.;\ h_{R_2(10\ minutes)} = -2.1\ mm.;\ h_{P\,\&\,R(10\ minutes)} = 4.0\ mm.$

$$h_{\text{Photo.}} = -\left[\tfrac{1}{2}\left((-0.2) + (-0.21)\right) - (-0.4)\right] = 0.605\ mm.$$

B. "Alternating light-and-dark periods" method: The following chart indicates the general relationships:

Condition	Dark		Light	Dark	Light	Dark	$\longrightarrow$
Processes	Respiration		P & R	R	P & R	R	$\longrightarrow$
Time (minutes)		0 5 10	15 20	25 30	35 40	45 50	$\longrightarrow$
Manometer readings taken	Equil-bration period	$\uparrow$ $\uparrow$ R_1	$(P\&R)_1$	$\uparrow$ $\uparrow$ R_2	$(P\&R)_2$	$\uparrow$ $\uparrow$ R_3	$\longrightarrow$

As indicated, the rate of respiration is measured during the second 5 minutes of each dark period. The first 5 minutes allows for the attainment of equilibrium conditions of gas exchange for respiration after a period of combined photosynthesis and respiration. On the other hand, while photosynthesis begins as soon as the plant cells receive light and ceases when the light is turned off, the last vestige of oxygen produced in photosynthesis requires one or two minutes to reach the gas space, and hence it would not be included in the measured oxygen if a manometer reading were taken the instant the light was turned off. The same reasoning holds when the rate of photosynthesis is less than the rate of respiration. Therefore, a manometer reading is taken at the end of the first 5 minutes of darkness. Manometer readings may be continued to be taken in this order for succeeding 10-minute light and dark periods for as long a time as is practical.

The true rate of photosynthesis is calculated as follows: Since respiration has been measured for two 5-minute periods (immediately before and 5 minutes after the photosynthesis-respiration period), the average respiration for the two periods is taken to represent the respiration occurring during each 5-minute period of photosynthesis-respiration. During the 15-minute period of photosynthesis-respiration, photosynthesis occurred for 10 minutes and respiration occurred for 15 minutes. Hence the true rate of photosynthesis for the 10-minute light period is obtained as follows:

$$\text{Photo}_{10 \text{ minutes}} = 3 \left(\frac{O_2{}_{R_1} + O_2{}_{R_2}}{2} \right) + O_2 \, (P\&R)_1$$

The result can be obtained more quickly by substituting the h values obtained for the different periods in the following equation:

$$h_{10\text{-min. Photo.}} = - \left[3 \left(\frac{h_{R_1} + h_{R_2}}{2} \right) - h_{P\&R} \right]$$

36

where the negative sign before the bracket allows for the correct substitution of either negative or positive values of $h_{P\&R}$. As an example: In a determination of photosynthesis in light of low intensity: $h_{R_2} = -5.1 \, \text{mm.}$; $h_{R_3} = -5.1 \, \text{mm.}$; $h_{P\&R_2} = -10.1 \, \text{mm.}$

$$h_{10\text{-min. Photo.}} = - \left[3 \left(\frac{(-5.1) + (-5.1)}{2} \right) - (-10.1) \right] = 5.2 \, \text{mm.}$$

From the above discussion of the methods of measuring photosynthesis by means of the differential manometer; it is evident that in the reaction vessel: (1) both carbon dioxide and oxygen are present in the gas space and are dissolved in the solution in which the plant cells are suspended; (2) during respiration carbon dioxide is added to and oxygen is removed from the gas and liquid phases; (3) during photosynthesis-respiration, if the rate of photosynthesis exceeds the rate of respiration, oxygen is added to and carbon dioxide removed from the gas and liquid phases; (4) if the rate of photosynthesis does not exceed the rate of respiration during the photosynthesis-respiration period the situation is the same as for (2) above, the rate of exchange only is decreased. In other words, both the oxygen and carbon dioxide content of the gas and liquid phases change. If, during respiration the CO_2/O_2 ratio is 1.0 the net difference in terms of total gas in the reaction vessel is zero; the same is true when the photosynthesis ratio, O_2/CO_2 is 1.0. There would be no change in the manometer reading were it not for the fact that α for oxygen is much less than the α for carbon dioxide. When oxygen is utilized in respiration V_g decreases due to the greater solubility of the carbon dioxide produced in the liquid present. By the same reasoning, V_g increases during photosynthesis.

In measuring photosynthesis manometrically three different methods have been employed. Each of these is described below, where the gas exchange is obtained using differential respirometers. (As pointed out above, appropriately calibrated Warburg respirometers may be used instead.)

1. "One-vessel" ("one-respirometer") method involving CO_2 and O_2 exchange between V_g and V_f:

As stated above, V_g increases during photosynthesis because the oxygen produced is less soluble than the carbon dioxide used in the liquid of the cell suspension. By using an acid (pH 4-5, to avoid CO_2 retention) mineral-salt nutrient solution or other medium in preparing the cell suspension it is possible to measure the rate of photosynthesis with a single differential respirometer. This, however, requires the following extension of the theory of the instrument:

(a) K of the gas space must be determined, since there is no way of determining what portion of its volume is occupied by oxygen and by carbon dioxide; (b) a means must be found to determine K_{O_2}, i.e., when we know what effect the addition of x amount of carbon dioxide and the removal of the same quantity of oxygen (or the reverse of this exchange) will have on h; (c) how a correction can be made when the photosynthesis ratio differs from 1.0. It does not matter what the respiratory ratio is if photosynthesis is calculated on the basis of the h values for the different periods (see equations 35, 36 above) for what occurs in the reaction vessel is essentially a change in h due to photosynthesis, and this is the only change measured.

a. Determination of $K_{gas-space}$ (K_{gs}): The K desired is the change in manometer reading, h, produced by adding x quantity of gas to the gas space when no gas is absorbed by the liquid present. It is assumed that the volume of liquid occupying V_f (and V'_f) is to be present during an experiment.

The K_{gs} may be determined by using a modification of the simplified equation. $V_f \underline{\alpha}$ in the third term of the equation, which accounts for the quantity of the gas introduced that dissolves in the liquid, is omitted and the equation used in this form:

$$K_{gs} = h \left[\left(1 + \frac{A\, P_0}{2\, V'_g} \right) \left(\frac{V_g \frac{273}{T}}{P_0} + \frac{A}{2} \frac{273}{T} \right) \right]$$

$\boxed{37}$

where the product of the terms within the brackets is the "gas space constant" of the respirometer. In reality this equation is a variant of the equation derived by Barcroft (1908). The original equation is:

$$K_{gs} = h \left(\frac{273}{T} \right) \left(\frac{V_g\, AP}{P_0} \right)$$

$\boxed{38}$

and was used by Warburg and Negelein (1922a) in deriving the constant of their differential manometer. Equation (37) has the advantage of allowing for different volumes of V_g and V'_g. The substitution of experimental values into equations (37) and (38) will yield the same results (within 2%) only if the cross-sectional area of the manometer capillary is less than 0.25 sq. mm.

b. Determination of K_{O_2} when equal amounts of carbon dioxide and oxygen are exchanged: The extension of the theory to determine K_{O_2} based on the difference in solubilities of carbon dioxide and oxygen in the liquids in the vessels has been described by Warburg and Negelein (1922a). It is as follows:

Let: P_o = normal pressure in mm. of manometric fluid.

V_f = µl. of liquid in reaction vessel (also in V').

Y_{O_2} = µl. of oxygen released or absorbed.

Y_{CO_2} = µl. of carbon dioxide released or absorbed.

h = manometer reading, in mm.

$\underline{\alpha} \, O_2$ = absorption coeff. of oxygen at T.

$\underline{\alpha} \, CO_2$ = absorption coeff. of carbon dioxide at T.

V = change in volume of the gas space in the reaction side of the respirometer.

BV = µl. of oxygen added to or removed from the gas space.

(B - 1) V = µl. of carbon dioxide added to or removed from the gas space.

hV = change in the partial pressure of oxygen when the volume of the gas space changes by an amount V.

(h - 1) V = change in the partial pressure of carbon dioxide when the volume of the gas space changes by an amount V.

Then, $V = BV - (B - 1) V$

and $h = Bh - (B - 1) h$

Thus, $Y_{O_2} = BV + \dfrac{Bh(V_f \, \underline{\alpha} \, O_2)}{P_o}$ **39**

and $Y_{CO_2} = (B - 1) V + \dfrac{(B - 1) \, h(V_f \, \underline{\alpha} \, CO_2)}{P_o}$ **40**

Since $Y_{CO_2} = Y_{O_2}$

on eliminating B and Y_{CO_2} after combining equations (39) and (40)

$$Y_{O_2} = \frac{\left(V + \dfrac{hV_f \, \underline{\alpha} \, CO_2}{P_o} \right) \left(V + \dfrac{hV_f \, \underline{\alpha} \, O_2}{P_o} \right)}{\dfrac{hV_f \, (\underline{\alpha} \, CO_2 - \underline{\alpha} \, O_2)}{P_o}}$$ **41**

In this equation, h represents the increase in pressure, $\triangle P$, on the reaction side of the respirometer. Actually h is less than $\triangle P$ because of the compensatory effect of the increase in pressure on the compensation-vessel side. A correction may be applied by substituting $\triangle P$ for h, where

$$\triangle P = h + P \left(\frac{V_g}{V_g - \frac{Ah}{2}} - 1 \right)$$

This correction reduces the value of Y_{O_2} by about 1%.

Since V is equal to hK_{gs},

$$X_{O_2} = h \left[\frac{\left(K_{gs} + \frac{V_f \alpha CO_2}{P_o}\right) \left(K_{gs} + \frac{V_f \alpha O_2}{P_o}\right)}{\frac{V_f (\alpha CO_2 - \alpha O_2)}{P_o}} \right] \qquad 42$$

and K_{O_2} is equal to the quantity represented by the bracketed terms in the above equation.

c. Correcting K_{O_2} when the photosynthetic ratio, O_2/CO_2, is not unity:

Let $\dfrac{Y_{O_2}}{Y_{CO_2}} = Z$

then equation (42) takes this form,

$$X_{O_2} = h \left[\frac{\left(ZK_{gs} + Z\frac{V_f \alpha CO_2}{P_o}\right) \left(K_{gs} + \frac{V_f \alpha O_2}{P_o}\right)}{K_{gs}(Z-1) + Z\left(\frac{V_f \alpha CO_2}{P_o}\right) - \frac{V_f \alpha O_2}{P_o}} \right] \qquad 43$$

The above equation is the complete equation to be used with the differential manometer in determining photosynthesis provided the photosynthesis ratio is known. It so happens, however, that a determination of the photosynthesis ratio is not an easy matter. Many workers have either assumed it to be 1.0, or they have used the value obtained by Warburg and Negelein (1922a). As a matter of fact, Warburg and Negelein did not determine this ratio under conditions strictly comparable to those which prevailed during their measurement of the quantum efficiency of photosynthesis. They used a glass vessel filled with a gas mixture and a suspension of algal cells, from which samples of gas were withdrawn from time to time and analyzed for oxygen and carbon dioxide. They obtained an average value of 1.1 in three experiments.

2. "One-vessel" ("one-respirometer") method involving only O_2 exchange between V_g and V_f:

Because of the difficulty of obtaining the photosynthetic ratio directly and because it effects a simplification of the whole procedure of determining photosynthesis, many workers favor the use of carbonate-bicarbonate CO_2-buffer solutions. Without going into the question of the effect of such solutions on the metabolism of the cell (Warburg, 1919; Manning, et al., 1938; Emerson and Lewis, 1943), it is readily understood that if the partial pressure of carbon dioxide in the gas space of the reaction vessel of the respirometer is maintained constant, the change in h is due solely to the oxygen added to or removed from the system by the plant cells. Thus, one need only determine the K_{O_2} for the respirometer containing the particular CO_2-buffer under the conditions of experimentation. There are certain precautions, however, to be borne in mind. In particular: the carbonate-bicarbonate CO_2-buffers change as carbon dioxide is added to or removed from solution; this in turn changes the partial pressure of the carbon dioxide in the gas space of the respirometer vessel. Warburg (1919) has called attention to this fact, and has indicated the working range in terms of the quantity of carbon dioxide that can be removed from or added to the solution without introducing an error of more than 1% in the h values obtained (but see Emerson and Chalmers, 1955). He also pointed out that the higher the pH of a carbonate-bicarbonate solution the shorter the period of time the plant cells, i.e., Chlorella, can remain in it without showing a decrease in photosynthetic capacity. Pratt (1943) has considered this question of the physiological effect of sodium and potassium bicarbonates on the rate of respiration and photosynthesis of Chlorella vulgaris. As a result of this study, he recommended a solution consisting of 0.035 M KHCO₃ and 0.065 M NaHCO₃. He found that in such a solution the accelerating and depressing actions of potassium and sodium salts, respectively, were balanced and the initial rate of photosynthesis was maintained virtually unchanged for fifteen hours.

Table 15 contains some of the pertinent data for various solutions of sodium carbonate-bicarbonate CO_2-buffers. Solutions of this type were used by Warburg (1919) in determining the effect of carbon dioxide concentration on the rate of photosynthesis in Chlorella.

Table 16
Carbonate-bicarbonate Mixtures

Mixture No.	Composition, mls.		Na millimoles Liter	CO_2 Moles/L 25°C.	pH* 25° C.
	Na₂CO₃ 0.1 M	NaHCO₃ 0.1 M			
1	85	15	185	0.53×10^{-6}	10.42
2	80	20	180	1.0 "	10.30
3	75	25	175	1.7 "	10.19
4	70	30	170	2.6 "	10.10
5	60	40	160	5.3 "	9.93
6	50	50	150	9.8 "	9.79
7	35	65	135	2.3×10^{-5}	9.51
8	25	75	125	4.3 "	9.32
9	15	85	115	9.1 "	9.08
10	10	90	110	15.0 "	8.91
11	5	95	105	33.0 "	8.69

*Routine determinations made with a glass electrode.

The data in Table 15 are presented only to show the composition of some CO_2-buffers that have been used, and to point out the relatively high pH values of such solutions. In case one desires to use such buffers, it is imperative that their effect on the particular process under investigation be determined. It certainly appears that the recommendations of Pratt (1943) should be considered.

3. "Two-vessel" ("two-respirometers") method involving exchange of CO_2 and O_2 between V_g and V_f:

Simply stated this is a means of measuring the rate of photosynthesis using the "indirect" method of Warburg (see Chapter 3). Two differential respirometers are used: one with rectangular vessels of the type A of figure 28; the other with rectangular vessels of exactly the same dimensions of the vessel-compartment as those of the A-type used with the other respirometer, but differing from these in having an extended neck (type B, fig. 28) to increase their volume to about 150% of that of the A pair (cf. Emerson and Chalmers, 1955, for a complete discussion of the effect seemingly minor differences in the shape and dimensions of the two pairs of vessels may have on the results obtained). The reaction vessels are supplied with equal aliquots of the same algal cell suspension (acid, pH 4-5, nutrient solution as suspending medium) and each of the two compensation vessels is supplied with a volume of the nutrient solution, without algal cells, equal to that in each of the reaction vessels. Thus the two respirometers when assembled contain the same volume of liquid, V_f and V'_f, but unequal volumes of gas, V_g and V'_g. The gas phase, usually 5% carbon dioxide in air, is obtained by flushing all four flasks with this mixture.

Representing the change in the height of the manometer liquid of the respirometer having the vessels with the larger gas volume by H, and that of the respirometer having the vessels with the smaller gas volume by h, over any period of simultaneous readings of H and h,

$$O_2 \text{ exchange} = \frac{HK_{CO_2} - hk_{CO_2}}{\dfrac{K_{CO_2}}{K_{O_2}} - \dfrac{k_{CO_2}}{k_{O_2}}} \qquad \boxed{44}$$

$$CO_2 \text{ exchange} = \frac{HK_{O_2} - hk_{O_2}}{\dfrac{K_{O_2}}{K_{CO_2}} - \dfrac{k_{O_2}}{k_{CO_2}}} \qquad \boxed{45}$$

The flask constants, K_{O_2} and K_{CO_2} for the respirometer equipped with the larger flasks and k_{O_2} and k_{CO_2} for the respirometer equipped with the smaller flasks are determined as described in Chapter 4.

In using the two-vessel method it is very important to remember that H and h, the corresponding pressure changes in the two respirometers, must represent the same gas exchange. Therefore, it is understood that all conditions which may affect the gas exchange must be exactly the same for both pairs of vessels. Potential sources of error in using this method of measuring photosynthesis have been discussed by Nishimura et al. (1951) and Emerson and Chalmers (1955). It would appear from the results obtained by the latter that the method is unsatisfactory in measuring photosynthesis during periods of transient rates of gas exchange (immediately following expo-

sure of the algal cells to light, and immediately following the exclusion of light), but
with suitable precautions being taken in the design of the vessels, rate of shaking, etc.,
it is capable of being used to determine the rate of this process under steady-state
conditions during alternating periods of darkness (respiration) and light (photosynthesis and respiration).

Another problem encountered in using the two-vessel method in measuring photosynthesis is that of supplying the two algal cell suspensions simultaneously with beams of
light of equal intensity (and preferably, uniform intensity over the cross-sectional area
of each beam). A suitable system of light source, prisms, and filters has been described by Nishimura et al. (1951). The use of commercial types of constant temperature baths provided with horizontal fluorescent lamps to illuminate the algal cell suspensions from beneath would appear to be satisfactory for some types of studies of
photosynthesis, but we have had no experience with any one of them.

RESPIRATION

The differential respirometer may be used in the same manner as the Warburg respirometer in determining oxygen uptake by the "direct method", i.e., alkali in the center wells,
with or without liquid in the sidearms; K_{O_2} is obtained by calculation using the simplified
equation (34), or the Münzer and Neumann method. The simplifying assumptions made in
deriving equation (34) should be kept in mind. Commercial Barcroft manometers with
capillary cross sectional areas over 1 mm.^{2} have appeared on the market; these will give
inaccurate results, because it is assumed in the simplification that a much smaller cross
sectional area will be used (an area of 0.1-0.2 mm.^{2} is desirable in the U-tube of the
manometer, but larger bore tubing may be used for the remaining portions of the manometer). The typical Barcroft flask has had a volume of 30-40 ml., but it is convenient to
use flasks as small as 7 ml.

Although it is less generally used than the Warburg respirometer, the differential respirometer is distinctly the more stable of the two. The closed differential system avoids the
errors introduced by the inevitable inaccuracies in the thermobarometric corrections
required with the Warburg respirometer. The Barcroft apparatus is particularly advantageous when small gas exchanges must be measured.

The differential respirometer also may be used to determine respiration by the indirect
method of Warburg (Chapter 3). Two respirometers are required. Unequal volumes of
liquid and unequal volumes of gas, unequal volumes of liquid and equal volumes of gas, or
equal volumes of liquid unequal volumes of gas may be used in the reaction vessels of the
two respirometers. K_{O_2} and K_{CO_2} may be obtained as described above, and x_{O_2} and
x_{CO_2} obtained by use of the equations (44) and (45).

In general, the differential respirometer can be used in any situation to which the Warburg
respirometer is applicable; it can be used in those cases where it is desirable to increase
or decrease the pressure of the gas in the reaction vessel above or below the pressure of
the atmosphere.

FERMENTATION

The differential respirometer is used without alkali in the center wells (if the flasks
possess these) and with or without liquids in the sidearms of the flasks. K_{CO_2} is obtained by using the simplified equation (34).

J. F. STAUFFER

Chapter 7
SPECIAL METHODS EMPLOYING MANOMETRIC AND ELECTROMETRIC TECHNIQUES

Most of the methods described in this chapter require some sort of specialized apparatus other than that normally accompanying a respirometer. In general, the methods have been devised to meet specific needs not covered by the usual instruments or to facilitate measurements which are difficult and time-consuming on the normal instrument. In some instances the method is described in principle only and references to detailed descriptions are cited.

DIXON-KEILIN METHOD: WARBURG MANOMETER

In this method CO_2 is present during the reaction period; after the reaction period acid is added to liberate all bound CO_2, and finally the CO_2 is absorbed with alkali. Appropriate controls permit one to measure oxygen uptake, acid production, and CO_2 production in buffers, bicarbonate, serum, etc., or mixtures of these. Although the method is somewhat complex, it is desirable to have some knowledge of its principles since the method eliminates many of the complexities and uncertainties inherent in other methods, although it does introduce a few of its own.

Figure 29
Dixon-Keilin Flask (see text for description

The type of flask used by Dixon and Keilin is illustrated in figure 29. Tissue is placed in compartment A, and acid in the sidearm A'. Alkali is placed in the stopcock insert B' which when turned to a point parallel with the center well (B) permits the alkali to enter the flask. B contains a glass rod and usually contains filter paper to increase the surface of the alkali. The glass rod drops into the stopcock insert and displaces the alkali into B so that it wets the paper.

Measurement of respiration, CO_2 output, and acid production are made with one flask, but two other flasks are required as controls. Details of the procedure have been adequately described in several places (Dixon, 1951, Dickens and Simer, 1933). A brief description of the method follows: In the main compartment of the reaction flask, the tissue is suspended in phosphate, in other buffers, or in serum and is allowed to respire for a measured interval. At the end of this interval acid is tipped in from the sidearm, and the CO_2 released is measured (= final "bound" CO_2). After the readings are constant, the alkali is added in the Dixon-Keilin flasks to absorb the CO_2. This is measured (= final CO_2 in gas phase). Oxygen uptake is determined by the decrease in the reading after all the CO_2 has been absorbed compared to the initial reading. This decrease is caused by (a) oxygen uptake, and (b) the absorption of the CO_2 which was in the gas phase at the start. A control flask is used to determine how much CO_2 is in the gas phase at the start; hence, the oxygen uptake can.be calculated from these data readily. The CO_2 in the gas phase not accounted for by the initial CO_2 in the gas, plus that derived from the bicarbonate (a second control flask measures initial "bound" CO_2) is that produced directly by respiration or fermentation. The decrease in bicarbonate is a measure of the acid production, but it must be corrected for "acid retention" (see later) to give the true acid produced. The relatively large changes in gas pressure which occur (<u>i.e.</u>, when bicarbonate is acidified, or all the CO_2 is absorbed) usually necessitate the use of mercury or Clerici's solution in the manometer. Whereas the method is quite useful, it has two limitations:

(1) "Acid retention" must be estimated and a correction applied for it. (See discussion in the latter part of this chapter.)
(2) It only serves to measure the reactions over an interval and does not provide a continuous measurement of respiration, CO_2 output and glycolysis, as has sometimes been supposed.

Undoubtedly this method deserves more general use than has been accorded to it. In our opinion the necessity for specialized apparatus has been a serious limitation in its use. A modification which permits one to use the method with ordinary respirometer flasks having two sidearms follows:

Figure 30
Flask which permits the mixing of two materials in the sidearm (see text for description)

Tissue, buffer, <u>etc.</u>, are placed in the main compartment of the flask (fig. 30). Acid is placed in the single sidearm. The double sidearm contains solid KI in its main compartment and 0.3 ml. of saturated $KMnO_4$ in 0.001 M H_2SO_4 in its side compartment. When it is desired to absorb the CO_2 from the gas phase (after acid has been added from the single sidearm and a measurement has been made), the $KMnO_4$ solution is tipped into the KI to produce an alkaline solution. The vessel may require 8-12 hours of shaking before absorption of CO_2 is complete; the tissue has been inactivated with the acid before the alkali is generated. The flask shown in figure 30 is suitable for a wide variety of manometric techniques and is recommended highly as a general utility flask. As these flasks occupy more space than the ordinary flasks, it may be necessary to stagger them in the bath, <u>i.e.</u>, if the sidearms of one flask point away from the manometer the sidearms of the adjacent flask will point toward the manometer.

DIXON-KEILIN METHOD: DIFFERENTIAL RESPIROMETER

This method is adequately described by Dixon (1943, 1951) together with several modifications for use with the differential respirometer. With this apparatus it is undoubtedly a very excellent method. Two flasks (Dixon-Keilin type) of exactly the same size (their size may be equalized by adding glass rods (Summerson, 1939)) and containing identical amounts of tissue, buffers, gas, <u>etc.</u> are attached to opposite sides of a differential manometer. At the start, acid is tipped into one of the flasks, giving the initial "bound" CO_2. Respiration, glycolysis, etc. continue in the other flask, causing a change in the manometer reading. At the end of a measured interval, acid is tipped into the second flask causing the liberation of "bound" CO_2 still remaining. Both flasks have now had the same treatment except that one has respired for a measured interval. Alkali is now introduced into both flasks simultaneously to absorb the CO_2 in the gas phase. From the resulting change in the manometer, the oxygen uptake can be determined readily. From the other readings mentioned one may determine the total CO_2 output and the change in "bound" CO_2. From the latter, by correcting for "acid retention", the acid produced may be calculated. Dixon (1937), Brekke and Dixon (1937), Elliot and Schroeder (1934) have described methods based on the Dixon-Keilin method. Dickens and Greville (1933b) and Summerson (1939) have provided essentially similar methods, but with improvements possible by the use of specialized apparatus. Dixon (1943) has discussed these in some detail.

W. W. UMBREIT

RETENTION

The measurement of CO_2 production is complicated by retention. Retention is a manifestation of the fact that the amount of CO_2 released from a buffered medium is less than would be released from a theoretical medium with no buffering capacity. Quantitatively, retention by a medium is a direct function of its buffering capacity.

Two manifestations of retention are encountered experimentally, and they will be discussed here under the terms "retention of CO_2" and "retention of acid". The difference between them is that "retention of CO_2" concerns the binding of a part of the metabolic CO_2 (determined as outlined in Chapter 3) as bicarbonate by reaction with the buffer, and "retention of acid" concerns the neutralization of a part of the metabolically formed acid (determined as outlined in Chapter 2) by the buffer present rather than by bicarbonate.

Retention of CO_2. When metabolic CO_2 is produced in a medium in the usual physiological range of pH, less CO_2 appears in the gas phase than is predicted by the equation for

the measurement of CO_2 exchange: $x_{CO_2} = hk_{CO_2}$. The flask constant $k_{CO_2} = \dfrac{V_g \dfrac{273}{T} + \alpha V_f}{10,000}$

is calculated with the absorption coefficient, α, for CO_2 as one factor. The values for α substituted in the equation are determined from the solubility of CO_2 in pure water, i.e., in a medium essentially without buffering capacity. The true absorption coefficient, α, is not affected greatly by a change in pH or by the presence or absence of buffers in the medium, e.g., the α value for CO_2 at 25° C. is 0.756 in water, 0.732 in 1.0 M HCl, and 0.692 in 1.0 M NH_4Cl. However, as was emphasized in Chapter 2, the observed solubility of CO_2 is complicated by the formation of bicarbonate in a medium with buffering capacity. Retention of CO_2 is the term used to describe the ability of a medium to bind CO_2 (as carbonate or bicarbonate) in excess of the amount predicted by its true α solubility.

Correction for retention of CO_2 is made most easily by using a flask constant derived by substituting an α' value for α in the equation for determining the flask constant. α' is defined here as the solubility of CO_2 at the pH of the medium, and it combines both the true α solubility and the solubility from the formation of bicarbonates. As pK'_a from the apparent first dissociation constant for carbonic acid is 6.317 (at 38° C.),

$$\frac{\alpha'}{\alpha} = \frac{(HCO_3^-) + (CO_2)}{(CO_2)} = \left[\text{antilog (pH - 6.317)}\right] + 1$$

where the pH is that in the reaction flask during the experiment. In figure 8, Chapter 3, $\dfrac{\alpha}{\alpha}$ is plotted against pH. An inspection of this figure indicates that below pH 5 retention is negligible and may be disregarded, that in the pH range 5 to 7 retention is considerable but may be corrected for with the anticipation of accurate results, but that retention above pH 7.0 is excessive and accuracy may be poor when the "direct method" for measuring CO_2 production is used.

As an example of the use of the α' value, assume that a flask of 18.5 ml. volume is being used to measure the CO_2 production by cells suspended in 3 ml. of medium at pH 6.5.

The temperature of the bath is $37°$ C. Figure 8 indicates that at pH 6.5 $\frac{\alpha'}{\alpha}$ = 2.50. At $37°$ C. the value of α for CO_2 is 0.567, so α' = 2.5 x 0.567 = 1.42. Therefore,

$$k'_{CO_2} = \frac{15{,}500 \times \frac{273}{310} + 3{,}000 \times 1.42}{10{,}000} = 1.79.$$

Under the conditions specified the true CO_2 production can be calculated simply by multiplying the observed change in mm. on the manometer (Brodie's or Krebs' fluid) by 1.79.

The use of α' in correcting for retention carries with it the assumption that the pH in the reaction vessel does not change. If the pH does change, the final as well as the initial pH should be determined to permit a more accurate calculation of the CO_2 retained. As reactions proceeding at a linear rate are normally measured, a knowledge of the initial and final pH will permit the reasonably accurate prediction of the pH at any time during the run; from the pH at any time the α' and the flask constant at that time can be calculated. In many cases the buffering capacity of the medium will be sufficient so that changes in the pH may be neglected.

Although the use of α' values for the calculation of retention of CO_2 is recommended for its simplicity, it also is possible to determine the retention empirically. This is done by generating CO_2 in a respirometer in the absence of the medium and in another respirometer in the presence of the medium. The procedure usually recommended is to place bicarbonate for generating CO_2 in the flasks primary sac of Siamese sidearm, fig. 30) and to fill the flasks with a gas mixture containing CO_2 in equilibrium with the bicarbonate. A simpler procedure is to substitute carbonate for bicarbonate so the determination may be performed in an atmosphere of air. The details of such a determination follow:

Flask 1 (A flask with 1 sidearm)	Flask 2 (A flask of the type shown in fig. 30)
0.2 ml. solution containing 1 mg. Na_2CO_3 (equivalent to 211 μl. CO_2) is dried in main chamber of flask at $250°$ C. for 1 hour.	0.2 ml. solution containing 1 mg. Na_2CO_3 is dried in primary sac of Siamese sidearm (fig. 30) at $250°$C. for 1 hour.
0.2 ml. 0.2 N H_2SO_4 in sidearm. (This is more than sufficient to liberate all the CO_2 from the Na_2CO_3.)	0.2 ml. 0.2 N H_2SO_4 in secondary sac of Siamese sidearm (fig. 30).
2.0 ml. H_2O in main chamber.	2.0 ml. of medium in main chamber (fig. 30).
Atmosphere, air.	Atmosphere, air.

After equilibration, tip in acid from the sidearm into the main chamber of flask 1. In flask 2 tip acid from the secondary into the primary sac of the Siamese sidearm (fig. 30). The addition of acid liberates the same amount of CO_2 in each flask, but more is taken up by the medium in flask 2 than by the water in flask 1. The amount of CO_2 liberated into the atmosphere of each flask is calculated from the observed change in pressure (corrected for any change in the thermobarometer) and the k_{CO_2} for each flask. As the same amount of CO_2 was liberated from the carbonate in each flask, the CO_2 observed in flask 1 minus that observed in flask 2 represents the retention of CO_2 by 2 ml. of the medium (the α solubility in the fluid in the flasks is corrected for in the calculation with k_{CO_2}). If, for example, only 80% of the CO_2 liberated is observed in the gas phase, all observed values for CO_2 liberation under the same conditions can be divided by 0.80 to give the true amount of CO_2.

It should be noted that in the example of the empirical determination of retention of CO_2 only the medium is considered and no enzymatic preparation is included in the test. When a homogenate or other preparation with considerable buffering capacity is added, the retention is changed substantially. Addition of heat inactivated enzyme, or enzyme plus inhibitor, to the medium for the test of retention capacity should correct for this, although denaturation and clumping of the protein upon heating may alter its buffering capacity somewhat.

Retention of Acid: Production of acid often is followed manometrically by measuring the CO_2 released by the acid from a bicarbonate medium. However, the acid produced does not release its equivalent in CO_2 because of the buffering capacity of the medium.

An electrometric titration curve of materials duplicating those contained in the reaction flask and a determination of the initial and final pH in each flask will permit the calculation of retention of acid. However, it is difficult to obtain accurate pH values because of the loss of CO_2 from the medium after the vessel is opened. The pH values could be found by inserting a glass electrode and bridge assembly through a ground joint in the flask, but this would require special equipment.

The empirical determination of retention of acid (especially by the method described by Bain in the next section) is the method of choice for obtaining a correction factor. A known amount of acid, insufficient to liberate all of the CO_2 from bicarbonate, is added to bicarbonate in one flask and to bicarbonate plus the medium in another flask; the output of CO_2 is measured in each case. Note that in this method the acid is added directly to the medium, whereas in the empirical determination of retention of CO_2 it is added to the carbonate in a chamber separated from the medium. An example of such a determination, carried out in ordinary flasks with one sidearm, follows:

Flask 1	Flask 2
Main chamber - 1 ml. 0.0177 M NaHCO₃ 2 ml. water	1 ml. 0.0177 M NaHCO₃ 2 ml. medium
Sidearm - 0.1 ml. 0.040 M lactic acid	0.1 ml. 0.040 M lactic acid

Gas mixture contains 5% CO_2; pH of medium, 7.0

After equilibration, acid is rinsed into the main chamber of each flask. The amount of CO_2 liberated is calculated from the change in the manometer readings (corrected for any change of the thermobarometer) and the flask constants. The μl. CO_2 liberated in flask 2 divided by the μl. CO_2 liberated in flask 1 gives the fraction liberated from the medium. If this be 0.8, subsequent values for CO_2 liberation, from this medium under the same conditions, when divided by 0.8 will yield the true amount of CO_2 equivalent to the acid produced.

The method described involves the addition of a constant amount of acid. If it is added in flasks of different volumes it will not establish the same pCO_2; therefore, retention of acid will not be the same in flasks of different volumes. Hence, calibration of each flask is necessary; this is a cumbersome operation when accomplished by the procedure outlined above. In the following section a very convenient method for determining retention of acid during a run is described.

R. H. BURRIS

MEASUREMENT OF RETENTION OF ACID

Warburg flasks, so designed as to allow the addition of two substances to the system at different times are required. Flasks with two sidearms were found to be convenient. In one sidearm is placed a measured amount of standard citric acid (0.1-0.2 ml. M/10). The flask is then placed in an oven at 75° C. until the acid is completely dried. This is done in order to avoid changes in volume when the standard acid is added to the system. In the other sidearm is placed the requisite amount of substrate solution while the main part of the flask contains the tissue to be studied, the $NaHCO_3$ buffer, and water to make a total volume of 3.0 ml. The flask is gassed and equilibrated in the usual manner and the substrate tipped in. The rate of CO_2 evolution is measured for two five minute periods; at the end of the second period the dried acid is washed into the main part of the flask and three more readings are taken. The first two and the last two readings give the steady rate of the system. The difference between this rate and the third reading gives the amount of carbon dioxide evolved by the standard acid. The variation between this value and the value obtained by tipping standard acid into $NaHCO_3$ alone allows a calculation of the retention correction to be made. The amount of acid introduced into the system is not large enough to change the pH appreciably and thus the activity of the tissue is not affected. The correction obtained is a function not only of the buffering capacity of the medium, but also of the volume of the flask and the amount of the gas evolved.

In the conventional method (Dixon, 1943, 1951) each flask is calibrated individually. A method has been devised whereby any number of flasks may be calibrated for retention from the data obtained by the use of just one flask provided the volume of each is known.

If the flask constants (k) are calculated for a series of flasks in the usual manner and plotted against the gas volumes (Vg) a straight line, hereafter referred to as the base line, is obtained. Suppose that a medium which retains carbon dioxide is introduced into these flasks. Each flask will now have a constant which is equal to k plus an amount "r" which will vary with each flask. If these new k values be plotted against V_g as before, a straight line will again be obtained, but will be found to lie above the base line and to have a different slope. The characteristics of this line are reflections of the facts that the amount of retention is a function of the buffering capacity of the medium, the volume of the flask, and the amount of gas evolved.

By introducing a given medium into three flasks of different volumes and measuring the amount of CO_2 given off when a known amount of standard acid was added, a retention line was determined directly. This was done with several media of different retentions and the data plotted (see Bain and Rusch, 1944). It was found that the slope (m) of these lines was proportional to the value of k at a given volume, *i.e.*:

When V_g is constant:

$$k_I m_{II} = k_{II} m_I \qquad \text{46a}$$

$$k_I m_{III} = k_{III} m_I \qquad \text{46b}$$

$$k_I m_{IV} = k_{IV} m_I \qquad \text{46c}$$

With this fact established it became apparent that the retention line for a given medium could be determined from the data of one flask if the base line and the volume of the test flask were known. The method of arriving at this conclusion is demonstrated as follows:

From Chapter 1, $k = x/h$, where k = the constant of the test flask of volume V_g, x = the theoretical µl. of carbon dioxide evolved by n ml. of standard acid, and h = the manometer reading produced by n ml. of standard acid.

Solving the established proportion for m, we find $m = km_{base}/k_{base}$, where m is the slope of the retention line, m_{base} the slope of the base-line and k and k_{base} the constants of the flask of volume V_g at retention and at base-line levels.

By solving a simple analytical equation for a straight line, we find $k' = m(V'g - Vg) + k$, where k' is the constant of the flask of volume $V'g$ at retention line level.

With V_g known and $V'g$ arbitrarily assigned, k and k' can be calculated from the above equations and the retention line (thus defined by the points (k, Vg) and $(k', V'g)$) constructed. The constant for any apparatus volume may now be read directly from the retention curve for the medium involved.

The use of these retention values in the Warburg "indirect method" (Chapter 3) is described by Dixon (1943, 1951), and in the Dixon and Keilin method (page 91) by Dixon (1937, 1943, 1951).

J. A. BAIN

MEASUREMENT OF GASES OTHER THAN OXYGEN AND CARBON DIOXIDE

HYDROGEN: Hydrogen exchange often may be involved in bacterial reactions. In the oxidation of hydrogen with molecular oxygen (the Knallgas reaction) a combination of oxygen and hydrogen takes place and difficulty arises in establishing how much of each gas reacts. If the reaction can occur at a low partial pressure of oxygen, the individual gases taken up in the overall reaction can be measured as described by Lee, Wilson, and Wilson (1942). Employing a mixture of 98% H_2 and 2% O_2 in the Warburg flasks they allowed the reaction to proceed until the oxygen was exhausted. The oxygen supplied was accurately measured in independent flasks containing pyrogallol and alkali, the alkali being added from the sidearm after temperature equilibrium was reached. Such a method is limited to gas mixtures containing not over 2.5% of oxygen. Subtracting the pressure change in the oxygen analysis flask (alkaline pyrogallol) from the total pressure change in the flask containing H_2 and O_2 indicated the pressure change attributable to H_2 uptake.

If hydrogen evolution is to be measured in an anaerobic system, for which independent analysis has demonstrated hydrogen and carbon dioxide as the only gaseous products, the carbon dioxide may be absorbed with KOH in the inset cup and gas pressure attributed to hydrogen production. Woods and Clifton (1937) have followed such hydrogen output with simultaneous estimation of carbon dioxide evolution in independent flasks. DeLey (1949) has used colloidal Pd to absorb H_2 produced in respirometers.

Schatz (1952) studied the metabolism of the hydrogen bacteria, and in the course of this work he developed a method for determining H_2, O_2 and CO_2 independently with commonly available manometric apparatus.

NITROGEN: Molecular nitrogen is involved in the biological reactions of nitrogen fixation and denitrification. The amounts of N_2 reacting are usually relatively small, but can be measured by manometric methods.

Nitrogen fixation may be followed directly in Warburg respirometers in the following way: The Brodie's fluid in the manometers is replaced with mercury which has been moistened with water; 1 to 5 mm. of water is kept above each mercury column to minimize the sticking of the mercury in the capillary tubes of the manometers. The biological agent to be studied is introduced into a Warburg flask arranged so the alkali may be mixed with pyrogallol at the end of the run (flasks shown in figs. 29 and 30 are applicable). The cultures are shaken in the Warburg bath in the ordinary manner, and pure oxygen is added to the flasks when needed as indicated by the manometer. If impure tank oxygen is used the amount supplied must be recorded so a final correction may be made for N_2 added with the O_2. After it is judged that the biological agent has accomplished its nitrogen fixation, the alkali which has absorbed CO_2 in the vessel is mixed with the solution of pyrogallol (initially slightly acidified to limit spontaneous oxygen absorption) and the manometer is shaken until equilibrium is reached. The absorption of oxygen will yield the percentage of oxygen initially present in the flask if no nitrogen has been fixed, however, if nitrogen has been fixed its removal will appear as an apparent increase in the oxygen content of the flask. For example, if the gas mixture initially supplied were air with 21% oxygen, and the final absorption of oxygen indicated that 23% of the gas supplied had disappeared, one would conclude that 2% of nitrogen had been fixed. Such measurements may prove useful in establishing nitrogen fixation by materials which by virtue of a high initial nitrogen content cannot be accurately analyzed with the Kjeldahl procedure. The method has been applied by Allison, Hoover and Minor (1942) and the theory of the method as used with Novy-Soule respirometers has been discussed by Hurwitz and Wilson (1940).

Burk (1934) demonstrated that nitrogen fixation could be followed indirectly by estimating the growth rate of nitrogen fixing organisms as measured by oxygen uptake. In a nitrogen free medium the growth of azotobacter is limited by its ability to fix nitrogen. The more rapidly the organism fixes nitrogen the more rapidly it multiplies and in turn the more rapidly it takes up oxygen. Thus a measurement of the increasing rate of oxygen uptake gives an approximation of the rate of nitrogen fixation, although the two reactions are not strictly parallel.

R. H. BURRIS

MISCELLANEOUS METHODS

GAS ANALYSIS: Two general procedures are employed in using the Warburg instrument for gas analysis. For gas mixtures containing less than 2 to 2.5% of the gas to be measured, the flasks are filled with the gas to be analyzed (either by the flow method or the evacuation method, see Chapter 5). A reaction is then caused in the flask (or a reagent added) which will absorb the gas. The decreased pressure observed is a measure of the gas content. This method has been used for oxygen (see page 97) by using slightly acidified solutions of pyrogallol in the main compartment and tipping in alkali from the sidearm after the system is equilibrated. It has been used for CO_2 by generating alkali by means of permanganate and iodide or by using Dixon-Keilin flasks (e.g., see Vogler, 1942).

The second procedure, for gas mixtures containing more than 2 to 2.5% of the gas to be measured, is as follows: the reagent for absorbing the gas is placed in the main compartment of the flask and the flask filled with an inert gas. After equilibration, the gas to be analyzed is introduced into the sidearm. The increased pressure, while the gas remains in the sidearm, is a measure of the total amount of gas introduced. As the gas diffuses into the main compartment the reagent absorbs it and the resulting decrease in pressure is a measure of the specific gas involved. Three methods of adding the gas to be analyzed may be used, as follows:

1. Addition to sidearm: Sidearm flasks equipped with a gas vent are employed (fig. 16, page 68). Before adding the reagent to the flask, the gas is allowed to flow from a reservoir through the sidearm plug until all the original gas in it has been displaced by the mixture to be analyzed. The reagent is added to the flask, the sidearm plug inserted (closed position so that there is no flow of the gas into the flask; reservoir remains attached to plug), and the gas in the flask is replaced with an inert mixture by evacuation procedure (see page 68). After equilibration (during which time the reagent absorbs any of the gas in question which may have entered the flask while inserting the sidearm plug), the plug is turned momentarily to allow gas to enter the flask. The increase in pressure is measured (giving the µl. of gas added). After the gas has diffused from the sidearm and been absorbed by the reagent, the pressure change may be used to calculate the composition of the gas added.

2. Addition to sidearm: This is essentially the same as above, except that the sidearm plug is filled with the gas mixture in question by evacuating and refilling with the gas mixture and is left attached to the gas reservoir. Several (4 or 5) evacuations and refillings are necessary.

3. Addition through manometer stopcock: Gas also may be added through the stopcock of the manometer after flushing out the connecting tubing through the tail-vent of the three-way stopcock. This is an especially convenient method of gas addition. However, the gas tends to remain in the capillaries for a long time. It may be forced into the flask by closing off the open end of the manometer and raising the fluid until it travels along the capillary connecting the manometer to the flask, but even then there is a "dead" space between the flask connection and the stopcock. This method is useful when great accuracy is not required.

The reagents one employs for absorbing gases, depend upon the nature of the gas. Standard works on gas analysis should be consulted for their preparation.

CATALYTIC HYDROGENATION: The Warburg respirometer can be used for the quantitative study of many catalytic hydrogenations. These take place at 1 atmosphere pressure even though on a larger scale several atmospheres of pressure may be necessary. Apparently the relatively enormous quantity of catalyst in the Warburg vessel in relation to the material to be reduced permits more effective operation of the catalyst, and hence higher pressures are not usually required. The procedure is useful to determine how much hydrogen is being absorbed, but is not intended to actually prepare the products of hydrogenation. Very small quantities of substances can be used and the general conditions for optimum reduction worked out before progressing to large scale reduction. The process is illustrated by an example: In a Warburg flask was placed 1.5 ml. 0.1 M borate buffer, pH 9, 0.5 ml. of a suspension of platinum black containing 1 mg. platinum per ml. In the sidearm was placed 0.2 ml. of a pyridoxal hydrochloride solution containing 5 mg. per ml. (m. w. = 204, hence the 1 mg. added = 4.9 µM) and 0.3 ml. of the borate buffer. Hydrogen gas was passed through the flask for 1 hour, after which the taps were closed and the slight residual uptake of hydrogen (required for the complete reduction of the catalyst) allowed to proceed to completion. The pyridoxal hydrochloride was then tipped in, and in 20 minutes 114 µl. of H_2 was taken up; at this time the reaction stopped. This represents 114/22.4 = 5.1 µM H_2 or 1.04 H_2 per mole of pyridoxal and indicates reduction of the free aldehyde group but no reduction in the ring. Upon using the same reagents but adjusting the buffer to pH 5, 2.63 H_2 per pyridoxal were absorbed indicating direct reduction of the pyridine ring. This method has not been used extensively by organic chemists for the quantitative measurement of hydrogenation, but it is convenient and worthy of more general application. One obvious precaution should be added—the buffer used must not be reducible in the presence of the catalyst. Phthalate buffers, for example, cannot be employed with most catalysts. The catalysts, such as platinum, palladium, Raney nickel, etc., are prepared in the same manner as for large scale reductions.

Mead and Howton (1950) have applied this method for the quantitative hydrogenation of small amounts of unsaturated fatty acid derivatives. They used palladium black on charcoal as their catalyst and found that hydrogen uptake usually differed from theory by less than 5% even when no more than a mg. of sample was used.

SPECIALIZED RESPIROMETERS

The Warburg instrument has been accorded general use primarily because of its range and versatility and because of the commercial availability of reliable instruments. Although, manometry need not be confined to Warburg respirometers but may be employed with a variety of instruments, most investigators are not interested in manometry per se, so they tend to use only readily available instruments. It has been our experience that many instruments, other than the conventional Barcroft and Warburg respirometers, suffer from some defect. We therefore have concentrated our efforts in describing the general all-around uses of the conventional systems. In this section, however, we describe modifications in the operation of the conventional system, other types of manometers usable with the conventional shaking and temperature control systems, and other types of respirometers which require further modification of the usual apparatus. The new respirometers which employ a plunger to maintain a constant pressure appear especially promising and may quickly gain general acceptance.

Modifications in the Operation of Conventional Respirometers.

To decrease sensitivity: Sometimes it is desired to measure larger gas exchange than can be conveniently handled with the standard Warburg instrument. Essentially this means one wishes each unit, h, on the manometer to represent more gas, i.e., one wishes to have a larger k. Since:

$$k = \frac{Vg\, \dfrac{273}{T} + V_f\, \alpha}{P_o}$$

one may increase k by increasing Vg (larger flask) or decreasing P_o. As P_o is pressure at standard conditions represented in mm. manometer fluid, an increase in the density of the manometer fluid from 1.033 (Brodie's solution, $P_o = 10,000$) to mercury (density = 13.6, $P_o = 760$) increases k; thus for the same set of readings more gas exchange is represented. Examples of manometry under "macro" conditions are given by Wells (1938) and Wood et al. (1940).

To increase sensitivity: On the basis of the preceding argument, k can be decreased with smaller flasks, and with manometer fluid of a lower density (e.g., hydrocarbons or oils of density ca. 0.7 gm./ml.). In this manner, an increase in sensitivity of about 2 fold can be obtained. However, Burk and Hobby (1954) have devised a system which will increase sensitivity 10-100 fold with only minor modification of the conventional instrument.

W. W. UMBREIT

OTHER TYPES OF RESPIROMETERS

Two types of constant-volume differential manometers have been devised which combine the advantages of the "Warburg" constant volume type and the "Barcroft" differential type. In the first of these, described by Dickens and Greville (1933a), the volume is maintained at a constant value by adjusting the vertical position of one manometer arm and flask so that the fluid in the manometer arms remains unchanged in its position. The difference in fluid levels in the two arms is read from a graduated scale. This permits one to employ a compensated system, independent of changes in barometric pressure, yet using the simple flask constants of the Warburg instrument. The second type, that of Summerson (1939), is illustrated in figure 31. It is an extremely adaptable instrument, being capable of serving as two ordinary Warburg manometers (which indeed comprise the main portion of the apparatus) or of serving as a constant-volume differential manometer in which case the fluid level in the two outer columns, attached to the flasks, is held constant and the difference in reading of the two inner columns is noted.

Several types of ultramicrorespirometers have been developed for measuring less gas exchange than can be measured accurately with the Warburg instrument. Certain of these have been described in some detail by Dixon (1943, 1951), Perkins (1943) and Tobias (1943).

Among the most sensitive instruments are those employing the Cartesian diver principle (Holter (1943), Linderstrom-Lang (1943), Anfinson and Claff (1947), Holter and Linderstrom-Lang (1951)). Another respirometer of comparable sensitivity has been described by Gregg (1947), and a modified form of it by Gregg (1950); it appears to be easier to operate than the Cartesian diver apparatus and permits measurements to 0.001 μl. Prop (1954) has described in detail a microrespirometer capable of simultaneously measuring O_2 consumption and CO_2 production. Whenever possible it is advisable to work with but when very small pieces of tissue or single small organisms are to be studied, measurements with the ultramicrorespirometers are indicated.

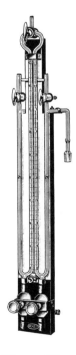

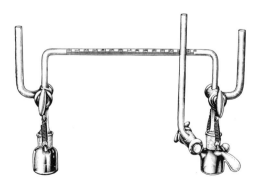

Figure 31
Summerson Manometer and Support

Figure 32
Fenn Respirometer

The Fenn (1928) respirometer is another type of differential respirometer. As illustrated in figure 32 this instrument consists of a control flask and an experimental flask connected by a graduated capillary tube. The latter contains a short thread of kerosene colored with a dye which serves as an index of the volume changes. It is readily understood that the Fenn respirometer is essentially the same as a Barcroft differential respirometer with the manometer portion raised to a horizontal position. Then, since the movement of the oil thread, d, is due entirely to the change in volume and since the change in pressure in the control flask is equal to the change in pressure in the experimental flask, the complete equation for the Fenn respirometer may be obtained in the same manner as that of the Barcroft instrument by substituting d for $\frac{h}{2}$ and by placing $\triangle P = \triangle P'$ in deriving equation 33 on page 80. The result is,

$$x = d \left[A\left(\frac{273}{T} \ \frac{P + \triangle P - p}{P_o}\right)\left(\frac{Vg\frac{273}{T} + V_f\alpha}{V'g\frac{273}{T} + V'_f\alpha} + 1\right)\right] \qquad \text{33a}$$

where the product of the terms within the brackets is the "constant" of the respirometer. To obtain the volume, x, of gas evolved at NTP it is necessary only to multiply the value of the constant by the distance, d, the oil thread has moved in the capillary.

It will be noted that the term $\triangle P$ appears in Equation 33a. As $\triangle P$ is quite small in comparison with P it is neglected when calculating the constant by substituting known values for the terms in this equation. The constant may be obtained also by using the Münzer and Neumann (1917) method.

Most of these ultramicrorespirometers as well as others not here mentioned have been described in detail in an excellent book by Glick (1961) to which the reader is referred.

Cruickshank (1954) has described a differential capillary respirometer which offers some advantages over those earlier described. Scholander et al. (1952) have developed an apparatus for which standardization of flasks is not required, in fact small bottles can be used. Kok (1955) has described in some detail several sensitive volumeters, some of which are suitable for recording, and Kok, Veltkamp and Gelderman (1953) have studied the movement of fluid columns in glass capillaries since this seems to be the principal limitation in the speed of response of manometers.

W. W. UMBREIT, J. F. STAUFFER and R. H. BURRIS

CONSTANT PRESSURE RESPIROMETERS

Winterstein (1912, 1913) described a volumetric respirometer, and since that time a variety of modifications and improvements have been made (Dixon, 1943, 1951; Scholander, 1942a, 1942b, 1949). A modification of the apparatus described by Dixon (1951, fig. 2 and pages 6-8) was discussed on page 111 of the 1957 edition of this book; the system for adjusting the volume was somewhat cumbersome. Despite the inherent advantages of constant pressure apparatus, it never has approached the popularity of the Warburg and Barcroft respirometers. Recent modifications, however, may make the constant pressure systems much more popular.

Scholander et al. (1952) described a compact and versatile volumetric respirometer and a micro version of it; Scholander and Iverson (1958) modified it somewhat. The apparatus (fig. 33) is now available from the Mark Co., Randolph, Mass. They furnish detailed directions for the operation of the respirometer as do Scholander et al. in their publications.

To operate the Scholander respirometer (fig. 33), the reaction mixture is placed in vessel A (no calibration of the vessel is required), and KOH and filter paper are placed in tray B. The respirometer is immersed in a glass-sided constant temperature bath and is agitated with a pivotal motion. After temperature equilibration, plug C is rotated 180°

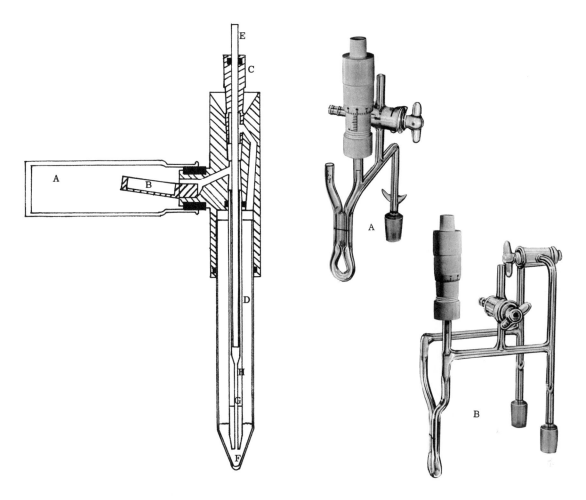

Figure 33
Scholander respirometer

Figure 34
Constant pressure respirometers with
micrometer control of plunger

from the position shown, so that compensating chamber D is isolated from reaction chamber A. Rod E is pushed down or pulled up to adjust the manometer fluid F to the reference mark G on capillary H of the rod chamber. The volume of gas taken up or evolved is measured by moving rod E up or down to bring the manometer fluid back to the reference mark G. The amount of rod moved in or out is measured with a vernier measuring device (not shown; one device serves all respirometers of a set). The cross-section of the rod (factory calibrated) is the only constant required for calibration other than temperature and barometric pressure. Seals are effected with O rings, tapered joints in the plastic, and a neoprene ring for attaching reaction vessels. Scholander et al. indicated how this apparatus can be gassed. Gas can be added, withdrawn, and compensated for during an experiment by the use of a hypodermic syringe and a rubber barrier. Attractive features of the apparatus include: no calibration of vessels is required; the system carries a compensating chamber to minimize thermobarometric changes.

Recently Roger Gilmont Instruments, Inc. has introduced a plastic micrometer unit (fig. 34) which can be used to maintain a constant pressure as in the Scholander apparatus. The micrometer is mounted directly above a shortened manometer whose fluid level is adjusted to a reference position before gas uptake or evolution is read directly in microliters from the micrometer. Open arm (fig. 34A) and differential manometers (fig. 34B) are available.

Gilson (1963) has described a constant pressure respirometer which introduces a number of important improvements. The stopcock arrangement is such that Warburg type manometers (fig. 35) and vessels can be evacuated and filled directly with gas by attaching only to the open arm of the manometer, because both arms of the manometer are evacuated simultaneously. A similar stopcock can be used on a differential respirometer of the Barcroft type. Gilson (1963) has arranged similar manometers, fabricated from plastic, above a water bath and has connected the open arms of all manometers to a common compensation vessel through a manifold (figs. 25 and 35).

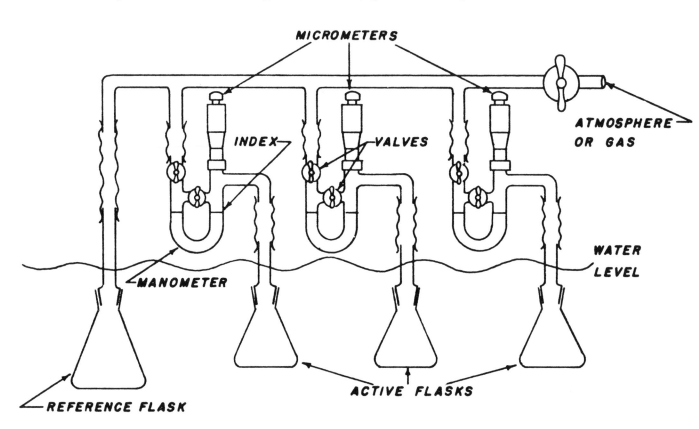

Figure 35
Illustration of the principle of the Gilson differential respirometer

This arrangement permits the simultaneous evacuation and gassing of all vessels, and the compensating vessel eliminates corrections for barometric changes and minimizes temperature errors. Stability comparable to that of the Barcroft respirometer and considerably better than that of the Warburg respirometer is achieved. Readout is digital for the volume changes which accompany the inward or outward movement of the plastic rod required to maintain the system at constant pressure. The micrometers and manometers remain stationary, while the vessels attached to plastic tubing are shaken. Micrometer reading can be plotted directly against time, and a single temperature-barometric pressure factor then can be applied to the slopes of all straight lines to reduce the gas exchange data to absolute terms.

Gilson's compensated constant pressure system is compact, rugged, remarkably stable, rapid and easy to read, and convenient to use. The vessels require no calibration, and data reduction is simple. Figure 36 shows a plot of data obtained with this respirometer.

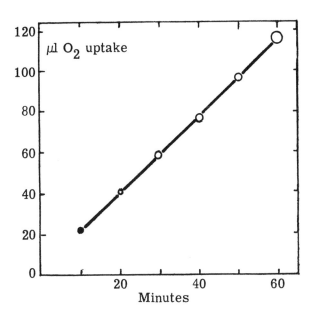

Figure 36
Oxygen uptake by Torula utilis as measured
with the Gilson respirometer

The reproducibility of the measurements is indicated by the fact that the readings for each of 5 replicate flasks fell within the diameters of the circles drawn.

R. H. BURRIS

AUTOMATIC RECORDING MANOMETERS

Manometry always has required numerous readings and time consuming data reduction. Part of the impetus for the development of spectrophotometric methods undoubtedly derived from efforts to simplify and to mechanize the measurement of enzymatic activity, and the same impetus has motivated the automation of manometry.

Recording respirometers were described in the past but were not commercially available. Recently, however, two automatic recording systems have been marketed. These are attachable to standard Warburg manometers, and will read, calculate, and record gas exchange in μl. gas without continual attention by the operator. One, called "Manomatic", was devised by Otto Koelle of Braun, Melsungen, Germany, and the other was devised by R. E. Steele of Mechrolab. Both systems work. The Manomatic is less expensive but requires more attention and is subject to greater fluctuation. The "Mechrolab" system is precise and reproducible, but relatively expensive. We shall discuss each system separately and then summarize the advantages and disadvantages of automatic recording.

The Manomatic System: These instruments are available in the U. S. through the Bronwill Scientific Company, 107 N. Goodman Street, Rochester 3, New York. The system is based upon a neglected principle outlined by Dickens and Greville (1933a). Its application in the Manomatic system is outlined in figure 37. In part A, at the start of the

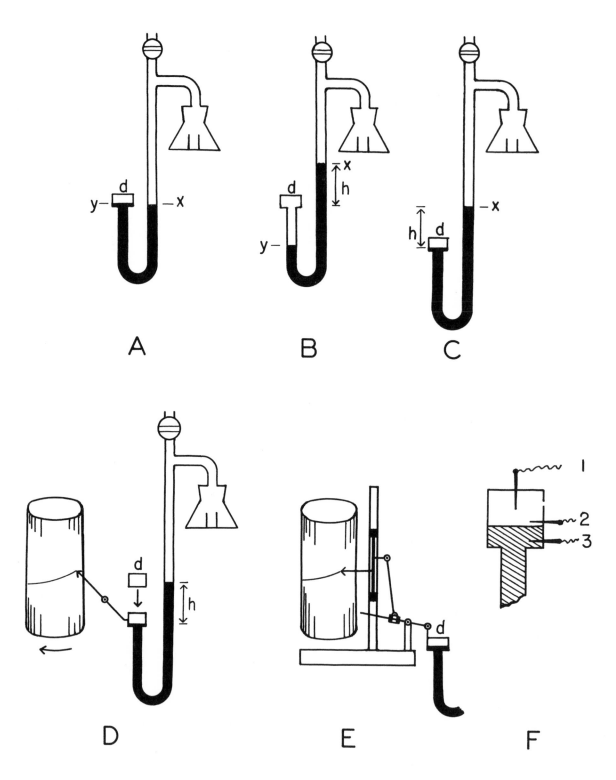

Figure 37
Illustration of the principle used in the Manometric
system of automatic recording respirometers

recording, the fluid in the closed arm of the manometer stands at x, and in what corresponds to the open arm it stands at point y, the open and closed arms of the manometer being connected by a flexible tube. At the level y, on the "open" arm, there is an electrical contact controlling a relay and motor which serves to detect the level of fluid in this arm. This is labeled "d" in parts A through E and illustrated in detail in part F of figure 37. When there is gas uptake in the flask (part B), fluid will rise in the closed arm by an amount h, but since the distance x to y must remain constant (since the amount of fluid is not changed and the bore of the manometer and the flexible tubing is approximately the same), there will be a corresponding drop in fluid in the open arm. A drop in the fluid level in the detector (part F) will activate it to move downward to follow the level of fluid in the open arm (as shown in part C). But when it does so, it also lowers the height of the fluid in the closed arm. Indeed, since the distance x to y (and the amount of fluid) in the manometer arms is constant, the net effect is to keep the level of fluid in the closed arm at a constant value (= x) and thus the operation of the detection system decreases the pressure exactly corresponding to the gas uptake. As this is precisely what occurs in the normal Warburg system, the same theory, flask constants, etc. apply. All that remains is to record this decrease in pressure in the detection system. This is done by recording the position of the detector on a rotating drum, as shown in part D.

Actually, this device has been modified (as indicated in fig. 37, part E) to make it adjustable for different flask constants. The detection system is attached to an inclined lever and its position on this lever can be set so that for each mm. that the detector system moves, the pen records the number of μl. of gas exchanged. The position of the detector on the lever is determined by the flask constant. Movement of the detector from the position occupied in A and B to that of C and D, causes the pen to write on the recorder as shown in part D.

The Manomatic system is a complete operating unit attachable to any Warburg manometer, 1 unit per manometer each with its own recording drum. The drum makes one complete revolution in two hours, and generally the system is adjusted so that the entire span of the drum is 200 μl. We have run these instruments continuously for twenty-four hour periods, and have left them untended overnight with no special difficulties. There is a very slight drift upward in the pen recording over long intervals (about 5 μl./hr.), perhaps arising from a small amount of evaporation from the detector; this is an advantage in overnight recordings because the lines do not run exactly in the same channels.

In attaching the apparatus to the normal unmodified Warburg instrument, it is convenient to insert the attachment to the detector into the bottom of the rubber bulb used for adjusting fluid height (this gives a degree of flexibility in initial adjustments of pen and zero point). The normal open arm of the manometer then must be plugged, because the detector serves as the open arm. We fill it completely with manometer fluid and close it with a small rubber or plastic stopper. It may be left open, as in the normal Warburg, but then the fluid level drops in both the detector system and the open arm of the usual manometer, and the calculation of the factor becomes difficult. Nevertheless, it can be used in this fashion by empirical standardization, i.e. a known quantity of gas is released or taken up and the position of the detector on the lever arm is adjusted so that the pen will transverse the proper distance on the scaled paper put on the drum.

It is sometimes more convenient to use a modified manometer prepared by drawing out the bottom of the closed arm side to a tip and removing the open arm side of the manometer.

The single manometer system does not correct for thermo-barometric changes. However, this usually is not too serious. Often the thermobarometer remains relatively constant, and one may take a reading at the start and at the end of the run and correct the observed readings for any changes (usually by simply tilting the base line of the recorded graph) by assuming that they are continuous throughout the run. A relatively smooth line recording indicates thermo-barometric stability. When instability is indicated by an irregular recording, such data must be discarded. Surprisingly, however, this is seldom necessary.

A Manomatic unit is required for each manometer. These occupy space and when several are in operation the tubing and shaking devices may become entangled. Mr. Koelle has devised a system in which several detector pens record on a single chart and automatic adjustment is made for changes in the thermo-barometer. We have had no experience with this system and so are unable to comment on it.

Since any change in the barometric pressure in the room acts equally on the open ends of all manometers, any such change will affect the readings of all manometers in the same way, even if their flasks are of different volumes. This is usually intuitively understood, but the effect of change in temperature is equally independent of the flask volume. This may be shown as follows:

$$PV = nRT \text{ may be rewritten as}$$

$$P = \frac{(nR)\ T}{V}$$

Where n = the number of molecules of gas, which does not change in the thermobarometer. Since n, V, and R are constants (V being held constant in the Warburg system)

$$P = (constant)\ T, \text{ and}$$

$$\triangle P = (constant)\ \triangle T$$

i.e., a change in temperature results in a change in pressure which is independent of the volume of the flask employed.

In the present Manomatic the detection system (fig. 37, part F) is so arranged that when the fluid breaks the contact between 2 and 3, the detector system rises, while when it makes contact between 1 and 2, the detector lowers. During most operation, fluid should be rising and falling between 1 and 2, or 2 and 3, depending on the system. This is easily accomplished when the manometers are shaking and there is a free swing imparted to the connecting tubing. We find that the system works best on a rectangular Warburg bath with reciprocal shaking, but it can be used on a circular Warburg as well. The principal difficulties arise from the stickiness of the fluid, which does not always flow freely in the narrow bore tubes of the manometer and connecting (plastic) tubing, and in an occasional stuck relay. The Manomatic system is one that requires some attention and should be worked with daily. If it is allowed to stand without use for several days, difficulties may be encountered because fluid has evaporated, pens have dried, or contacts have corroded; until these are corrected the system will operate erratically or not at all. We also find that the tube connecting the detector system and the manometer should be relatively short. If the detector is connected to a long tube so that the recorder may be placed at some distance (i.e., 5 to 10 feet) from the manometer, the system works poorly.

The Mechrolab System: This system is manufactured and sold by Mechrolab, Inc., 1062 Linda Vista Avenue, Mountain View, California. A lamp and a red sensitive photoelectric detecting device is attached at the chosen zero point (usually 15 mm.) of the closed arm of the Warburg manometer. When the red fluid in the manometer is below the level of the light path, the photocell is activated and fluid is pumped from the system to the manometer. When the meniscus is just in the light path, the reflection of the light is caught in a mirror and the pumping mechanism is stopped.

The pumping mechanism consists of a metal bellows, mounted between two micrometers, one run by the motor in the pumping mechanism, the other adjusted by hand to level the fluid initially. The mechanically actuated micrometer is attached to a potentiometer, and its position is converted into a potential which is recorded on a multiple point recorder. The bellows (chosen because it is more stable and less subject to creeping than a syringe) expands or contracts and is attached to the manometer by capillary plastic tubing. The system is so adjusted at the start that the fluid at both the open arm and the closed arm (which bears the detector) is at the zero point chosen, and the mechanically controlled micrometer is adjusted so that the pen controlled by it is at a convenient zero point on the recorder. The stopcocks are closed and as gas is taken up the fluid rises in the closed arm, but is withdrawn by expansion of the bellows under the control of the zero point detector, such that fluid is kept at the zero point in the closed arm but drops in the open arm. The change in potential registers on the recorder and is converted into μl. of gas. One dial on the convertor sets the flask constant. The other adjusts for the calibration of the manometer bore, i.e., a value which relates these amounts of fluid withdrawn to the drop in height of the open arm. The range of the recording paper (using a Leeds and Northrup "Speedomax" recorder) may be set so the active range may represent 50 or 5000 ml. The system is corrected for thermobarometer changes by employing the same kind of detection system on the thermobarometer and imposing this potential electronically within the recorder so that the reading of any manometer comes out as μl. of gas corrected for thermobarometer. No further calculations are required unless reduction to normal temperature and pressure is desired. This system may cost well over $1000 a manometer. A 4 manometer system will do as much and with greater precision than the usual 9 manometer manual system.

Advantages of Recording: As is usual in most instrument developments, a suitable system has unexpected advantages. Obviously, the automatic recording systems free the operator from calculations and from being tied closely to the instrument. In addition it speeds up experiments several fold. It usually is easy to tell in the first few moments of the reaction what the actual result is going to be. Hence, one can begin to set up the next experiment while the recorder is collecting the data on the first. Furthermore, continuous recording gives one a more precise picture of what is happening and slight pauses or accelerations in reaction rate are easily discernible that otherwise would be obscured.

The recording system is suitable for measuring very rapid reactions, since the system responds so rapidly to gas changes. By speeding up the paper in the recorder, one may record changes occurring in fractions of a minute. Likewise, by slowing the recording paper, one may conveniently measure slow reactions. For the latter, it is especially convenient to begin an experiment in the late afternoon and record the gas exchange overnight.

MEASUREMENT OF DISSOLVED OXYGEN

In the 1957 edition of this book, p. 112-116, the use of the dropping mercury electrode for the measurement of dissolved oxygen was described in some detail. This electrode now has been generally replaced by other types of electrodes for oxygen. Beckman Instruments Inc. markets an oxygen electrode, employing a gold cathode and a silver anode embedded in a conducting cellulose gel and enclosed by a teflon membrane through which oxygen diffuses. A potential of 0.8 volt is applied between the electrodes, and oxygen is reduced at the cathode producing a current proportional to the oxygen concentration. This electrode might be adapted to respiring systems. The cadmium electrode also is very promising (Neville, 1962). However, the system which has gained wide acceptance incorporates a rotating or vibrating bright platinum electrode. The "Oxygraph" (Gilson Medical Electronics), illustrated on page 111, gives rapid and sensitive measurements of dissolved oxygen with a vibrating electrode. Additions of substrates, cofactors, inhibitors, and various reactants can be made during measurement of oxygen evolution or absorption, and if they have any influence it is registered quickly by a change in the slope of the trace being recorded.

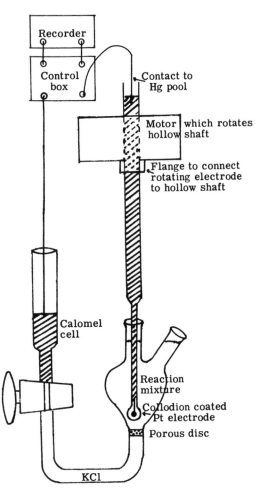

Figure 38
Rotating platinum electrode for the
measurement of dissolved oxygen

Hagihara (1961) has described a simple oxygen electrode which can be constructed readily at modest cost. The instrument employs a rotating platinum electrode as illustrated in figure 38. This electrode is constructed by melting a piece of platinum wire to form a 1 mm. knob at one end and sealing this wire into soft glass tubing. The glass then is ground away to expose the platinum knob which in turn is polished with fine abrasive and coated with dilute collodion. The circuit is completed from the calomel electrode through saturated KCl and the porous disc to the reaction vessel and thence from the platinum electrode through the well of mercury in the rotating electrode tube to a wire immersed in the mercury. Current is supplied through this circuit by a mercury battery, and suitable resistances are incorporated to adjust the voltage to the 0.5 to 0.8 volt range. The cathode reaction current is essentially a linear function of the dissolved oxygen concentration in the reaction vessel. Output from the circuit can be fed to a strip chart recorder.

Figure 39 shows a measurement of oxygen uptake by a suspension of plant mitochondria (Tamaoki et al., 1960) with an electrode such as described by Hagihari (1961). In a period of 19 minutes (read strip chart from right to left; the figures indicate the slopes of the various sections which are a measure of oxygen uptake rates as $m\mu$. atoms/ml.) the electrode indicated endogenous respiration, and the influence of succinate, ADP, malonate, citrate, DPN, DPNH, antimycin A and ascorbate.

Measurements can be performed on very small amounts of material. The reaction vessel can be small and can be jacketed so that the temperature can be kept constant by circulating water. The reaction vessel can be illuminated readily for the measurement of photosynthetic liberation of oxygen by chloroplasts or algae.

The platinum electrode has much to recommend it in terms of speed of response and measurement, simplicity of calculation, sensitivity, and the small amount of reaction mixture required.

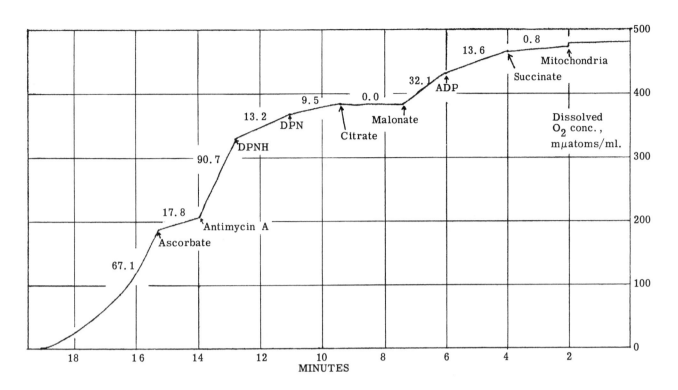

Figure 39
Utilization of dissolved oxygen by mitochondria from tomato
tissue cultures, as measured with a platinum electrode

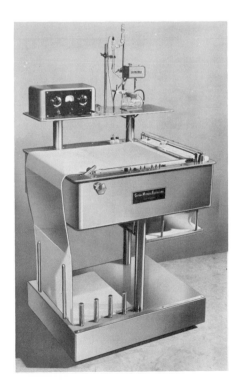

Figure 40
"Oxygraph" platinum electrode apparatus
for measuring dissolved oxygen

DETERMINATION OF THE TYPE OF INHIBITION

In interpreting the mechanism of enzyme action it frequently is very helpful to understand the manner in which specific inhibitors function. The usual basic distinction is that of competitive, uncompetitive and noncompetitive inhibitors. In competitive inhibition, the substrate and inhibitor are competing for an active site, and hence changes in either the substrate or inhibitor concentration will affect the degree of inhibition observed. To determine the type of inhibition one should apply the equations that have been described by Lineweaver and Burk (1934). The discussions by Wilson (1939), Ebersole et al. (1944), Alberty (1956), Reiner (1959), and Cleland (1963 a, b, c) should be consulted for adequate derivation of the theory upon which the tests for type of inhibition are based. As Cleland (1936b) points out, the graphical tests which we will describe fit only the uncomplicated linear inhibitions and cannot be expected to fit complex enzymatic reactions involving a number of substrates and products. Cleland (1963d) has described computer programs for processing kinetic data which define non-linear responses.

To apply the tests, determine the velocity constants, v, of the reaction over as wide a range of substrate concentrations as is practical and at two or more concentrations of inhibitor. Plot the reciprocals of the velocity constants, $1/v$, against the reciprocals of the concentrations of substrate, $1/S$; draw the line to conform to the line defined by the method of least squares. The lines should have the following characteristics:

1. In the <u>absence of inhibitor</u>, a straight line results whose slope/intercept equals K_s, the dissociation constant of the enzyme-substrate complex.

2. In strictly linear <u>competitive inhibition,</u> the intercept remains constant, but the slope is increased by $(1 + (I)/K_i)$, where (I) is concentration of inhibitor, and K_i the dissociation constant of the enzyme-inhibitor complex. The apparent K_s = slope/intercept increased by the same factor, <u>i.e.</u>, $(1 + (I)/K_i)$. This is illustrated in fig. 41A. (The dissociation constant, $\overline{K_s}$, closely approximates the Michaelis constant, K_m, but as Dalziel (1962b) has pointed out, they are not identical and in complex reactions may be distinctly different.)

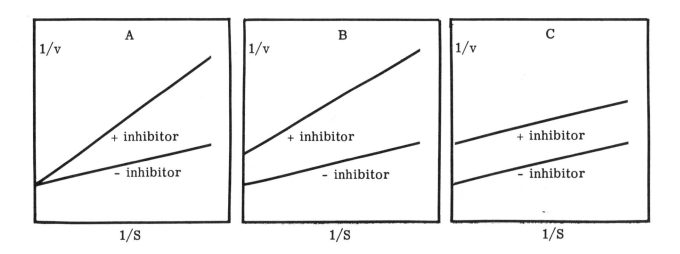

Figure 41
Examples of Lineweaver and Burk plots illustrating competitive (A),
non-competitive (B), and uncompetitive (C) inhibition

3. In strictly linear <u>non-competitive inhibition,</u> both the slope and intercept are increased by the <u>same factor, viz., $(1 + (I)/K_i)$</u> so that K_S remains constant (fig. 41B).

4. In strictly linear <u>uncompetitive inhibition,</u> the slopes of the lines remain constant, but the intercepts change (fig. 41C).

Dixon (1953) introduced a graphical means of determining K_S and K_i (dissociation constant of the enzyme-inhibitor complex). If $\frac{1}{v}$ is plotted against $\frac{1}{S}$ the line intersects the x axis to the left of the y axis; the value of the intercept is $\frac{-1}{K_S}$ (fig. 42A). To determine the type of inhibition, rates are measured at two substrate concentrations at various inhibitor concentrations, and $\frac{1}{v}$ is plotted against i (inhibitor concentration).

The two straight lines defined for the two substrate concentrations intersect on the negative side of the y axis. For competitive inhibition the point of intersection of the lines lies above the x axis at a point $-K_i$ from the y axis (fig. 42B). For non-competitive inhibition the two lines meet on the x axis at a point $-K_i$ from the y axis (fig. 42C).

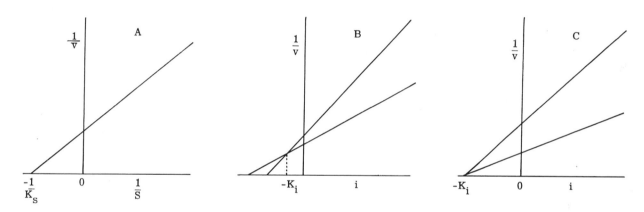

Figure 42
Plots described by Dixon (1953) for determining the K_S, the dissociation or Michaelis constant (A); K_i (dissociation constant of the enzyme-inhibitor complex) for competitive inhibition (B); and K_i for non-competitive inhibition (C)

THE USE OF ISOTOPIC TRACERS

The use of isotopic tracers to follow enzymatic reactions can be very helpful in the elucidation of reaction mechanisms. The extreme sensitivity of the tracer technique permits its application on a micro scale, and the conventional Warburg apparatus is ideally suited for conducting a wide variety of enzymatic and non-enzymatic tracer experiments. This apparatus provides a system in which the gas atmosphere, the temperature and the shaking can be controlled conveniently, gases can be generated or absorbed internally, components can be added to the reaction mixture, and the course of the reaction can be followed manometrically. Furthermore, the all glass apparatus is easy to decontaminate.

It is outside the scope of this book to discuss the instrumentation, and techniques involved in the use of isotopic tracers. For a discussion of isotopes and working methods the reader is referred to the books by Kamen (1957), Calvin, Heidelberger, Reid, Tolbert and Yankwich (1949), Hevesy (1948), Friedlander and Kennedy (1955), Comar (1955), Aronoff (1956), Chase (1959), and Overman and Clark (1960).

R. H. BURRIS

Chapter 8
METHODS FOR PREPARATION AND STUDY OF TISSUES AND ENZYMES

INTRODUCTION

The manometric methods described are accurate and capable of measuring certain reactions with speed and precision. When applied to living tissues or preparations therefrom they will establish the rate and the course of many important processes. It must be recognized that the limitations of the methods are those always associated with in vitro measurements, that is, it may not be possible to extrapolate the findings in a quantitative sense to in vivo conditions since a number of physical and physiological conditions cannot be reproduced in vitro. In any case, that some of the multitude of interrelated chemical reactions which occur in vivo could be obtained in vitro has permitted the advances which have occurred in our knowledge of respiration and metabolism.

A problem which faces every investigator is the development and study of the means by which reactions occurring in intact tissues may be separated and studied. The techniques applicable to one type of tissue are not necessarily suitable for another. It is, in fact, the knowledge of the physiology of the tissue being studied which permits the selection of a technique of preparation which will be suitable for the tissue employed and the reaction or process one wishes to measure. We wish to emphasize that the techniques described below are not mutually exclusive nor are they all equally applicable. The question of which method to apply (if any) of the techniques listed is the responsibility of the individual investigator just as is the responsibility for the interpretation of the results. The techniques described below are useful but modifications of these or even the development of entirely new ones may be necessary to approach specific problems.

The subjects considered in this Chapter are divided into four sections dealing with Animal, Plant and Microbial Tissues, and Purification of Enzymes.

METHODS OF PREPARING ANIMAL TISSUES

TISSUE SLICE TECHNIQUE - INTRODUCTION

The tissue slice technique was developed in most of its details by Warburg and his co-workers in their studies of tumor metabolism (Warburg, 1926). By the use of tissue slices, the more complicated and uncontrollable aspects of whole organ or organism metabolism are minimized on the one hand, and the less certain effects of mincing, homogenizing or extracting are excluded on the other hand. In a word, the tissue slice is thought to represent organized surviving tissue, the metabolism of which qualitatively, if not quantitatively, reflects that of the original tissue. Further, the tissue slice technique allows for controlled variations in the suspending medium in addition to chemical analysis of the latter for changes in metabolite content. It should be pointed out that most investigators assume that simple substrates are freely diffusible into slices. That this may not be true in all instances, is seen in the case of liver slices which have a limited permeability for sodium glutamate (Cohen and Hayano, 1946). A critical analysis of the tissue slice method in manometric experiments has been published by Laser (1942).

PREPARATION OF SLICES OF ANIMAL TISSUES

It is usually possible with practice to slice most animal organs free hand with either a straight edge or a safety razor. However, where the size of the organ is very small, as for example a small tumor nodule, a mouse kidney, etc., or where the organ lacks consistency, such as brain, the free hand method of slicing even by the expert leaves much to be desired. A simple and most effective improvement in the technique of tissue slicing applicable to all organs and tissues is that introduced by Deutsch (1936). The principle of this technique is as follows:

The piece of tissue to be sliced is held firmly between two pieces of frosted glass and the tissue sliced by means of a razor blade, the latter being guided by the top frosted glass. In practice it is soon appreciated that the pressure necessary to keep the tissue fixed while slicing varies from tissue to tissue, and further that the thickness of the slice can be estimated by its translucency through the frosted glass.

The method of Deutsch has proved to be applicable to a wide variety of tissues. The following equipment and procedure has proved most satisfactory.

EQUIPMENT:

1. A piece of frosted glass, approximately 5 cm. square, mounted by means of paraffin on a heavy base, 5-6 cm. in height (an inverted cold cream jar has been found very satisfactory).
2. Frosted microscope slides; these are readily prepared from ordinary glass slides by rubbing with emery powder.
3. Razor blades. The three-holed variety broken in half lengthwise are satisfactory.
4. Razor blade holder. This is conveniently made from a piece of brass approximately 10 x 8 x 2 mm. with a hole drilled through one end holding a brass bolt and nut. The nut should have a diameter of about 8 mm. so as to provide a good purchase on the razor blade. The broken blade is placed so that the bolt fits into one of the end holes. The blade is fixed by tightening the bolt with a screwdriver.

PROCEDURE:

The procedure will vary somewhat from tissue to tissue. It is best to carry out the following general procedure in a 4° C. room if it is available.

A piece of hard filter paper, approximately 2 cm. square, is placed over one corner of the frosted glass and moistened with saline. The piece of tissue to be sliced (usually about 1 cm. in diameter) is placed on the filter paper. The frosted slide is then dipped in saline and applied to the top of the piece of tissue with gentle pressure and held in place with one hand. The razor blade is then moistened with saline and by means of the holder the blade is closely applied to the under surface of the frosted microscope slide. With experience it will be found possible to adjust the pressure on the tissue with the one hand and effectively slice with the other. The thickness and uniformity of the slice can be readily appreciated by the appearance of the slice through the microscope slide (by cutting across the corner of the frosted-glass base the operator's hand, and the razor blade and holder, will be free of obstruction). The slice is then transferred to a petri dish containing a suitable saline mixture. The slices should be handled by means of a pair of fine but blunt-ended forceps. When transferring the slices to the Warburg flasks, the slices are gently dried by touching with a piece of hard filter paper.

The use of specially designed devices for cutting tissue slices has occupied the attention of many investigators in this field. Very few of these devices have proved to be practical. However, the Stadie-Riggs microtome has had an enthusiastic reception by some workers (fig. 43). Details of construction and application are given in the paper by these investigators (Stadie and Riggs, 1944). The microtome and blades are obtainable from the Arthur H. Thomas Company, Philadelphia. An excellent review and discussion of the preparation of tissue slices has been published by Field (1948). A device suitable for preparing slices of brain suitable for respiration studies has been reported by Graca and Makaroff (1952).

McIlwain and Buddle (1953) have described an apparatus for preparing slices and suspensions of fresh animal tissues (and particularly suitable for brain) with minimum disruption of cellular structure. The machine is capable of cutting slices down to 0.2 mm. in thickness and of producing "prisms" of

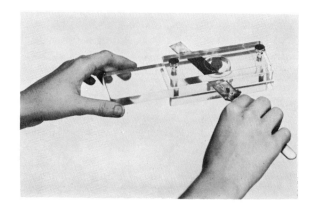

Figure 43
Stadie-Riggs tissue slicer

tissue down to 0.067 x 0.067 mm. in cross section. The authors report that a convenient preparation which can be made from many tissues in 30 seconds consists of prisms 0.2 x 0.2 mm. in section and 2 mm. in length. This preparation can be readily suspended in saline and sampled as a suspension. Comparison of metabolic activity of such suspensions using a glucose-saline medium with slices and homogenates revealed respiratory O_2 uptakes within 3% of slices and markedly more rapid than with homogenates.

ESTIMATION OF THE THICKNESS OF TISSUE SLICES

Since the rate of diffusion of gases and metabolites will be determined in part by the thickness of the tissue slices, it is essential that they be of uniform thickness within certain limits. These limits are determined by the diffusion constants of the reacting substances, the rate of metabolism of the tissue in question, etc. As derived by Warburg (1930), the limiting thickness in cm., d', for O_2 consumption of slices of a given tissue can be calculated from the equation

$$d' = \sqrt{8\, C_o\, \frac{D}{A}}$$

where D = the diffusion constant for O_2 in ml. (N.T.P.). According to Krogh, the rate of diffusion of O_2 at 38° through a tissue of 1 cm.^{2} cross section is 1.4 x 10^{-5} ml. per min.

A = the rate of respiration $\left(\dfrac{\text{ml. } O_2 \text{ uptake}}{\text{ml. tissue x min.}}\right)$

C_o = the O_2 concentration outside the slice (in atmospheres).

Taking 5 x 10^{-2} as the value for A for liver slices, 1.4 x 10^{-5} for D, and 1.0 and 0.2 for C_o for pure O_2 and air respectively, d' is calculated to be 4.7 x 10^{-2} cm. for pure O_2 and 2.1 x 10^{-2} cm. for air. In other words, if the gas phase is air, liver slices no thicker than 0.2 mm. can be used. Slices of this thickness are not only difficult to prepare, but also are very fragile and consequently very difficult to work with. On the other hand, slices 0.3 mm. in thickness can be cut with little difficulty and can be handled and shaken without danger of damage. However, even with slices of this thickness the gas phase must be pure O_2. Under these conditions the O_2 tension at the center of the slice will be about 0.6 atmospheres. Similar calculations have been carried out for CO_2 by Warburg (1930).

In practice it is quite easy to estimate the thickness of a given slice by its translucency and by the manner in which it curls up on itself when held up by a pair of fine forceps. However, in order to establish the correct thickness in terms of the above visual criteria it is best to measure a few selected slices of the different tissues. This is most readily done by placing the slices in a petri dish of Ringer's solution under which is placed a piece of squared millimeter paper. The slices are trimmed to a rectangular shape and their areas measured by counting the squares covered. The volumes of the individual slices are then calculated from their wet weight. The thickness of a given slice is then obtained by dividing the volume by the surface area.

TEMPERATURE OF TISSUE AND MEDIUM

It has been found desirable, and in some instances essential, to keep the tissue and medium at low temperatures while the slices are being cut. This is readily accomplished by keeping the petri dish containing saline and slices on cracked ice, and by filling the cold cream jar with cracked ice and placing it in a petri dish. The latter insures the tissue being kept cold while it is being sliced. The medium to be used for suspending the slices is cooled by storage in the refrigerator up to the time of use. The organs or tissues when removed from the animal are placed on cracked ice directly to chill rapidly and are then placed in small beakers which are surrounded by cracked ice.

DRY WEIGHT OF TISSUE SLICES

Metabolic quotients are usually expressed in terms of mg. dry weight of tissues. As pointed out in Chapter 1, this procedure may give rise to erroneous comparisons of metabolic rates of different tissues. Since the metabolic activity is associated more directly with the nitrogen (protein) content of a given tissue, it would seem desirable to include nitrogen determination when comparing tissues. Experiments in which tissues from an animal on one diet are compared with those from an animal on another diet may show differences which are more apparent than real on the basis of dry weight. This is particularly true in the case of liver the composition of which is so markedly influenced by diet. Thus it is possible to demonstrate an apparent increase in the content of certain enzymes of liver by merely starving the animal. This can be shown to be due in part to the decrease in glycogen with a consequent increase in protein (enzyme) concentration. This precaution of evaluating metabolic quotients, such as Q_{O_2}, on the basis of dry weight in comparative experiments cannot be overemphasized.

Tissue slice dry weights may be obtained in one of two ways:

1. Weighing moist slices on a small torsion balance and then taking a sample to dryness to determine the wet weight/dry weight ratio.
2. Determining dry weights of the tissues in each flask at the end of the incubation without regard to wet weight.

With good slicing technique and care in handling the slices, reliable and consistent results are obtained with either method. The chief objection to the first method is that it is difficult to insure a uniform H_2O and saline content when transferring the slices from the saline to the balance. The question as to whether the one or the other method gives more nearly correct values is not possible to answer. With the first technique it is assumed that the added weight of tissue is maintained and is metabolically active throughout the experimental period. This is certainly not true for all tissues. In the second method, the tissue removed from the experimental flask does not include, usually, the fragments broken off during the course of shaking. It is assumed in this instance that these fragments are not contributing to the metabolism of the system. Whether or not this is actually the case it is not possible to say. However, it may in part explain why the Q_{O_2} values obtained with the second method tend to be somewhat higher than those obtained with the first method.

For the purpose of determining dry weights of tissue slices, it is convenient to use containers of small weight to allow accurate weighing of a few milligrams. Small flat bottomed vials measuring approximately 10 mm. in length and 8 mm. in diameter, and which weigh between 300-500 mg., can be used. These vials are numbered and their weights recorded. Vials of this size are satisfactory for dry weights of 10-20 mg.; larger vials are used where the quantity of tissue exceeds this amount. Another convenient technique is to use tared glass slide cover slips. These can be used and discarded after a single use, thus eliminating the cleaning problem.

MINCING OF ANIMAL TISSUES

The purpose in mincing tissues for metabolic study is to reduce them to particles of such size as to permit adequate diffusion of the suspending medium, and also to provide a uniform tissue suspension of relatively high concentration. In comparison with the tissue slice, the mince particles contain a high per cent of damaged cells. The chief use of the tissue mince in recent times has been in the study of muscle metabolism, and in particular, pigeon breast muscle. Several mechanical devices for reducing tissues to a uniform mince have been described and successfully employed in metabolism experiments. A few of these will be discussed.

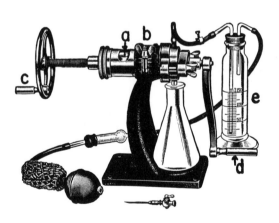

Figure 44
The Latapie tissue mincing mill. The material to be ground is fed into opening "a" and is gradually forced against the cutting discs at "b" by turning wheel "c". The material is ground by turning the crank "d"; the remainder of the apparatus is designed to supply fluid if necessary from "e"

The feature of the <u>Latapie Mincer</u> (fig. 44) instrument is that it is possible to control not only the rate of turning of the cutting discs but also the rate at which the tissue is forced against these discs. It is thus possible to obtain minces of different degrees of fineness, by varying the rates of turning of the two cranks, (see fig. 44). In most metabolic experiments it is desirable to have a mince which can be pipetted after it is suspended in the proper medium. This permits more rapid manipulation and uniformity of tissue content from flask to flask. On the other hand, too fine a mince is usually avoided in order to maintain some degree of integrity of the cells making up the particles. An additional feature of the Latapie is that sterile conditions may be maintained if desired.

The popular Latapie Mincer (obtainable from Arthur H. Thomas Company, Philadelphia) is intended for use with relatively large amounts of tissue, that is, of the order of 25 grams or more. It is thus particularly suitable for a tissue like pigeon heart muscle. However, where small animal tissues are to be employed the instrument is too large. A smaller model is available for this purpose (Arthur H. Thomas Company, Philadelphia, Pennsylvania).

SEEVERS AND SHIDEMAN MINCERS:

Other types of small mincing apparatus have also been used. A micromincer has been reported by Seevers and Shideman (1941) which appears to be ideally suited for use with small amounts of tissue since it is adaptable to varying quantities of material. Thus the authors report that amounts of tissue from 0.25 to 30 grams can be conveniently minced. The yield of mince from 250 milligrams of tissue is reported as 200 milligrams. In common with the Latapie Mincer principle, the tissue cannot be forced through without being cut since the cutting blades are synchronized to turn as the plunger advances. This feature guarantees a uniform particle size of tissue. A comparison of the respiration of homogenized liver and liver minced by this apparatus has been reported by Potter (1941b).

WARING BLENDOR:

Where relatively large amounts of tissue are available and a fine mince, of the consistency of a homogenate, is desired, the Waring Blendor is recommended.

Figure 45
The Waring Blendor with various containers

This device has had increasing use in the preparation of homogenates. At present it is possible to obtain a variety of containers varying in content from 25 ml. to 500 ml. (fig. 45). Further, stainless steel and aluminum containers which can be sterilized or the contents of which can be handled aseptically are available.

Modifications of the Waring Blendor container for low temperature use and a low temperature micro container have been reported by Sorof and Cohen (1951). The design of these vessels is shown in figure 46.

The Virtis Homogenizer (The Vertis Company, 160 Ashburton Avenue, Yonkers, New York) (fig. 47) can handle varying volumes; a micro unit capable of homogenizing volumes of 0.2 to 0.5 ml. also is available.

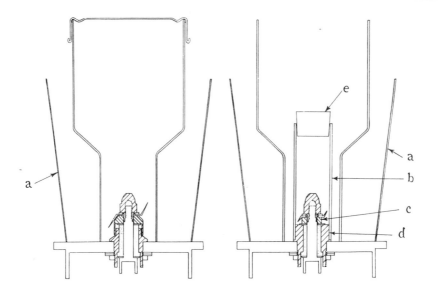

Figure 46
Semi-micro-blendor bowl with outer ice jacket (a) is on the left.
On the right is the micro-blendor bowl with outer ice jacket (a),
stainless steel tube (b), modified bearing cap (c), modified bearing
holder (d), and rubber stopper (e). From Experimental Cell
Research 2, 299 (1951).

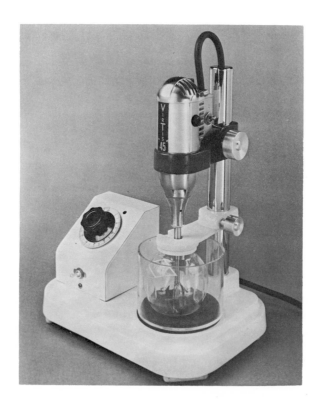

Figure 47
The Virtis homogenizer

Another high speed homogenizer and emulsifier is marketed under the name Omni-Mixer (Ivan Sorvall, Inc., P.O. Box 230, Norwalk, Connecticut). This unit is shown in figure 48.

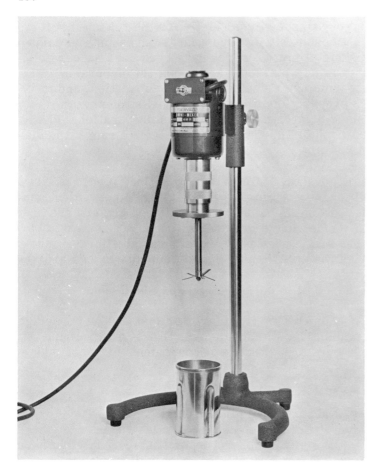

Figure 48
The Sorvall Omni-Mixer

Figure 49
Colloid Mill

COLLOID MILL:

The colloid mill (fig. 49) has a number of advantages over the Waring Blendor when the preparation of large quantities of tissue homogenate are desired. It is much more efficient with regard to cell breakage, it can be efficiently cooled and it can rapidly process large quantities of material. Small colloid mills with a capacity of as little as 15 ml. are now available (Gifford-Wood Company, 122 West Burlington Avenue, LaGrange, Illinois). A procedure which has been highly successful in the preparation of homogenates which were later used to recover mitochondria is as follows:

Fresh slaughterhouse tissue is first diced in a food chopper and then fed into the colloid mill at 0° C. together with the suspending medium. (Sucrose, 0.25 M, has been used successfully in the author's preparations.) For liver and kidney tissue, a gap setting of 0.03 - 0.05 inch has been used to process 100 gms. of tissue in one liter of sucrose solution in a period of 30 seconds (Garver, J. and DeLuca, H. F., unpublished).

SPECIAL TISSUE PREPARATIONS

MUSCLE:

Skeletal muscle does not yield satisfactory tissue slices chiefly for the reason that the muscle cells are relatively large. As a result, slices have a large percentage of damaged cells per slice. Two preparations of skeletal muscle which have been used successfully are fiber bundles described by Richardson, et al. (1930), and young rat diaphragm. The former has been prepared particularly from dog muscle by careful dissection, and the technique was found to yield a uniform preparation of intact fibers. Rat diaphragm is a very convenient muscle preparation since it involves a minimum of preparation. The rats should preferably weigh in the neighborhood of 100 grams. In this weight range, the diaphragm will have a thickness of about 0.3 mm.

Smooth muscle preparations have the disadvantage of contracting to thick pieces of tissue and consequently may not be suitable because of diffusion difficulties. A convenient and little used source of smooth muscle for slicing is bird gizzard. Pigeon gizzard has been found very suitable for slicing since it yields very thin slices which do not contract appreciably. It is further convenient in that a single gizzard will yield enough slices for the most elaborate metabolic experiment. Other convenient smooth muscle sources are:

1. The inner circular layer of the small intestine, which may be dissected free from mucosa and outer layers, and
2. The medial layer of middle-sized arteries from large animals. The advantage of the latter source of mammalian smooth muscle over that of many others is that one may obtain relatively pure preparations of convenient thickness and amount.

INTESTINE - Everted sacs for studies of absorption and transport:

A number of very useful techniques for the study of absorption or transport in vitro have been developed by Wilson and Wiseman (1954). Of these, the most widely used is the everted sac technique. The sacs are prepared in the following manner:

Animals are killed by decapitation and the upper sections, or if desired the other sections, of small intestine are quickly removed and dissected free of fat and connective tissue. They are then chilled in ice-cold saline until used. From this point on, all operations should be carried out at 0-4° C. if possible. A 2 mm. stirring rod, which has been pulled out to a point and then blunted by heating to form a 2 mm. nob on the point, is inserted through a 10 cm. section of small intestine to within 1 cm. of the other end. The intestine is quickly tied with surgical thread just behind the glass nob and the intestine beyond that trimmed off with a razor blade. The rod is now carefully withdrawn so that damage to the mucosa is kept at a minimum. This results in rapid eversion of the intestine. The section tied to the stirring rod is cut away and discarded. The remaining portion of intestine is tied into 3-4 cm. sausages and then cut into segments. Each segment now has one open end and one tied-off end. These sacs can be easily filled with a blunt-needled syringe. A loop of thread is placed over the syringe needle, and as the needle is inserted into the open end of the sac, the thread is tightened around the intestine to tie it to the needle. The sac is now filled with a physiological salt solution by means of a syringe, and at the end a bubble of oxygen is introduced. The syringe needle is withdrawn and the thread is pulled tight and tied at the same instant to give a leak-free sac. The sacs are then incubated in the desired medium. They may be weighed before and after incubation to determine water movement, although considerable error is experienced in this measurement because of the easy loss of mucosa. The transport of both ionic and nonionic materials has been measured with this technique.

INTESTINE - Isolated villi:

Considerable interest has been focused recently on the preparation of isolated intestinal villi as described by Crane and Mendlestam (1960). These villi are particularly suited to the study of metabolism associated with absorption.

Intestines are removed and dissected free of fat and mesentery. The intestine is slit lengthwise with a fine scissors and placed in ice-cold saline. The intestine is washed with cold saline and then placed, mucosal side up, on a flat porcelain or glass plate on cracked ice. One end of the intestine is held with a glass slide while another is used to scrape off the mucosa (be careful not to scrape off any muscle). The mucosa is transferred to a centrifuge tube containing a physiological salt solution at $0°$ C., and suspended in this medium by first gently breaking up the tissue with a stirring rod and by sucking up and gently blowing out the suspension in a serological pipette. The suspension is centrifuged at 50 x g. for 10 minutes and the supernatant plus floating fat discarded. The villi are resuspended as previously in the salt solution and centrifuged. After resuspension the villi are ready for use. An aliquot of the cells must be taken to determine tissue nitrogen, or other suitable composition upon which to express the data.

SEPARATED KIDNEY TUBULES:

Recently kidney tubules have been prepared for the purpose of studying reabsorption phenomena (Burg and Orloff, 1962). This is accomplished by injecting collagenase solution (0.375%) into the renal arteries of excised rabbit kidneys and then incubating the diced cortex obtained from these kidneys in the collagenase solution for 45 minutes at room temperature. The mixture is passed through surgical gauze, and the tubules are centrifuged at 50 x g. for 90 seconds. The preparations are washed three times and are used in an incubation medium containing 5% serum. The incubations can be carried out either in a manometric apparatus or in the special tubes described by the above investigators.

TESTIS:

The preparation of testis suitable for metabolic experiments is best accomplished by "teasing out" the tissue. The outer capsule is cut with a scissors and the testicular tissue is expressed into saline by manual pressure. The seminiferous tubules are then teased apart by combing the tissue with two pairs of blunt end, curved forceps. This technique insures practically intact tubules.

RETINA:

This structure can be used directly in metabolic experiments by merely stripping the sectioned eye ball. Sheep and pig retinae are particularly useful since they represent easily obtainable material. Rat retinae may be used but, of course, a large number of eyes are required to yield a sufficient amount of tissue. Extreme care must be exercised in handling this delicate tissue particularly if anaerobic experiments are to be performed. In the absence of substrate, retina may lose a large share of its metabolic activity if kept anaerobic for as little as 2-3 minutes.

H. F. DeLUCA and P. P. COHEN

THE PREPARATION OF MITOCHONDRIA ON A LARGE SCALE
FROM SLAUGHTERHOUSE MATERIAL

It is now well established that many enzymes which are involved in the principal metabolic sequences in the animal body are located in mitochondria. One may, therefore,
take advantage of such knowledge and use mitochondria rather than whole organs as a
source material for the isolation of these enzymes.

Methods for the preparation of mitochondria, which fulfill the presently adopted morphological and enzymatic criteria of intactness and purity are reported elsewhere in this
volume (Chapter 10). In general, the organs of small laboratory animals are the source
material for such preparations. Investigators who intend to carry out a multistep procedure for the purification of a mitochondrial enzyme may be forced to look for a more
abundant source of mitochondria and they may be willing in this instance to compromise
as far as the purity of the mitochondria is concerned, provided ample starting material
can be conveniently obtained. These considerations led to the development of the methods
outlined in this chapter which were primarily devised to serve the needs of the preparative enzymologist.

The tissues used were obtained from a large packing house and were packed in ice immediately at the kill floor (beef) or after their delivery from the processing line (pig). The
handling of slaughtered animals is probably standardized on this continent in a way that
the processing of the same animal and the same organ may be expected to be similar in
other packing houses. Although in some cases (pig) hours may elapse after the death of
an animal before the organ is obtained, no deleterious effects of such delay on enzymatic
activities studied in our laboratories were observed. The assumption that laboratory animals have to be used as source material because fresh tissues can be obtained only from
these animals is certainly not generally valid.

The preparation of acetone powders of organs and of microorganisms is an old practice
in enzymology. The subsequent solubilization of enzymes and separation of associated
enzymes may be greatly facilitated after this treatment. The same technique has therefore also been applied to mitochondria. Many enzymes have recently been successfully
isolated from acetone powders of beef, pig, or sheep liver mitochondria.

Beef Heart Mitochondria: Hearts are cut in strips (about 2.5 cm. wide) and packed in ice
when obtained. All fat and connective tissue is trimmed off and the meat is cut into small
pieces (about 2.5 cm.^{3}) and passed through a precooled electric meat grinder (plate with
holes of 4 mm. diameter). The material is then homogenized in lots of 400 gm. in a large
capacity, high speed blendor. (A 1/5 horsepower motor was fitted with a 25 cm. long shaft
and a 3-pointed blade which rotated at 18,000 r.p.m. without load. Because of easier
temperature control, an overhead type blendor was found advantageous.) To every 400
gms. are added 1,200 ml. of 8.5 per cent sucrose solution (0.25 M) containing 1.85 gm.
of K_2HPO_4 per liter (approximately 0.01 M). The blendor is operated for 30-45 seconds
at full speed. The pH should be kept around 7.2 to 7.4. For this purpose 2 to 3 ml. of
6 N KOH are added at the outset of blending and 3 to 4 ml. at the end, as required. The
homogenate is immediately centrifuged for 13 minutes at 1900 r.p.m. (1600 x g.) in a
refrigerated International serum centrifuge (Model 13 L) or under corresponding conditions in similar equipment. (n. b., All gravity values given are for the bottom of the
centrifuge tubes.) The red supernatant is decanted through a single layer of cheese cloth
and the sediment and a partially sedimented buff layer are discarded. Depending on the
requirements of the subsequent procedures, sucrose or KCl solution is now added to the
decanted supernatant. If mitochondria as such or mitochondrial fragments (see below)
are required, the sucrose addition may be preferable. For the preparation of acetone
powders, however, addition of more sucrose should be avoided.

1. <u>Sucrose</u>-<u>Mitochondria</u>: Two liters of 8.5 per cent sucrose solution are added to every 8 liters of original supernatant. The mixed fluid is now passed through a refrigerated Sharples supercentrifuge (Model T-1P) at 50,000 r.p.m. (62,000 x g.). A nozzle is used which permits the passage of 100 ml. per minute. The mitochondria, which have been sedimented in the bowl of the centrifuge by this procedure, are scraped out in a cold room. They are blended with 400 ml. of 8.5 per cent sucrose solution for 10 to 15 seconds and further at low speed until they form a smooth paste. The mixture is finally brought to a volume of 2 liters per contents of one bowl with the same sucrose solution. The resulting suspension is again passed through the Sharples centrifuge at a rate of 10 liters in 20 minutes. The residue is removed as before and blended with the desired volume of 8.5 per cent sucrose solution. When mitochondria are to be stored in the frozen state the sediment is suspended in an equal volume of sucrose solution.

2. <u>KCl</u>-<u>Mitochondria</u>: Eight liters of 0.9 per cent KCl are added to every two liters of original supernatant from the first centrifugation in the serum centrifuge. The suspension is mixed and passed through the refrigerated Sharples centrifuge at a rate of 10 liters in seven minutes. The residue in the bowl of the centrifuge is removed as described above and blended with 0.9 per cent KCl solution to the desired dilution.

3. <u>Acetone</u> <u>Powder</u>: For the preparation of an acetone powder the sediment in the bowl of the centrifuge is suspended in a minimal volume of 0.9 per cent KCl solution and is poured into 10 volumes of cold acetone at a temperature not exceeding -5° C. and under mixing with a high speed mechanical stirrer. Alternatively, a less efficiently mixed material may be blendorized for 20 seconds to break up aggregates of particles. The mixture is poured into a large size Büchner funnel equipped with a coarse filter paper (<u>e.g.</u>, Eaton and Dikeman No. 617 or No. 640). The liquid is removed by suction and the residue is washed twice with a total volume of cold acetone which equals approximately that of the filtered liquid. In order to avoid cracks in the filter cake the acetone used for washing should be added just when the sediment is barely covered with liquid. The filter cake may be dried by various means depending on the requirements of the subsequent procedures and on the humidity of the room air. Experience has taught that certain enzymes are more readily extracted when the material is dried to a fine fluffy powder, others when the powder is slightly granular. Under the conditions of humidity which prevail in heated or air-conditioned buildings the latter may be achieved by drying the material in room air. The acetone-moist mass is smeared on paper and is reshuffled with a flat spatula under an air stream from an electric fan. When the room is very humid this procedure is not advisable, because too much water is taken up by the acetone precipitated material and lumps are formed from which proteins cannot be readily extracted. There are also indications that some enzymes are inactivated if too much moisture is taken up by the powder. A fine fluffy acetone powder may be obtained by drying in a sealed drum. In our laboratory such a drum has been constructed from an 8 liter stainless steel beaker which is filled with the acetone treated material, fitted to a base plate and rotated horizontally at a slow speed. A moderate stream of dry nitrogen is introduced through a tube in the hollow shaft which rotates the base plate. The hollow shaft likewise serves as the exit for nitrogen and acetone vapor. Drying may be accelerated by directing a stream of warm air towards the drum. One drying operation takes 30 to 45 minutes under these conditions.

The following figures may serve to give an estimate of the material and time consumed and the yield to be expected in these procedures: about 6 kg. of meat are needed for one load of the Sharples centrifuge; about 2 loads may be processed in an average working day by 2 or 3 workers; and about 10 gm. of acetone powder may be obtained per kg. of meat or a yield of 100 to 125 gm. per day.

<u>Pig</u> <u>Liver</u> <u>Mitochondria</u>: Pig livers are packed into crushed ice when obtained at the slaughterhouse. Since liver tissue swells rapidly when in contact with water or wet ice the livers are placed into dry cold metal containers after arrival at the laboratory and are stored at 0 to 4° until prepared for immediate use. The outer swollen part of the liver (about 0.5 to 1 cm. deep) is trimmed off in a cold room and major blood vessels or strands of connective tissue are also removed. 500 gm. of tissue is cut into cubes of about 2 cm.^{3} with large scissors. 1500 ml. of 8.5 per cent sucrose solution is added which contains 1.85 gm. of K_2HPO_4 per liter. The mixture is homogenized for 30 seconds at 75 per cent of the full speed of the large capacity blendor (about 10,000 r.p.m. under load). Neutralization is carried out as described for heart. The homogenate is centrifuged for 6.5 minutes at 1,200 r.p.m. in the 13 L serum-centrifuge (650 x g.). The supernatant is poured through one layer of cheese cloth and the sediment together with incompletely sedimented material is discarded. In case mitochondria are wanted as the final product, sucrose solution may be added as described for heart. When one intends to prepare an acetone powder one may add KCl solution. Eight liters of 0.9 per cent KCl solution are then added for every 2 liters of supernatant. The mixed fluid is passed through the Sharples centrifuge at 50,000 r.p.m. at the rate of 10 liters in 20 minutes. The residue in the bowl of the centrifuge is removed in the cold and suspended in a small volume of 0.9 per cent KCl solution. The suspension is blended in a Waring blendor for 10 seconds at full speed and at low speed until a smooth paste is obtained. This paste is then stirred into acetone and further treated as described for heart.

<u>Beef</u> <u>Liver</u> <u>Mitochondria</u>: Beef liver is treated in a way analogous to that described for pig liver. About 3 kg. of usable material may be obtained from one liver. When first obtained the beef liver is cut into about 6 pieces to facilitate rapid cooling in ice. Before trimming, the membrane surrounding the liver is removed.

Requirements and yields for the liver preparations are similar to those mentioned above for heart.

Mitochondria or mitochondrial acetone powders may be obtained in a similar fashion from other organs and other animals.

The mitochondrial preparations described above will be suitable for the isolation of most mitochondrial enzymes. When, however, studies of the cytochrome and associated oxidative phosphorylation system are intended more carefully controlled preparations are preferable. Two methods, which utilize beef heart as starting material and lend themselves to operation at a reasonably large scale, will be described here. Mitochondria prepared by the routine method outlined above can be separated into so called "light" and "heavy" mitochondria (Hatefi and Lester, 1958; Ziegler <u>et al.</u>, 1958). The latter appear to be closer in properties to undamaged mitochondria.

"Heavy" Mitochondria <u>from</u> <u>Beef</u> <u>Heart</u>: 100 ml. of packed fresh mitochondria, prepared as described above, are homogenized with a sucrose solution, 0.02 M in Tris chloride of pH 8.0, to give a total volume of 780 ml. The suspension is centrifuged in the Spinco centrifuge (rotor No. 30) at 18,000 r.p.m. (38,000 x g.) for 13 minutes. (<u>n.b.</u>, Unless otherwise specified, the centrifuging time includes the acceleration of the particular rotor.) Somewhat more than half of the supernatant is decanted. The layer of light mitochondria overlaying the heavy mitochondria is stirred up with a glass rod and the resulting suspension is decanted from the heavy mitochondria. The remaining sediments are combined and homogenized with neutralized (KOH) 0.25 M sucrose to a volume of 390 ml.

The suspension is centrifuged in the Spinco centrifuge as above. Before the caps are removed from the tubes after centrifugation, the tubes are inverted and well shaken so that the enclosed air bubble separates the remaining loosely packed light mitochondria from the sediment of heavy mitochondria. The caps are then removed and the supernatant is discarded. The heavy mitochondria are combined and homogenized with a small amount of neutralized 0.25 M sucrose. They may be kept frozen.

Another method, which leads to mitochondria of high integrity, utilizes a bacterial proteinase to liberate mitichondria (Chance and Hagihara, 1960; Hatefi et al., 1961).

"Nagarse" Mitochondria from Beef Heart: Fresh beef heart (obtained from a slaughterhouse) is stripped from fat and connective tissue. The lean meat is diced and passed through a meat grinder into a beaker containing cold 0.25 M sucrose. The suspension is neutralized with 1 M Tris. It is then poured into a double layer of cheesecloth and drained thoroughly. Two hundred grams of the meat are weighed out and suspended in about 400 ml. of cold 0.25 M sucrose. The pH of the medium is adjusted to 7.2 to 7.4 with the dropwise addition of 1 M Tris. Then 400 mg. of Nagarse proteinase (manufactured by Teikoku Chemical Industry Co., Osaka, Japan, and obtainable in the U.S.A. from Biddle Sawyer Corp., 20 Vesey Street, New York, N.Y.) are added. The suspension is slowly stirred for 20 min. at $0°$ C. and the pH is maintained between 7.2 and 7.4 by the addition of Tris. After digestion, the suspension is homogenized in a 50 ml. glass homogenizer fitted with a teflon plunger and centrifuged 20 min. at 2,000 r.p.m. (12,000 x g.) in rotor No. 30 of the Spinco Model L. The supernatant material is discarded and the residue suspended in about 100 ml. of 0.25 M sucrose containing 0.01 M Tris, pH 7.7, homogenized as before and centrifuged for 10 min. at 17,000 r.p.m. (34,000 x g.) in rotor No. 30 of the Spinco. The sediment after centrifugation consists of three layers; a top, relatively pale layer which is sloughed off and discarded; a bottom, dark layer which is left behind in the centrifuge tubes; a middle layer, which consists of the desired particles. This material is suspended in 0.25 M sucrose, homogenized and washed by recentrifuging as before. The yield is about 600 mg. of mitochondrial protein from 200 gm. of ground heart muscle.

Mitochondrial Fragments: Interest has recently arisen in mitichondrial fragments which are readily sedimentable at high speed centrifugation, which are therefore of relatively large size, and which still possess some of the characteristic enzymatic activities and structural characteristics of mitochondria. Since such preparations have proven to be extremely useful in detailed studies of mitochondrial electron transfer and associated phosphorylation reactions, some of the techniques presently used to obtain such fragments will be mentioned. For the details of these procedures, the original publications will have to be consulted. The methods of fragmentation are generally based on treatments such as sonic or mechanical disintegration, freezing and thawing, exposure to media of low osmolarity or extreme pH, extraction with organic reagents (e.g., digitonin) or solvents (ethyl-, butyl-, isobutyl-, isoamyl alcohol) and enzymatic digestion. In many cases several of the mentioned procedures have been used in sequence, since any one treatment by itself may not be sufficiently effective.

1. Mechanical Disintegration and Treatment at Low pH: Heart preparations have been described in which the disintegration of mitochondria is achieved by exposure to low osmolarity, or by extensive mechanical comminution either by blending at high speed or by prolonged grinding with sand and finally by exposing the resulting extract to a low pH.

   A preparation of this type is the classical horse heart preparation of Keilin and Hartree (1947). Since the early work of these investigators, a variety of modifications of their procedure has been developed and it should be kept in mind that different workers referring to the use of a "Keilin-Hartree preparation" may actually have used quite different types of preparations. A modification in which blending is substituted for the grinding procedure will be described here:

One and one half kilos of pig or beef heart are cleaned of fat and connective tissue and minced in an electric meat grinder (butcher's size) and then washed by decantation with 20 liters of tap water until the washings are only slightly opalescent (usually 6-7 washes). The washed mince is collected on cheesecloth and excess moisture removed by squeezing. Aliquots of 100 gms. are now blended with 500 ml. of cold 0.02 M Na_2HPO_4 for one minute at full speed in a Waring blendor. The homogenate is centrifuged at 1,400 x g. for 20 min. in a refrigerated centrifuge and the supernatant collected. The cold supernatant is adjusted to pH 5.2 - 5.4 by the addition of cold 1 N acetic acid. The precipitate which forms is collected by centrifugation at 1,400 x g. for 40 min. and suspended in a suitable buffer to yield the particles.

The original method involved disruption of the mince by grinding in a mortar with sand. A useful modification of this original method utilizing a mechanical mortar has been described by Slater (1949). A more recent modification of King (1961) retains the grinding procedure, but substitutes differential centrifugation at neutral pH for the precipitation at lowered pH. certain activities appear to be better preserved by the grinding as compared to blending and by avoiding exposure to low pH.

All preparations of the Keilin-Hartree type have the advantage of being free of hemoglobin, myoglobin and most cofactors and have, therefore, proven to be extremely suitable for spectroscopic studies of the cytochrome system. They show succinic and DPNH oxidase activity, but are not able to carry out significant oxidative phosphorylation.

2. Sonic Disintegration and Differential Centrifugation: "Electron transport particles". Twenty five milliliters of packed fresh beef heart mitochondria prepared by the routine method described above, are diluted to 200 ml. by gentle homogenization with neutralized (KOH) 0.25 M sucrose. The suspension is centrifuged in the Spinco centrifuge (rotor No. 30) at 30,000 r.p.m. (150,000 x g.) for 5 minutes. The supernatant is discarded. The thus washed mitochondria are combined and homogenized gently to a final volume of 100 ml. with 0.25 M sucrose. The resulting suspension is then treated with a Raytheon 10 kc. sonic oscillator in 50 ml. batches. Each batch is exposed for 4 min. while the temperature is kept between 0 - 4° C. by circulating liquid from a bath maintained at -7° to -10° C. through the cooling jacket. The material is centrifuged in the Spinco centrifuge (rotor No. 30) at 30,000 r.p.m. for 30 minutes. The sedimented fraction is discarded, and the supernatant is now spun (rotor No. 40) at 40,000 r.p.m. (144,000 x g.) for 90 minutes. The red gelatinous sediment is collected and homogenized to the desired consistency with 0.25 M sucrose.

The particals have excellent optical properties and are almost transparent at high concentration. They lend themselves well to spectroscopic studies of their cytochrome components.

A variant of this basic procedure leads to similar particles which are capable of oxidative phosphorylation (Linnane and Ziegler, 1958). In this case the starting material is frozen heavy mitochondria. They are allowed to thaw slowly in the refrigerator over a period of several hours (over night if convenient). One apparently obtains a better yield after slow thawing. The volume of the suspension and its protein content are determined. The biuret method is used for protein determination with addition of cholate to a final concentration of 0.1% to clear the mixture. The mitochondrial suspension is diluted to a protein concentration of 20 mgs. per ml. with 0.25 M neutralized (KOH) sucrose. Concentrated solutions of $MgCl_2$ and ATP are then mixed in to give final concentrations of 15 and 1 mM, respectively. For best results in oxidative phosphorylation, Smith and Hansen (1962) recommend a 5 mM concentration of $MgCl_2$ and 10 mM $MnCl_2$. In other work, however, Mn^{++} may be undesirable. ATP may be omitted without resulting in complete failure of the procedure. Aliquots, 25 ml., of the mitochondrial suspension are then sonicated as above with the exception that the exposure time should only be 30 seconds. The suspension is centrifuged in the Spinco centrifuge (rotor No. 30). The rotor is accelerated to 15,000 r.p.m. (26,000 x g.) with the speed set at 30,000 and then spun six more minutes at the same setting. The milky supernatant is carefully decanted and centrifuged for 40 minutes in rotor No. 40 at 40,000 r.p.m. (144,000 x g.). The supernatant is discarded. The red residue is suspended with the aid of a Potter-Elvehjem homogenizer in approximately 10 volumes of a solution of neutralized sucrose, which is 1 mM with respect to ATP and 10 mM with respect to $MgCl_2$. The suspension is centrifuged for one hour in rotor No. 40 at 40,000 r.p.m. The sediments are combined and homogenized in a small amount of the sucrose-ATP-$MgCl_2$ mixture. Again, ATP may be omitted and $MnCl_2$ partly substituted for $MgCl_2$ in these latter steps.

3. Treatment with Organic Reagents and Solvents: A type of mitochondrial fragment has been described and extensively used by Lehninger and his associates (Cooper et al., 1955a; Devlin and Lehninger, 1958), which is obtained by extraction of rat liver mitochondria with 0.8% digitonin (final concentration) followed by differential centrifugation. For details the paper by Devlin and Lehninger (1958), which reports an improved method, should be consulted. This preparation is able to carry out oxidative phosphorylation concomitant with the oxidation of β-hydroxybutyrate and ascorbate.

Treatment of tissue fractions with n-butanol (Morton, 1950) has in several instances facilitated the extraction of enzymes in a soluble form. The action of this reagent is generally thought to effect a dissociation of proteins from lipid material. In a similar fashion, treatment of mitochondria with aqueous ethyl-, isobutyl-, or isoamyl alcohol has been successfully applied to the separation of active mitochondrial fragments (Green et al., 1955; Mackler and Green, 1956) of a particulate nature. Cholate and desoxycholate have been widely used for the separation of units which contain components of the cytochrome system of mitochondria (Eichel et al., 1950; Dannenberg and Kiese, 1952; Smith and Stotz, 1954; Griffiths and Wharton, 1961).

4. Treatment with Lipolytic Enzymes: More recently a variety of bound mitochondrial enzymes have been successfully solubilized by the action of phospholipase from snake venom. Procedures for extraction of α-L-glycerophosphate and choline dehydrogenases from acetone powders of pig brain and rat liver mitochondria, respectively, by the action of cobra (Naja naja) venom are described by Ringler and Singer (1961) and Kimura and Singer (1961). A careful study of the conditions of solubilization and the effects of cobra venom on DPNH dehydrogenase from beef heart mitochondria has been published by King and Howard (1962a, 1962b).

H. BEINERT

PREPARATION OF ACETONE POWDERS

The method of preparation is essentially that of Green, Needham, and Dewan (1937) as follows:

"The skeletal muscles of a freshly killed animal (rabbit) are cooled by packing with ice and thoroughly minced. The mince is mixed with 2 volumes of iced water and allowed to stand for ca. 30 minutes. The mixture is squeezed through muslin. 2 volumes of cold acetone are then added to the filtrate. The precipitate is filtered immediately on Büchner funnels with suction and then washed with acetone and ether. If the washings are effected before the cake of precipitate has cracked, it is possible to pulverize the precipitate in a mortar and dry it within an hour in vacuo over liquid paraffin. The dried acetone powder (10 g.) is rubbed up with water (120 ml.) until a homogeneous paste is formed. The mixture is then dialysed for 15 hours at 0° C. in cellophane sacs. The large amount of insoluble material is centrifuged off and discarded. The clear supernatant fluid contains the active enzymes. The activity is maintained for at least 10 days if the enzyme solution is kept at 0° C. The enzymes are best kept in the form of the dry powder."

In our experience, the final dehydration of the precipitated protein with pure acetone and peroxide-free ether, must be done quickly and in the cold. Furthermore, in trying to suck the precipitate dry, one is likely to hydrate it simply by contact with air. When this occurs, the color of the precipitate changes to a dark brown, and the dried precipitate is dark in color instead of almost white. The dark precipitate contains much more water-insoluble and presumably denatured protein than is the case with the light colored powder which is obtained when the dehydration is properly carried out. We have used from 0.5 to 1.0 ml. of the enzyme solution per Warburg flask in studies involving the addition of dehydrogenases. Further work needs to be done on the fractionation of the enzymes in this preparation, and on the factors affecting their solubility and denaturation.

Other workers, e.g. Kaplan and Lipmann (1948) have prepared acetone powders by adding the tissue directly to chilled acetone in a Waring mixer. Chilled, scissor-minced livers were added to 20 volumes of acetone, blended for 2 minutes and rapidly filtered on a Büchner funnel, washing the residue with pure acetone and peroxide-free ether, avoiding hydration as noted above. We have found that the filtration can advantageously be done in winter in cold regions, when interior humidity is very low. The powder is dried further in a vacuum desiccator over P_2O_5. Kaplan and Lipmann reported 15 to 20 gm. of pinkish powder from 100 gm. of fresh pigeon liver from 10 to 12 pigeons. They prepared acetylating extracts free from coenzyme A by grinding 10 gm. of acetone powder with 100 ml. of 0.02 M sodium bicarbonate and centrifuging to obtain 60-75 ml. of supernatant extract. This was frozen and stored overnight, thawed to room temperature and allowed to stand 4 hours to inactivate coenzyme A. It was then recentrifuged, the residue discarded, and the extract stored in a deep freeze or used for further fractionations.

Further discussion of the general problem of obtaining soluble enzymes from insoluble tissue components is given by Morton in an excellent discussion in volume 1 of the handbook edited by Colowick and Kaplan (1955).

V. R. POTTER

SUSPENDING MEDIA FOR ANIMAL TISSUES

The choice of a suspending medium for a given tissue preparation is to a large measure determined by the nature of the metabolic experiment. In the case of tissue slices it is ordinarily assumed that the purpose of the medium is to provide a solution which because of its ionic composition and its osmotic relation to the cells will maintain the integrity of the latter. Thus, the commonly employed Krebs-Ringer solution (Krebs and Henseleit, 1932) is so constituted as to closely approximate the ionic composition of the mammalian serum. This medium would seem to provide a physiological extracellular environment and so insure the metabolic integrity of the surviving cells. While this may actually be the case, it would appear from the literature that optimum conditions for a given metabolic reaction with slices often require a medium which is different from the balanced, physiological salt solution. Thus, the synthesis of glycogen from pyruvate by liver slices is most rapid when a medium high in potassium is used (Buchanan, et al., 1942). The medium the latter investigators found to give optimum glycogen formation consisted of (per liter) $CaCl_2$, 5.6 mM; KCl, 75 mM; K pyruvate, 60 mM; and $KHCO_3$, 43 mM. As can be seen, this medium can hardly be considered a balanced solution in the usual sense of the word. The respiration of brain tissue is markedly sensitive to variations in ionic composition of the suspending medium. When compared with other tissues such as kidney cortex, testis, liver, yolk sac, and retina, brain stands out as being unusually sensitive to the effects of changes in ionic concentration (Dickens and Greville, 1935).

Many other such instances of the effect of varying ionic concentrations on metabolic reactions with tissue slices have been reported. It is only necessary here to stress that the choice of a nutrient medium for a given metabolic experiment with tissue slices may require considerable experimentation with the composition of the medium before optimum conditions are realized.

The Use of Serum as a Suspending Medium: The use of mammalian serum in place of balanced salt solution would seem to represent the ideal physiological medium for suspending tissue slices. While some differences in Q_{O_2} and R. Q. have been reported (Dickens and Simer, 1931; Canzanelli and Rapport, 1939) the magnitude of the difference is usually not great enough to warrant its routine use. As a matter of fact, in some instances respiration is greater in salt solutions than in serum. Some of the difficulties attending the use of serum are:

1. Its preparation
2. The considerable CO_2 retention, and
3. The uncontrollable variability in its make up from sample to sample.

The latter would seem to be particularly undesirable since it represents an introduction of unknown variables in a system which has as one of its features the control of the tissue's environment.

Suspending Media for Tissue Minces: Since tissue minces contain a higher per cent of broken cells, the choice of a suspending medium would seem to favor one more closely approximating intra- rather than extracellular fluid. However, here again it is not possible to predict what type of medium will be most suitable for any given experiment. In the case of pigeon heart muscle mince, a phosphate-saline medium containing NaCl, KCl, $MgSO_4$ and Na_2HPO_4 was found to give higher metabolic rates than phosphate buffer plus NaCl, or phosphate buffer plus $MgCl_2$ (Krebs and Eggleston, 1940). A study of the effect of electrolytes on the respiration of pigeon breast muscle mince has been reported by Kleinzeller (1940). It was found that the optimal K concentration was 0.0385 M if the medium contained 0.02 M phosphate and 0.0425 M NaCl. When the medium contained 0.02 M phosphate, 0.092 M NaCl and 0.00085 M $MgSO_4$, the optimal K concentration was

0.0034 M. The optimum concentration of Mg was dependent on the concentration of other ions in the medium. Thus in a medium containing "physiological" concentrations of Na, K, and Cl the optimal Mg concentration was 0.0025 M. With a K concentration of 0.0385 M, the optimal Mg concentration is about 0.00125 M.

Phosphate, CO_2-Bicarbonate and other Buffers: From a quantitative standpoint, the CO_2-bicarbonate system of the extracellular fluid is the chief buffer system in the body. In the case of tissue slices, the use of phosphate buffer is somewhat more common since it is easier to use. Dickens and Simer (1931) found no significant difference in the Q_{O_2} or RQ of tissue slices in bicarbonate (or phosphate) Ringer solutions. However, Laser (1942) has shown that in the absence of CO_2 the maximum activity of tissue slices and reactivity to substrates are maintained for only a short time. Further, it was found that CO_2 stabilized the Q_{O_2} of slices in the presence of substrate for several hours and also insured their ability to oxidize substrates added after an incubation period without substrate. Since it is customary to "gas" phosphate buffered systems with 100% O_2, it should be pointed out that Laser has demonstrated that the rate of O_2 uptake without added substrate declined more rapidly in 100% than in lower O_2 tensions.

The use of buffers other than bicarbonate and phosphate has received relatively little study. In a comparative study of various media buffered with phosphate, bicarbonate and borate, Feinstein and Stare (1940) found that with liver slices there was no essential difference in the O_2 uptake. On the other hand, minced liver showed a higher O_2 uptake with the borate buffer than with phosphate or bicarbonate.

Preparation of Krebs-Ringer-Phosphate and Bicarbonate Solutions:

Solutions:

1. 0.90% NaC1   (0.154 M)
2. 1.15% KCl   (0.154 M)
3. 1.22% $CaCl_2$ (0.11 M)   (5 ml. equivalent to 11 ml. 0.1N AgNO₃)
4. 2.11% KH_2PO_4 (0.154 M)
5. 3.82% $MgSO_4 \cdot 7H_2O$ (0.154 M)
6. 1.30% $NaHCO_3$ (0.154 M)   (gas with CO_2 for 1 hour)
7. 0.1 M phosphate buffer, pH 7.4   (17.8 g. $Na_2HPO_4 \cdot 2H_2O$ + 20 ml. 1N HCl; dilute to 1 L.)

To prepare the Krebs-Ringer solution, the following amounts of the above are mixed:

100 parts of solution 1
  4 "   "   "   2
  3 "   "   "   3
  1 "   "   "   4
  1 "   "   "   5

Note: All solutions are isotonic with rat serum, hence can be mixed in any proportion yielding mixtures (of differing composition) which are still isotonic.

If Krebs-Ringer-Bicarbonate is desired, 21 parts of solution 6 are added. The solution is then gassed for 10 minutes with 5% CO_2. For aerobic experiments 5% CO_2-95% O_2 mixture is usually used, and for anaerobic experiments, 5% CO_2-95% N_2. After mixing and gassing the solution, it should be kept in a glass stoppered vessel in the cold, until ready for use. The manometric flasks containing the solution should be attached to the manometers and "gassed" as soon as possible.

If Krebs-Ringer-Phosphate is desired, omit solution 4 from the Krebs-Ringer solution and add 20 parts of solution 7. This solution after mixing, is gassed with either O_2, H_2 or air, depending on the gas phase desired. A precipitate of calcium phosphate forms; this is suspended by shaking before use.

To simplify the preparation and handling of the above solutions, it has been found convenient to make up solutions 1 to 5 in concentrations five times those listed. The more concentrated solutions are stable for months when stored in the cold. To make a stock Krebs-Ringer solution, solutions 1 to 5 are made up in the proportions indicated above (taking into account the fact that these stock solutions are five times the concentration required). This stock Krebs-Ringer solution will keep in the cold for about one week. To make up the Krebs-Ringer bicarbonate solution, 16 ml. of solution 6 are diluted to 100 ml. with the stock Krebs-Ringer solution. To make up the Krebs-Ringer phosphate, 10 ml. of solution 7 are diluted to 100 ml. with the stock Krebs-Ringer solution.

Robinson (1949) has devised a stable medium buffered with phosphate which was found to be particularly suitable for kidney slices. Except for the absence of bicarbonate the medium resembled mammalian extracellular fluid. The medium had the following composition:

Constituent	Concentration (M)	Parts Mixed For Whole Medium (ml.)
NaCl	0.154	232
KCl	0.154	8
MgSO$_4$	0.154	2
CaCl$_2$	0.110	6

The mixture is adjusted to pH 7.4 by the addition of 0.1 N NaOH. To this is added 12 ml. of M/15 phosphate buffer, pH 7.4. (This is prepared by mixing 80.8 ml. of M/15 Na$_2$HPO$_4$ with 19.2 ml. of M/15 KH$_2$PO$_4$.) To avoid precipitation the calcium solution and phosphate buffer were not brought together in less than the final volume. The completed solution however was found to be stable.

Glucose was added to this medium in the amount of 0.4 ml. of 5% solution to 19.6 ml. of medium. The resulting medium contains in millimoles per liter approximately the following: Na$^+$, 140; K$^+$, 5; Ca^{++}, 2.5; Mg^{++}, 1; Cl$^-$, 144; P, 3 and SO$_4^=$, 1, giving a total ionic strength of 0.158.

H. F. DeLUCA and P. P. COHEN

METHODS OF PREPARING PLANT TISSUES

HIGHER PLANTS

In general, the higher plant does not possess organs constituted of massive tissues as does an animal. The most actively metabolizing regions of a plant are those where growth, in the sense of increase in number of cells, is progressing most rapidly, namely the meristem regions of the stem and root, the developing flower and fruit, the germinating seed, and seedling. As a rule every plant cell progressively develops from the meristematic to the mature state. The rate of respiration also decreases as the cell matures; too, as the organ of the plant matures, cells are transformed into dead xylem elements, for example, which further lowers the respiratory rate of the organ.

Because the course of many experiments on respiration is dictated by the very practical consideration of using enough tissue to be able to accurately measure the carbon dioxide and/or oxygen exchange over a convenient period of time, the introduction of the manometric methods requiring relatively small quantities of tissue has allowed considerably more latitude in the choice of plant material and type of experiment. The development of other methods, particularly those involving the use of spectrophotometers (see Chapter 12), chromatograms (see Chapter 13) and isotopes, have in many instances made possible also the use of quantities of plant material much smaller than ever used before in investigating various phases of plant metabolism. With all of these methods becoming increasingly readily available, the most important problem when selecting the plant as the experimental object is not one of obtaining a sufficient quantity of material of the desired quality, but of making the tissue preparations. These include slices, breis, extracts, homogenates, acetone powders, and cellular fractions representing in varying degree isolated wall material, chloroplasts, mitochondria, microsomes, and the so-called "nonparticulate" matter.

It is not proposed to discuss at length all of the various types of plant preparations of use in the study of the several aspects of respiration, fermentation, and photosynthesis. Rather, the discussion will be limited to a few general cases together with indications as to where other accounts can be found.

Storage organs of a number of different types of plants are used extensively. Tubers of the potato and Jerusalem artichoke, roots of carrot and turnip, and the cotyledons from young pea, bean, and peanut seedlings are good examples. All have a high food content and contain a relatively high percentage of uniform parenchymatous cells. Berry and Steward (1934) have described the preparation and have measured the rate of respiration of samples of such tissues from a variety of plants (cf., Beevers and Gibbs, 1954).

In preparing slices, e.g., of potato tuber, cylinders of tissue are removed from the interior by means of a cork borer having a diameter of 6-12 mm. These are worked up into slices 0.4-1.0 mm. thick with a hand microtome. In many cases a set of razor blades separated by washers and bolted together as a unit has been used to speed up this operation. The slices are then washed in running tap water or some type of physiological salt solution, rinsed several times in distilled water, blotted with filter paper, and transferred to the suspending solution in the respirometer vessel. This washing period may be short or extend over 12-24 hours. Washing serves to remove the broken protoplasts of the cut cells and also eliminates certain inequalities in respiration partially associated with the period immediately succeeding cutting (Steward, 1932; also see below). In preparing slices of carrot root, Turner (1938) recommended that the whole organ be sliced and discs cut from the slices to minimize bruising the tissue. Marsh and Goddard (1939) used carrot slices 6 mm. in diameter and 0.5 mm. thick suspended in M/60 pH 5.9 Sorensen phosphate buffer in determining the effects of cyanide, azide and carbon monoxide on respiration. Beevers (1956) used discs of the same organ, and slices of parts of several other plants, in a study of the pentose pathway. Tissue slices of peanut cotyledons from maturing seeds and seedlings, prepared by free-hand sectioning and washing twice in distilled water, were used by Newcomb and Stumpf (1953) in in vitro studies of fatty acid synthesis.

Potato tuber slices when kept under favorable conditions in a suspending medium (termed "washing") may develop a zone of meristematic cells near their surfaces (Steward et al., 1940). This possibility is worth considering when using this tissue, and one should not overlook the possibility of a similar change occurring when using other tissues supposedly composed entirely of mature cells. This is particularly important since meristematic and young cells may have metabolic process patterns differing significantly from those of mature cells, e.g., substrate utilization (Albaum and Eichel, 1943) and terminal oxidase system (Marsh and Goddard, 1939; Thimann et al., 1954). It remains to be established whether or not there is any correlation between the resumption of meristematic activity by the cells in tissue slices and the observed induced respiration -- a two to five fold increase in the rate of respiration over an aging period of about 24 hours (cf., Laties, 1957). There is sufficient evidence that concomitant with the increase in the rate of the induced respiration the metabolism of some, if not all, of the cells alters qualitatively (ApRees and Beevers, 1960; Hackett et al., 1960; Laties, 1962); therefore, the time elapsing between the preparation of a tissue slice and the assessment of some facet of its metabolism is a significant point in interpreting the results obtained.

It should not be necessary to state that none of the tissue slices mentioned above consists entirely of parenchymatous cells; some vascular tissue at least is always included. However, should one desire to use slices containing only this type of cell, it is recommended that slices be prepared from pith segments from young internodes of vigorous, rapidly growing tobacco plants according to the technique described by Bryan and Newcomb (1954). Naylor, Sander, and Skoog (1954) have shown that there are no nuclear or cell divisions in segments of this tissue in contact with a mineral salts-sucrose-vitamins-agar medium, even after a relatively long period.

Root tips, segments of roots, coleoptiles and, to a lesser extent, epicotyls and hypocotyls of seedlings are also favored as experimental material. Since the latter two parts, e.g., of pea and bean seedlings, normally contain chlorophyll and are capable of photosynthesis, they are seldom employed even in the absence of light in experiments involving measurement of gas exchange. On the other hand, these parts from seedlings grown in darkness (etiolated) are used extensively in preparing breis, homogenates, etc.

It is a relatively easy matter to grow plants in liquid culture until the root systems have developed sufficiently to yield the desired quantity of material. Machlis (1944) has given in detail a method for producing barley roots 12-15 cm. long, relatively free of the very fragile root hairs and of uniform diameter slightly under 0.5 mm. Incidentally, Jackson (1962) has reported that carbowaxes present in the nutrient solution in concentrations much lower than that required to plasmolyze the cells of the root completely inhibited the production of root hairs by seedlings of redtop grass. Machlis described also a method of preparing segments of the roots (cf., Eliasson, 1955) for use in a study of the effects of certain inhibitors and acids of the tricarboxylic acid cycle on respiration. Root tips from seedlings are easily obtained and convenient to use. If it is unnecessary to exclude all contaminating organisms, the seed may be germinated in moist sand, or granular expanded vermiculite, under normal conditions of day and night or in complete darkness. Variations of this method include sterilizing the substrate, disinfecting the seed, and watering the seedlings with mineral salt nutrient solution.

Root tips, entire seedlings, and other plant parts can be produced readily under aseptic conditions. The seeds are steeped for a few minutes in a solution of some wetting agent, surface sterilized for 15 minutes in a freshly prepared and filtered 10% solution of calcium hypochlorite, washed thoroughly in sterile water and, after soaking for several hours in sterile water, placed on moistened, sterile filter paper in petri dishes or covered crystallizing dishes of a size that will accommodate the seedlings. The root tips or other seedling parts are excised, washed or not washed, blotted lightly and transferred directly to the experimental solution or otherwise worked up as a tissue preparation. For details regarding the culture of root tips, isolated plant tissues, etc., (cf.: White, 1963; Gautheret, 1959).

Breis and extracts (saps) of plant tissues are easy to prepare. The simplest method is to grind a representative sample of the whole plant, organ, or tissue to a pulp in a mortar and express the liquid from the macerated material by pressing it out through 2-4 layers of fine cheesecloth. The addition of a small amount of sand may facilitate the grinding. For larger samples, a food chopper equipped with a fine-toothed cutter or a blendor may be used to advantage. The liquid may be further clarified by centrifuging (ca. 500 x g for 5 minutes, minimum) or by allowing it to stand 10-12 hours at 2-4° C. The latter treatment appears to work well in obtaining clear extracts from chlorophyllous tissues; but, the trend is definitely toward using extracts as soon as possible. The preparation of an acetone powder (see later discussion) or the use of etiolated plant parts often suffices when the presence of the plastid pigments is objectionable. Extracts prepared from barley seedlings and barley shoots by freezing the material overnight at -12° C. and pressing out the sap by hand through muslin were used respectively by Bunting and James (1941) in a study of carboxylase and cocarboxylase and by James and Cragg (1943) in investigating the ascorbic acid system as an agent in respiration. A method similar to this, but including grinding in a mortar after thawing and centrifugation of the strained liquid at ca. 6000 x g. for a few minutes, was used by Beevers (1954) to prepare extracts of cucumber fruit in a study of the oxidation of reduced diphosphopyridine nucleotide by an ascorbate system. Wang et al. (1962), in a study of the hexose monophosphate pathway in tomato fruits, prepared a water soluble fraction of an 80% alcoholic extract of blendorized fruits, freed the solution of amino and organic acids by sequential passage through columns of Dowex-5 (H form) and Dowex-3 (OH form) resins, and separated the sugars by paper chromatography.

Berger and Avery (1943) ground oat coleoptiles with twice their weight of water, and filtered or centrifuged the extracts for use in determining dehydrogenase activity by means of the Thunberg technique (see Chapter 12). Price and Thimann (1954b) in carrying out a quantitative comparison of dehydrogenase activity and respiration of oat coleoptiles and stem segments of etiolated pea seedlings, ground the chilled and diced tissue in a mortar at 3° C. with 2-5 volumes of 0.2 M sucrose-0.03M pH 7 phosphate solution, extracted the residue three more times with smaller amounts of this solution, and used the combined volumes of extract. Noll and Burris (1954), in a study of the nature and distribution of glycolic acid oxidase in plants, ground the tissue in a mortar with quartz sand, or in a Nixtamal mill, chilled the resulting brei and strained it through a double layer of cheesecloth, adjusted the pH to 8, centrifuged the suspension at 2500 x g. for 10 minutes and used the supernatant liquid. Black and Humphreys (1962) used a dialyzed extract of the roots of etiolated corn seedlings in some of their experiments in determining the effect of 2,4-D (2,4-dichlorophenoxy acetic acid) on the enzymes of glycolysis and pentose phosphate cycle. The chilled roots were ground in a mortar with a cold solution of Tris buffer and EDTA (ethylenediaminetetraacetic acid, tetra sodium salt), and the liquid extracted through cheese cloth, centrifuged at 900 x g. and dialyzed against tris buffer.

Regardless of the details of the procedures, these methods of preparing tissue breis and extracts result in preparations in which the cell components have been diluted to some extent by vacuolar sap or the extracting fluid. Because of this, it is not at all unusual to find that such preparations are fortified by the addition of substrates, coenzymes, inorganic ions, and the like.

It would appear that homogenates (see Chapter 9 for a description of this technique) of plant tissue would be more active, in respect to metabolic activity in general, than breis and extracts, because the cell debris on which some of the enzymes may be absorbed and yet remain active is not removed. It is of interest to point out that Bryan and Newcomb (1954) found that most of the pectin methylesterase activity of whole cell homogenates of tobacco pith tissue could be recovered in the washed cell wall fraction. Homogenates have been used successfully by Albaum and Cohen (1943) in a study of transaminase from oat seedlings, and by Albaum and Umbreit (1943) in determining phosphorous transformations in oat embryos.

Although other studies could be cited to indicate the range of usefulness of homogenates of whole plant cells, this is considered unnecessary in view of the present emphasis on the fractionation of breis, homogenates and extracts to determine the intracellular localization of enzymes and enzyme systems. All such fractionations are patterned after the well known method of Hogeboom, Schneider and Palade (1948) (and see Chapter 10). Particular attention has been given to the isolation of mitochondria (e.g., Stafford, 1951; Millerd et al., 1951; Millerd, 1953; Price and Thimann, 1954a; Stumpf, 1955; Lieberman and Biale, 1956; Lund et al., 1958; Hanson, 1959; Marcus and Velasco, 1960; Jackson et al., 1962; Baker and Lieberman, 1962) and to the isolation of smaller particles, i.e., microsomes (e.g., Humphreys et al., 1954; Martin and Morton, 1956; Lund et al., 1958; Hackett and Ragland, 1962; Smillie, 1962) and ribonucleoprotein particles (e.g., Tso et al., 1956; Webster, 1957). Typically, isolation of subcellular particles smaller than chloroplasts has been effected by differential centrifugation in which a high centrifugal force is applied during one or more stages of the process. A method which represents quite a departure from the general procedure is the utilization of a maximum centrifugal force of 1000 x g. in combination with the stabilized sucrose-gradient technique, as applied by Pierpoint (1960) to chloroplast and mitochondrial fractions prepared from leaves of tobacco. Because the details of handling the plant material have varied considerably, it appears advisable only to refer the reader to the literature cited above for the possible selection of a method that may be suited, or adapted to his need. That just any method may not suffice for a plant tissue is indicated by the unusual requirement of bovine serum albumin as a protective agent in the medium used in isolating subcellular particles from cotton seedlings which were capable of oxidizing Krebs cycle intermediates and of oxidative phosphorylation (Throneberry, 1961, 1962).

Chloroplast suspensions prepared from leaves are widely used, particularly in studies relating the activities of these cell organelles to the process of photosynthesis. Arnon et al. (1956) (and cf., Whatley et al., 1960) obtained whole chloroplasts by grinding 100-200 gms. of spinach leaf lamina with 100-200 ml. of ice-cold 0.35 M NaCl in an ice-cold mortar with sand, squeezing the slurry through a double layer of cheesecloth, removing debris by centrifuging for one minute at $0°$ C. and 200 x g., and removing the chloroplast fragments and smaller cellular particles in the supernatant liquid following a second centrifugation of seven minutes in the cold at 1000 x g. The sedimented chloroplasts were washed by resuspending them in ca. 100 ml. of ice-cold 0.35 M NaCl and centrifuging again, and a final suspension made up in ca. 25 ml. of 0.35 M NaCl. They stress the importance of maintaining the solutions and apparatus ice-cold during all the manipulations. Chloroplasts prepared in this manner were active in the Hill reaction, photosynthetic phosphorylation, reduction of triphosphopyridine nucleotide, and CO_2 fixation and reduction to the level of carbohydrate with simultaneous evolution of oxygen.

As a variant of Arnon and coworkers method of preparing whole chloroplasts, Jagendorf and Avron (1958) found that spinach chloroplasts maintained their activity longer with respect to photosynthetic phosphorylation when prepared and stored in a solution consisting of 0.40 M sucrose, 0.05 M Tris buffer, pH 7.8, and 0.01 M NaCl rather than in 0.35 M NaCl (cf., Duane and Krogman, 1963, for a simple method of storing chloroplasts with little loss of activity - Hill reaction and photophosphorylation - for at least one month). Other variants of the isolation medium are exemplified by those employed by Stumpf and James (1963) in investigating the biosynthesis of long-chain fatty acids by lettuce chloroplasts. The density gradient technique has been applied by Leech (1963) to obtain chloroplasts free of mitochondria. Crude chloroplast suspensions, prepared in the usual manner, were centrifuged through a glycerol-sucrose density gradient (cf., James and Das, 1957, for details). The efficacy of this method of fractionation was established by electron microscopy of the chloroplast preparations.

In obtaining chloroplasts capable of photophosphorylation from leaves of young corn plants Miflin and Hageman (1963) found that the inhibitor in the cell sap could be removed by adding Carbowax 4000, which presumably precipitated tannins, to the grinding medium. The most favorable isolation medium developed consisted of 0.40 M sucrose, 0.05 M Tris buffer, pH 7.8, 0.01 M NaCl, 0.005 M glutathione and 6 mg./ml. Carbowax 4000.

Higher concentrations of either glutathione or the Carbowax were inhibitory, although up to 20 mg./ml. of the latter was indicated as optimal in isolating chloroplasts from old leaves. They mention Stocking's (1956) finding that Carbowax precipitates proteins in accounting for the inhibitory effect of higher concentrations of this substance.

Chloroplasts have been isolated in nonaqueous media, following lyophilization of the cells or tissue (cf., Stocking, 1959), to prevent or minimize the loss of proteins and other water-soluble components, especially in studies of their chemical composition and enzyme content. The reader is referred to an article by Smillie (1963) for an extensive discussion and comparison of the aqueous and nonaqueous methods, and for details of a nonaqueous density fractionation procedure applied to the single-celled organism Euglena gracilis, together with suggestions for modifying this procedure when using green leaves.

An earlier devised procedure for obtaining chloroplast fragments (Whatley et al., 1956) (also cf., Avron et al., 1957) has been modified (Whatley et al., 1959) to include ascorbate in all of the solutions used in isolating, washing, and disrupting whole chloroplasts. The leaves are ground in 0.35 M NaCl containing 0.02 M Tris buffer, pH 8.3, and 0.01 M Na-ascorbate, washed in the same solution minus buffer, and disrupted in a solution of 0.035 M NaCl-0.01 M Na-ascorbate. While this method proved satisfactory for obtaining broken chloroplast particles from a number of plant species, they state that 0.5 M NaCl instead of 0.35 M NaCl was used in the grinding and washing media when using leaves of tobacco and sugar beet.

Recently Park and Pon (1961, 1963) have described a method of isolating green, uniformly-sized particles of about 20 mμ. diameter following sonification of isolated chloroplasts. (As constituents of the chloroplast lamellae, these particles plus their attached membranes are called "quantosomes". It is stated that possibly these are the smallest units which are capable of performing the light reactions in photosynthesis.) Whereas unwashed lamellae preparations were active in the Hill reaction and in photophosphorylation, washing in water eliminated all activity toward the latter.

Chloroplast extract has been prepared from whole chloroplasts isolated as described above following their disruption in distilled water (Whatley et al., 1956) or in 0.035 M NaCl (Whatley et al., 1959) by centrifuging out the suspended particles at 20,000 x g. for 10 min. at 0° C. In another method (Avron and Jagendorf, 1957) the chloroplasts are suspended in cold 0.04 M sucrose, 0.05 M Tris buffer, pH 8.0, and 0.1 M KCl solution for 30 minutes and the suspension centrifuged at 17,000 x g. for 30 min. at 0° C. In some instances the clear centrifugate has been used directly, in others after purification by dialysis or by treatment with ammonium sulfate.

Acetone powders of plant material also have proved to be useful. The procedure of Stafford and Magaldi (1954) is an example of the preparation of such a powder, in this case from green tissue and one that could be extracted to yield a suspension of D-glyceric acid oxidase sufficiently pigment-free to permit the spectrophotometric determination of the activity of the enzyme. Washed fresh tissue, 10-20 gms. was ground for one minute in 200 ml. of cold (-18° C.) acetone in a Waring blendor at 4°C; the powder filtered off and washed with 200 ml. of cold acetone in successive small portions, dried, and stored at 4° C. over CaCl$_2$ in a vacuum desiccator. The powder sample was extracted for 0.5 hour at 4° C. in 25-50 ml. of 0.001 M pH 7.4 phosphate buffer, and the extract filtered off through glass wool and centrifuged at high speed. Two other, and more recent, examples are: the use of 0.1 M phosphate buffer, pH 8.2, containing 0.03 M EDTA as the grinding medium and 0.01 M phosphate buffer, pH 7.2, containing 0.0015 M EDTA as the powder-extracting medium (Black and Humphreys, 1962); acetone powders of mitochondrial preparations from leaves and roots, but containing material from contaminating chloroplast fragments (leaves) and, perhaps, leucoplast fragments (roots) (Hiatt, 1962).

ALGAL CELL SUSPENSIONS

There are a number of unicellular green algae which may be grown in the laboratory under standardized conditions as a source of plant material. The suitability of these forms for studies of photosynthesis has been outlined by Manning et al. (1938), and the same considerations favor their use in many other types of investigations. Laboratory cultures of Chlorella are probably used more extensively than those of any other alga to prepare cell suspensions used in studies of photosynthesis and respiration. This is due to its rapid rate of growth, adaptability to sometimes rather severe changes in environment, its non-colonial habit of growth and lack of any accessory cell structures, the similarity of it to a green cell of the higher plants in possessing the same complex of pigments in the plastid, ability to form starch and a cellulosic cell wall, and the absence of any gelatinous sheath about the cell.

Many species of green algae have been used, of course, as well as species of genera of some of the other Divisions of Algae (including chlorophyll-containing protozoa) (cf., Smith, 1951, for algal taxonomy, morphology, pigment content, etc., and Lewin, 1962, for taxonomy, pigments, laboratory cultures, and various aspects of the biochemistry and physiology of algae). It is often possible to obtain a particular species from one or another of the following culture collections maintained at: Department of Botany, Indiana University, Bloomington, Indiana; Department of Bacteriology, University of Georgia, Athens, Georgia; Botany School, Cambridge University, Cambridge, England. Sources of chlorophyllous protozoa and their culture are among the listings in a catalogue of references in the Journal of Protozoology, Vol. 5, p. 1, 1958. Reprints of this catalogue are available at $1.00 per copy from Dr. D. M. Lilly, Department of Biology, St. John's University, Jamaica, N.Y.

Without any intention of implying that Chlorella is the only alga recommended, but because of its wide use and because of our experience with it, a general method of culturing this alga is outlined below. With slight modifications of conditions such as the composition and concentration of the mineral salts in the nutrient solutions, light, temperature, etc., this method can be used for the production of large numbers of cells of many other algae. It has been used in culturing C. pyrenoidosa, C. vulgaris, C. miniata and a species of Dactylococcus. The method probably had its inception during the course of the experiments of Warburg (1919) and Warburg and Negelein (1922b) on photosynthesis. In its present form it approximates the description given by Manning et al. (1938) and Moore and Duggar (1949).

It is necessary to have a pure, unialgal culture to begin with. Impure cultures can be diluted, plated out on an agar medium in petri dishes, and an uncontaminated colony picked off and propagated. This is rather time consuming with a long period of waiting until colonies develop, not to mention the problem of the identity of the alga, so it is best to obtain a culture from a laboratory where the alga is being maintained. To continue the stock, and as a source of inoculum for the liquid cultures described below, the alga can be grown on slants of agar-solidified medium (see below) in culture tubes. Of course, one must exercise the usual bacteriological methods to avoid introducing contaminants. These stock cultures can be easily maintained by bi-monthly transfers of cells onto fresh slants. The cells multiply readily when exposed to natural or artificial light.

The algal cells to be used in preparing the suspensions are grown in liquid cultures. A loopful of cells from a stock culture is introduced into 100-150 ml. of sterile nutrient solution (see below) contained in a sterile, cotton-plugged culture vessel with attached air filter. The culture vessel is a 38 x 300 mm. test tube bearing a 5 mm. O. D. glass gas-inlet tube fused in at a point 7 cm. below the rim and extending to the bottom. The lower rim of the gas-inlet tube is notched to cause the gas to exit into the culture medium as several streams of small bubbles. The air filter, fashioned from a 10 cm. $CaCl_2$ drying tube loosely packed with cotton, is attached to the outer end of the gas-inlet tube. The liquid cultures are incubated in a suitable rack between two industrial-reflector type two-lamp banks of 40 watt "daylight" fluorescent lamps placed horizontally and facing each other at a distance of about one foot. Temperature regulation can be obtained by placing the set-up in a constant temperature room. The culture vessels are connected to a manifold and air or a mixture of CO_2 in air (4-5%, from a tank, or prepared by flow-meter mixing of compressed CO_2 and air) is constantly bubbled through the culture vessels at a rate of about 100 cc. per culture vessel per minute. This rate ordinarily is sufficient to supply more than enough CO_2, from a 5% CO_2 in air mixture, and to maintain the algal cells in suspension.

As one would suspect, many variations of the above technique and apparatus for culturing Chlorella have been used. This applies especially to the culture vessels, illumination and temperature control, e.g., Warburg et al. (1950) used Drechsel gas washing bottles as culture vessels in a thermostatted glass aquarium and supplied light, either from tungsten or fluorescent lamps, from the side.

The following media are given for the growth of Chlorella since we have found them to be satisfactory:

Medium for agar-slant stock cultures		Medium for liquid cultures	
$NaNO_3$	0.25 gm.	KNO_3	2.53 gm.
KH_2PO_4	0.25 gm.	KH_2PO_4	2.72 gm.
$MgSO_4 \cdot 7H_2O$	0.25 gm.	$MgSO_4$	2.40 gm.
$CaCl_2 \cdot 1H_2O$	0.25 gm.	$CaCl_2$	0.155 gm.
Cane sugar	4.0 gm.	$FeSO_4$	0.0015 gm.
Bacto-peptone	0.5 gm.	Micro-element solution	1.0 ml.
Micro-element solution	1.0 ml.	Distilled water to make	1.0 L.
Distilled water, to	1.0 L.	Adjust pH to 6.8 with KOH	

The particular micro-element solution used contains in 18 liters of distilled water: 30 ml. of 18 N HNO_3; LiCl, 0.5 gm.; $CuSO_4 \cdot 5H_2O$, 1.0 gm.; $ZnSO_4$, 1.0 gm.; H_3BO_3, 11.0 gms; $Al_2(SO_4)_3 \cdot 18H_2O$, 2.7 gms.; $SnCl_2 \cdot 2H_2O$, 0.5 gm.; $Ti_2(SO_4)_3$, 1.8 gms.; $MnCl_2 \cdot 4H_2O$, 7.0 gms.; $NiCl_2 \cdot 6H_2O$, 1.0 gm.; $Co(NO_3)_2$, 1.0 gm.; KI, 0.5 gm.; KBr, 0.5 gm.; Na_2WO_4, 0.5 gm.; $K_2Cr_2O_7$, 0.2 gm.; $(NH_4)_6 Mo_7O_{24} \cdot 4H_2O$, 0.5 gm.; Na_3VO_4, 0.5 gm. Its use does not appear to be absolutely necessary when ordinary reagent grade chemicals are employed in making up the medium with boron and manganese added (0.5 μg./ml. of each).

The contents of a culture vessel may be used directly as an algal cell suspension, or greater concentrations of cells can be obtained by centrifuging the culture. The usual procedure is to centrifuge out the cells in a graduated 15 ml. centrifuge tube, wash once or twice and after the final recentrifugation suspend them in whatever medium one wishes to use. For experiments of short duration no precautions against contamination by other organisms are necessary. The dry weight, algal nitrogen or phosphorus, etc., can be obtained from an aliquot. The suspension can be used immediately, or for certain types of experiments it may be stored in a refrigerator at 4° C. for several days. The quantity required can readily be measured out with a pipette. Chlorella cell suspensions prepared in such a manner have been used in studying photosynthesis (Manning et al., 1938; Fan

et al., 1943; Moore and Duggar, 1949) and phosphorylation (Emerson et al., 1944).
Most investigators who have used algal cell suspensions in experiments on photosynthesis
and respiration prepared them in somewhat the same manner (e.g., Kok, 1948; Warburg
et al., 1950; Kratz and Myers, 1955; Yuan et al., 1955; Bassham et al., 1955; Good and
Brown, 1961; Casselton and Syrett, 1962; Allen et al., 1962).

In some instances growing an alga in single step culture as described above is inconven-
ient or unsatisfactory for some reason. The solution, then, may be to use a continuous
and automatic culture system (cf., Myers and Clark, 1944; Bassham and Calvin, 1957;
Hauschild et al., 1962), or to grow the alga under conditions where at any one time all of
the cells are in the same growth phase, i.e., synchronous culture (cf., Tamiya et al.,
1953; Sorokin and Myers, 1957; Lorenzen, 1957).

J. F. STAUFFER

PREPARATIONS FROM MICROORGANISMS

PREPARATION OF BACTERIAL CELLS

Washed bacterial cells have been used widely in studies of respiratory enzymes. Washing
is considered to remove most nutrients and thus render the cells "non-proliferating" or
"resting". Among the advantages rightly claimed for such preparations are: (a) various
bacteria present a wide variety of enzymes for study; (b) the organisms can be grown
readily under reproducible conditions; (c) the cells give a uniform suspension that can
be pipetted accurately; (d) most washed cells can be stored for some time at refrigerator
temperatures without appreciable change in activity; (e) respiration remains linear with
time; (f) bacteria are extremely active per unit of tissue; and (g) gas diffusion into the
cell is not a limiting factor normally.

The media required for best growth of bacteria vary widely with the organisms concerned.
With organisms which produce gums or capsules, it may be necessary to grow the cells on
media which are low or lacking in carbohydrate to facilitate centrifugation and to limit the
high endogenous respiration characteristic of cells abundant in reserve materials. Aside
from such considerations, the cells should be grown on as favorable a medium as possible.

When small quantities of aerobic cells will suffice, they are most conveniently grown on
an agar medium in liter Roux bottles. These bottles present a large area which is adequately covered by 75 to 85 ml. of agar. Inoculate the slanted, hardened agar surface with
2 or 3 ml. of a suspension of fresh cells, and distribute the suspension over the agar.
After incubation, harvest the cells when they are young and active, even at the expense of
a reduction in total crop. To harvest, add 10 ml. of buffer or mixed salt solution (e.g.,
Ringer's solution, page 132) to each Roux bottle and scrape the organisms from the agar
surface with a curved glass rod. Filter through cheesecloth to remove lumps of agar (by
using 2% rather than the usual 1.5% agar less difficulty with breakage of the medium is
experienced). Rinse with another 5 or 10 ml. portion of solution. Sediment the cells by
centrifugation; resuspend in fresh solution and recentrifuge. Repeat. Place the washed
cells in a tube or flask equipped for aeration, i.e., with a rubber stopper holding a glass
tube leading to the bottom and an exit tube from the top. Aeration at room temperature
before the cells are used serves to exhaust metabolites and reduce the endogenous respiration. Store the cells at temperatures somewhat above freezing.

Large quantities of aerobes can be produced in aerated liquid culture. The Sharples supercentrifuge provides a rapid means of handling large volumes of a culture medium. When anaerobes are to be used, they usually can be grown in stagnant carboys of liquid media and recovered by passage through a Sharples supercentrifuge. Precautions are frequently necessary to maintain reducing conditions during harvest to minimize inactivation of the enzymes.

The washed cell suspensions are adjusted by dilution to a point where they will induce a gas exchange of 100 to 200 μl. per hour in a Warburg flask; correspondingly, a dilution such that they will reduce methylene blue in 15 to 30 minutes on a suitable substrate is desirable for dehydrogenase studies. The first dilutions will be empirical, but activity can be correlated with turbidity measurements on a colorimeter or spectrophotometer. Subsequent suspensions can be adjusted to a reasonably constant activity by dilution to a standard turbidity. When measuring turbidity photometrically in the usual yellow bacteriological medium, it is customary to employ a red filter (620 or 660 mμ.) to minimize the effect of the yellow interfering color. With washed suspensions of bacteria in the absence of such color, it is advantageous to use a blue filter, since the instrument is more sensitive to turbidity changes under such conditions. Most stock bacterial suspensions will require about a 10 fold dilution to adjust the turbidity to a range suitable for standardization on a photoelectric colorimeter. For example, a suspension of Rhizobium trifolii is of about the proper concentration when 1 ml. added to 9 ml. of water gives 45% transmittance in a colorimeter at 420 mμ., distilled water being used as blank.

Turbidity serves as a means of judging activity for adjusting suspensions, but final cell activity is best expressed as the $Q_{O_2}(N)$, or μl. of oxygen taken up per hour per mg. nitrogen content of the cells. The relative merits of dry weight, total nitrogen, nucleic acid phosphorus, total carbon, and cell numbers as bases for expression of activity, are discussed by Burris and Wilson (1940) and in Chapter 1 of this book. In Chapter 11 directions are given for micro Kjeldahl determinations. Duplicate nitrogen determinations should give a basis for expressing $Q_{O_2}(N)$ values for all observations made with one particular suspension.

CELL-FREE ENZYME PREPARATIONS FROM BACTERIA

The advances in knowledge of yeast fermentation, which resulted from studies with cell-free preparations, emphasize the value of such experimental material. In their early review of methods employed in producing cell-free bacterial juices, Werkman and Wood (1940) enumerated the advantages and disadvantages of these preparations. Among the advantages were cited the facts that, the results are not affected by growth and reproduction of cells; cellular permeability is no factor in the measurements; it is possible to isolate and follow single reactions through the use of inhibitors and specific substrates; and it is possible to reconstruct a chain of enzymatic reactions by the combination of the individual components of the system. The disadvantages include the change in environment suffered by the enzymes isolated from the cell, and the destruction or incomplete solution of certain enzymes.

Werkman and Wood (1940), Hugo (1954) should be consulted for a listing and description in some detail of all the methods which have been employed in liberating bacterial enzymes from the cell. In this discussion we shall confine our attention to methods in current, practical use; many require only simple, readily obtainable equipment.

GRINDING WITH POWDERED GLASS OR ALUMINA

Wiggert, Silverman, Utter and Werkman (1940) describe a simple method for macerating bacterial cells by adding powdered glass and grinding with a mortar and pestle. The bacterial cells are best grown in liquid culture and recovered with a Sharples supercentrifuge, as in most cases several grams of wet cells are required. A subsequent wash and recentrifugation is often advisable to remove excess nutrients. The cells should be harvested while young and active; the loss in total crop by early harvest is largely compensated for in greater unit activity. Obviously the manner in which the bacteria are grown will vary with the organism concerned, and the individual investigator will be best acquainted with the nutrient and environmental requirements of the organism with which he is dealing.

Pyrex glass is powdered by grinding in a ball mill; 24 hours with stone balls, but not over 4 hours with steel balls usually suffices for proper powdering. Sift the glass through a 30 mesh screen to remove large particles. When handling the glass powder wear a dust mask.

Mix 3 g. of bacterial paste, 25 g. of powdered glass and 7 ml. of pH 7.0, M/15 phosphate buffer; the consistency will be that of a firm batter. Place 10 g. of this mixture in a chilled 4.5 inch mortar and grind vigorously for 5 minutes. Do not use larger than 10 g. portions; observe the 5 minute grinding period, for additional grinding results in inactivation rather than increased yields. Combine the separately ground portions, and for each 10 g. portion add 2 ml. of phosphate buffer; mix well. Transfer to centrifuge tubes and sediment the glass by 5 to 10 minutes centrifugation at 3,000 to 5,000 x gravity. With particularly viscous preparations longer centrifugation may be necessary. Remove the supernatant and clarify by centrifugation in a Spinco Model L centrifuge or by 2 to 15 minutes centrifugation in a Beams, Weed and Pickels (1933) "spinning top" air driven centrifuge equipped with a screw top with rubber gasket seal. Such a centrifuge can be constructed at low cost by a competent mechanician or instrument maker. The centrifugal force it will develop will depend largely upon the rotor diameter and the pressure of air used for driving the rotor; hence, it is impossible to state exactly the time necessary for sedimentation. This can be determined empirically by observation of the degree of clarification with varying periods of centrifugation. With a 1.25 in. rotor Wiggert, et al., (1940) reported suitable sedimentation in 2 minutes at 175,000 r.p.m.; this speed is obtained with 80-90 pounds air pressure. Other preparations may require considerably longer sedimentation; cooling the juice is sometimes helpful in hastening sedimentation. Remove the supernatant with a pipette; the sediment is tightly packed on the walls of the rotor and is not appreciably dislodged when the rotor is decelerated evenly with the fingers.

In operating the Beams "spinning top" centrifuge the hollow rotor can be completely filled, since sedimentation appears to be as effective as when the rotor is only partially filled. Screw the top of the rotor "finger-tight" against the rubber gasket. Open the air line completely, so full pressure is applied to the stator and lower the rotor into position on the stator. Release the rotor, guiding it as it starts to rotate by having the fingers and thumb encircle it in an "eagle-grip". As the rotor gains speed and passes the "chatter-point", line it up by touching the edge gently with the thumbnail. To stop the rotor, leave the air pressure on at full force, place the fingers around the rotor in an "eagle-grip" and apply pressure gently from all sides. The air stream, upon which the rotor revolves, serves to cool the fingers, so there is no discomfort in stopping the rotor. Even deceleration of the rotor can be judged by the uniform drop in pitch of the audible note from the centrifuge.

The method of grinding with glass requires simple equipment, is successful with most organisms tested, and comparative studies indicate it has about the same effectiveness as the bacterial mill of Booth and Green (1938) in respect to both speed and completeness of cell disintegration. The Booth-Green mill will not be described here; it no longer is being manufactured.

Grinding with powdered glass now is less favored than grinding with aluminum oxide, a method introduced by McIlwain (1948). McIlwain recommended a grade of aluminum oxide such that 50% of the particles were less than 1 micron in diameter and 45% were 1-3 microns in diameter. There is no general agreement on the best alumina to use, and trial of a number of samples may be desirable to establish the one best for a particular application. Some samples are improved by washing and drying. Dockstader and Halvorson (1950) have compared the effectiveness of a variety of grinding agents and have found diatomaceous earth and alumina fully as effective as powdered glass for breaking bacterial cells. They did not test for retention of enzymatic activity.

The methods for grinding with alumina and with powdered glass are very similar. Equal weights of packed bacterial cells and alumina are mixed (the ratio of cells to alumina may be varied to find the optimal mixture). About 5 grams of the mixture is chilled in a mortar and is left in the cold room or ice bath for the grinding. The chilled mixture is ground vigorously for 3-5 minutes; during the grinding the mixture loses its original dry appearance and becomes pasty. It is inadvisable to grind more than 5 grams at a time or to grind for longer than 5 minutes; larger amounts than 5 grams require longer grinding, and the chances of inactivation are greater. After grinding is completed, buffer is added to reduce the viscosity, and the preparation is centrifuged to remove alumina, intact cells and cell debris. Subsequent treatment is as described for the preparations with powdered glass.

Juices prepared in this way are essentially free from intact cells. They can be employed directly in respirometer vessels, spectrophotometer cells or Thunberg tubes with appropriate additions of buffers and substrates. Any considerable dilution should be avoided, as it may involve a greater than proportionate loss in activity. Wiggert, et al. (1940) discussed the activity of cell-free juices obtained from a variety of bacteria in relation to grinding time, volume of extracting fluid, buffers and substrates employed, addition of viable cells, storage and filtration. Juices from Aerobacter indologenes were completely inactivated by passage through Seitz, Jena glass, or Chamberland filters. With cell-free preparations of Azotobacter vinelandii, Lee, Burris and Wilson (1942) and Lee, Wilson and Wilson (1942) found very little inactivation of the enzymes examined after passage through a Berkefeld N or Mandler 15 filter.

DISINTEGRATION BY SHAKING OR GRINDING WITH BEADS

Bacterial cells can be disrupted by shaking them vigorously with beads. The very small beads used for reflective highway markers and beaded projection screens normally are used (Superbrite glass beads, grade 110, Minnesota Mining and Manufacturing Co., St. Paul 6, Minn., or ballotini beads, English Glass Co. Ltd., Leicester, England). The beads should be washed with HCl and with water before use. The Mickle disintegrator (manufactured by H. Mickle, 4 Ormond Drive, Hampton, Middlesex, England) normally is loaded with a suspension of organisms equivalent to 30-50 mg. dry weight plus glass beads. The suspension is shaken from 20-60 minutes.

Nossal (1953) has designed a disintegrator that shakes much more vigorously than the Mickle shaker; the shaking rate is 5,600 cycles per minute. A typical load in a 25 ml. metal capsule used on the shaker is 0.5-1.0 g. fresh, packed bacterial or yeast cells, 10 ml. of buffer and 10 g. grade 110 Superbrite glass beads. Considerable destruction of the cells is achieved with 10 seconds shaking, and Nossal has found that certain enzymes liberated in 10-15 seconds are largely inactivated by shaking a minute. Some of these rapidly liberated enzymes have been inactivated by all other preparative methods tested by Nossal.

Lamanna and Mallette (1954) have reported that bacteria can be broken with small beads agitated in a Waring or Virtis blendor.

The method of Garver and Epstein (1959) is perhaps the most successful means for rupturing microorganisms in large quantities. They broke 300 to 500 ml. batches of heavy cell suspensions of yeast and bacteria mixed with small glass beads by circulating the slurry between the shearing plates of an Eppenbach colloid mill model QV-6. The homogenizing zone was kept cool by circulating antifreeze at -25° C. through the jacket. 60 ml. of Superbrite glass beads 120-130 µ in diameter were used per 100 ml. of suspension, and the clearance between the plates of the colloid mill was set at 0.03 inch. Under these conditions, 99% breakage of yeast was obtained in 20 minutes and of Escherichia coli in 15 minutes. 95% breakage of Aspergillus niger mycelium was achieved in 3 minutes. The shearing forces obtained in a colloid mill are far greater than those produced with glass beads in a Waring blendor.

DISRUPTION BY EXTRUSION

Hughes (1951) described a press which has the distinct advantage that it keeps the cells at low temperature both before and after disruption. A paste of bacterial cells is placed in a cooled stainless steel block (obtainable from Shandon Scientific Co., Ltd., 6 Cromwell Place, London, S.W. 7, England), and a close-fitting piston is lowered onto the cells. The entire unit is placed in a fly-press (Denbigh No. 4 fly-press, manufactured by Thomas Ward, Ltd., Sheffield, England) and the press is used to subject the piston in the block to a series of vigorous momentary blows. The high pressure transmitted by the piston forces the bacteria through a narrow orifice into a reservoir chamber in the block, where they freeze again. The cells are disrupted by the pressure and in passing through the orifice. The halves of the block are separated to recover the preparation. Abrasives mixed with the cell paste may enhance the breakage, but if the block is cooled to a sufficiently low temperature, the use of abrasives is not obligatory. As a substitute for the fly-press, H. Gest has placed a piece of pipe several feet long over the Hughes press and has repeatedly dropped a weight down the pipe to strike the piston of the Hughes press. Colab Laboratories, Chicago Heights, Ill., manufactures both the Hughes press and a drop hammer for use with it. The Hughes press has been a very successful device for preparing cell-free enzymes from microorganisms, and it provides a preparation which is more concentrated that that obtained by most other methods.

Milner et al. (1950) described a device (manufactured by American Instrument Co., Silver Spring, Md.) for breaking algal cells by extrusion. The suspension of algae is placed in a cylinder, and pressure is applied to a piston above with a hydraulic press. A needle valve at the bottom of the cylinder is opened slightly to provide a small orifice, and the cells are broken as they are extruded through the needle valve.

Fraser (1951) found that cells of Escherichia coli, placed under 500 to 900 lbs./sq. in. of N_2O (the gas of choice), N_2, A or CO_2 in a gas cylinder, were disrupted when they were discharged quickly from the cylinder and the pressure was released. With this method, the breakage resulted from the release of pressure rather than from extrusion through the orifice. Foster, Cowen and Maag (1962) modified the apparatus so that disruption of pathogens could be accomplished in a closed system.

BREAKING CELLS WITH SOUND WAVES

It is not clear how sound waves disrupt bacteria, but enormous transient pressures are produced locally in liquids subjected to sonic or ultrasonic waves. Breakage of cells accompanies the cavitation produced in the liquid. Hughes and Nyborg (1962) have analyzed the process of cell disruption by ultrasound in considerable detail.

Waves in the ultrasonic region normally are generated with an oscillator and with a piezo-electric crystal to serve as transducer. Frequencies between 400 and 600 kilocycles/sec. have been used most often to break microorganisms; the exact frequency used does not appear to be critical. Stumpf et al. (1946) described the use of a 600 kilocycle generator for the preparation of a number of enzymes from bacteria. Heat was dissipated by immersing the transducer and the flask containing bacterial cells in cooled transformer oil. Commercial ultrasonic oscillators are sold by Bronwill Scientific, Rochester, N.Y., Branson Instruments, Stamford, Conn., and others.

Magnetostrictive oscillators operating in the sonic range have been more popular in the United States than ultrasonic oscillators for disintegrating bacteria. An alternating magnetic field, from a coil connected to an electronic oscillator, if imposed on a laminated nickel rod induces changes in dimensions of the rod; the rapid oscillations of the rod can be transmitted to microorganisms in suspension by attaching a sample cup to a diaphragm on the nickel rod. Commercial sonic oscillators are produced by the Raytheon Manufacturing Co., Waltham, Mass., and Measuring and Scientific Equipment, Spenser St., London, S.W. 1 (sold in U.S. by Instrumentation Associates, 17 W. 60th St., New York City). Much more rapid disintegration is accomplished by the 10 kilocycle/sec. than by the 9 kilocycle Raytheon unit because of the greater power output of the 10 kilocycle apparatus. Provision can be made conveniently for cooling the material being treated in the sonic oscillator. The 10 kilocycle unit normally is operated with 50 ml. of suspension, and treatment usually is for 10 to 30 minutes. The use of the MSE disintegrator has been described by Hughes (1962). As relatively heavy suspensions of microorganisms can be disintegrated, the sonic oscillator provides a means of obtaining larger quantities of cell extracts in a reasonable time than by most other methods. Many enzymes have been obtained from microorganisms by sonic oscillation, although the method has not been successful with all enzymes investigated.

AUTOLYSIS OF CELLS

One of the simplest means of preparing cell-free enzymes is by autolysis. The ease and the conditions under which different cells will autolyze vary widely. Some cells will autolyze while other cells are growing in the same culture medium, so that the filtered medium will at times carry a usable concentration of freed intracellular enzymes. Many bacteria, however, are refractory to autolysis, or the autolysis requires such a prolonged time that many enzymes are inactivated during the interval. Again the individual must determine the proper conditions for autolysis of the particular cells with which he is concerned.

Stephenson (1928) prepared cell-free lactic, succinic, and formic dehydrogenases from Escherichia coli. In studying the correlation of enzyme activity with number of viable cells present she found that aging suspensions increased in activity on lactate. This observation suggested that autolysis was freeing the enzyme, and optimum conditions for the autolysis were determined. The organisms were harvested, washed, suspended in pH 7.6, M/2 phosphate buffer and incubated at 37° C. for 5 or 6 days in a stoppered bottle. Addition of 1% sodium fluoride prevented putrefactive deterioration, but did not alter the enzyme. The preparation could not reduce molecular oxygen but could reduce methylene blue in the presence of any of the three substrates listed. Filtration through a porcelain filter resulted in complete inactivation. Passage through kieselguhr gave an almost water clear preparation which retained only lactic dehydrogenase activity.

To deal in general terms, it is customary to allow cells to autolyze in heavy suspensions under a layer of toluene at room or incubator temperatures. To determine optimum conditions, a series of samples of cells may be suspended in buffers at a variety of pH's. The supernatants should be tested at intervals to determine the time of greatest activity. After such a survey, a standard practice for autolyzing particular cells may be adopted.

LYSIS BY ADDED AGENTS

Lysis can be induced readily by the addition of foreign agents to certain sensitive species of bacteria. A notable example is Micrococcus lysodeikticus which is rapidly lysed by the addition of raw egg white, saliva, tears, or purified lysozyme to a suspension of the organism. Fleming and Allison (1924) found that a heavy suspension could be completely cleared in 30 seconds at 50° C. by the addition of 1% egg white. On incubation for 24 hours at 37°, lysis was observed in a one to 50 million dilution of egg white.

Penrose and Quastel (1930) compared the enzyme activity of intact and lysed cells of M. lysodeikticus, and reported that lysis increased the rate of p-phenylenediamine oxidation, increased the activity of catalase, fumarase, and urease, left peroxidase activity unchanged, and destroyed or reduced the activity of the dehydrogenases for glucose, fructose, lactic acid, succinic acid, glutamic acid, and glycerophosphoric acid. Krampitz and Werkman (1941) grew M. lysodeikticus on a glucose, peptone, yeast extract medium, and washed and recovered the cells by centrifugation. To a 10% suspension of wet cells they added 1/10 volume of saliva, and incubated the mixture for 1 hour at 36° C. The cell-free supernatant exhibited an active oxalacetic acid decarboxylase.

In his studies of formic acid decomposition by Escherichia coli, Stickland (1929) found that autolysis would not liberate the enzymes involved. He resorted to digestion of the cells at 37° C., pH 7.6, with crude trypsin, using 5 ml. of Benger's "liquor pancreaticus" to 100 ml. of cell suspension. Periodic tests for dehydrogenase activity showed an initial rise followed by destruction of lactic and succinic dehydrogenases, whereas formic dehydrogenase activity continued to increase. The treatment yielded a cell-free formic dehydrogenase, whose activity appeared to be associated with cell debris, but completely destroyed formic hydrogenlyase and hydrogenase thus preventing the production of H_2 and CO_2 anaerobically or H_2O and CO_2 aerobically from formate.

Sylvester (personal communication) suggested the possibility of inducing lysis by bacteriophage, for the lytic action is rapid and, one might anticipate that enzymes would be liberated with little inactivation. Sher and Mallette (1953) applied this method for releasing lysine and arginine decarboxylases from Escherichia coli B. It yielded preparations with higher total and specific activities than any other method tested. Sher and Mallette believed that lysis by bacteriophage had particular promise as a general method for obtaining cell-free preparations from bacteria on a large scale.

Morton (1950) has employed butanol to release enzymes from various animal tissues. The facility with which it releases cytochromes from Azotobacter vinelandii (Tissières and Burris, 1956) suggests that it may prove a useful agent for solubilizing a number of enzymes from microorganisms.

OSMOTIC SHOCK

Great interest developed in the preparation of protoplasts following the work of Weibull (1953). Protoplasts, being devoid of cell walls, remain intact only in isotonic media, and transferring them to water or buffers of low osmotic pressure ruptures them and liberates their enzymes. Thus an organism which will yield protoplasts, in turn should yield cell free preparations with rather mild treatment.

Cells can be disrupted by allowing them to equilibrate in a medium of high osmotic pressure and then transferring them suddenly to distilled water or a weak buffer. Pangborn et al., (1962) mixed packed cells of Azotobacter vinelandii with an equal volume of 3 M glycerol, allowed them to equilibrate for 5 minutes, and then ejected them with a syringe into 10 volumes of rapidly stirred buffer. They estimated that 96% of the cells were disrupted. The preparation was treated with deoxyribonuclease to decrease its viscosity before centrifugation.

FREEZING AND THAWING OF CELLS

Bacterial enzymes often may be released into solution by rupturing the cell with alternate freezing and thawing. By such a method Avery and Neill (1924) prepared a cell-free extract of pneumococci that formed peroxide when exposed to oxygen. The cells from a broth culture were recovered by centrifugation and suspended in one volume of phosphate buffer or nutrient broth for each 35 volumes of the original culture. This suspension of unwashed cells was placed in long, narrow tubes, sealed with vaseline, and alternately frozen and thawed rapidly 6 to 9 times. The cell debris was sedimented by 3 or 4 high speed centrifugations. The material did not lose its activity on passage through a Berkefeld filter under an atmosphere of nitrogen.

Koepsell and Johnson (1942), in their studies of the pyruvic acid metabolism of Clostridium butylicum, used a cell-free solution prepared by freezing the bacteria. Wet cell paste, as taken from the Sharples supercentrifuge, was packed in stoppered tubes and frozen immediately after harvest. While frozen, the cells slowly ruptured and released their contents. After 12 days 85 g. of cell paste was evenly suspended in boiled, cooled water, to give 250 ml. volume, and centrifuged. The supernatant liquid contained most of the original activity of the cells. This supernatant was dried under high vacuum and as a dry powder remained stable for some months.

COMMENTS

It has been our purpose to emphasize means of preparing cell-free juices which require relatively simple equipment, to stress the methods we have personally employed, and to describe briefly and cite references to other procedures. Unquestionably sonic and ultrasonic apparatus, the Hughes press, the colloid mill, and the Nossal disintegrator will yield excellent enzyme preparations from bacteria, but the equipment necessary is specialized. Grinding with alumina (McIlwain, 1948), with powdered glass (Wiggert et al., 1940) or using osmotic shock (Pangborn et al., 1962) often is entirely adequate; the methods have much to recommend them because of their simplicity, general applicability and mildness. Dried cells also frequently yield active soluble preparations, and they can be prepared readily by the methods described in the following section.

R. H. BURRIS

DRYING CELLS

Drying is one of the most efficient and convenient methods of preparing enzyme preparations from bacterial cells, and a surprising number of enzymes have proved stable to the treatments described. Dried preparations are normally of two types: those obtained by acetone treatment and those obtained by lyophilization (drying from the frozen state in vacuo).

Acetone Preparations: These are similar to the preparations made from animal tissues. A bacterial suspension, usually a thick cream, is added dropwise to at least 10 volumes of ice cold, dry acetone which is vigorously stirred. When the entire suspension has been added it will usually flock, and if stirring is discontinued the cells will settle rapidly. If flocking does not occur, more dry acetone should be added. After settling for 5-10 minutes, the supernatant is decanted and the remainder filtered (usually with suction). The residue on the filter is treated with a small portion of dry, cold acetone which is sucked off as rapidly as possible. Some prefer to wash the preparation with alcohol or alcohol-ether mixtures but our own experience is that this is usually best omitted. The residue is spread on filter paper and dried either in air or under a slight vacuum.

Vacuum Dried or Lyophilized Preparations: The bacteria are suspended in distilled water to form a heavy suspension. This should contain enough water so that it will flow freely and must be more dilute than a paste. Various methods for drying the cells then are used. The suspension may be placed in a flat dish in a desiccator over Drierite (or P_2O_5, $CaCl_2$, conc. H_2SO_4, etc.) and the desiccator evacuated with a rotary oil-sealed pump. The water is drawn off rapidly enough so that the cells freeze during the first five minutes of evacuation and subsequent drying is from the frozen state. Normally, one leaves the pump on for about 3-4 hours, and allows the preparation to remain under the vacuum in the desiccator for 8-10 hours more before opening. In another method, the cell suspension is first frozen (usually in dry ice) before the evacuation is begun. In a third, the suspension is frozen in a thin layer by rotating the container in a bath of dry ice ("shell dry") before the evacuation.

Many commercial lyophilizers are on the market, but any laboratory equipped with a high vacuum oil pump can make an adequate lyophilizer merely by adding a manifold and freezing trap to the pump. As in all vacuum work, the lines in the vacuum system should have a large bore.

Use of Dryed Preparations: After drying, the preparation first is tested for activity and if active, the preparation is likely to be stable for relatively long periods (especially if it is kept cold and dry). However, the enzyme usually is not yet in the cell-free state, and permeability of the cells may not have been altered sufficiently to permit extraction of the enzyme. Autolysis or suspending in buffer may extract the system desired. When extraction procedures of this type do not work, it frequently is possible to obtain the enzyme desired in a cell-free state by grinding the powder in vacuo. This may be accomplished by a method developed by Gunsalus and Umbreit (1945).

PREPARATION OF MOLD AND ACTINOMYCES TISSUES

Both molds and actinomyces normally grow as a heavy mat over the surface of media. This mat may be handled in much the same manner as animal tissues. It may be removed, washed with water and cut into slices. Semeniuk (1944) has used a process roughly equivalent to the homogenate technique in which the mycelium was ground with sand. Our experience with the homogenizer itself (see Chapter 9) has not been very satisfactory, since most of the activity of the tissue was lost and various supplements had little effect.

Foster (1949) has discussed growth of molds and actinomyces in detail and also has reviewed the literature on their use as a source of enzymes.

The mycelium of both molds and actinomyces also may be grown submerged with aeration (Woodruff and Foster, 1943). This is done either by forcing sterile air through the medium or by continuous shaking of the culture flasks. For shaking, the usual procedure is to place a 250 or 500 ml. Erlenmeyer flask carrying 100 ml. of inoculated medium in a shaker which operates with a 2 to 4 cm. stroke at 60 to 100 cycles a minute. Under these circumstances "pellets" of mycelium are formed which can be pipetted readily. One precaution should be noted; such pellets may not have the same metabolism as the mycelium grown on the surface. Knight (1948) has studied the 1-amino acid oxidase of penicillin-producing molds in preparations of mycelium that were treated with acetone, dried and ground. Various preparations of mold and actinomyces tissue also may be employed in the study of phosphorylation. So far as present knowledge of phosphorylation extends, it apparently differs from the known processes in animal tissues (Mann, 1943; Semeniuk, 1944), if, indeed, it exists in molds (Nord, Dammann and Hofstetter, 1936; Nord, 1939).

W. W. UMBREIT

PURIFICATION OF ENZYMES

The following discussion of enzyme purification is aimed at the student or research worker in fields peripheral to enzymology. Although superficial, it is intended to indicate the common methods of approach and wherever possible references to more detailed reviews or appropriate publications are given in lieu of a wealth of experimental detail.

In general the purification of an enzyme consists of the sequential application of a variety of well established procedures. In this section an indication of the nature of the various techniques and an outline of one method of approach will be given.

Assays (cf., Dixon and Webb, 1958): Before one embarks on an enzyme purification, it is essential to be able to measure the quantity of enzyme which is present in a sample. This is most conveniently done by measuring its biological activity in one of two ways. One can either measure the disappearance of the substrate, or one can determine the appearance of the product. Assays can be kinetic (when a continuous record of the reaction is obtained) or static (when the extent of the reaction preceding in an arbitrary time interval is measured); the former is to be preferred. Preliminary experiments should be performed to determine the optimum conditions of temperature, pH, substrate concentration and nature of buffer ions. If possible, conditions should be chosen so that the measured activity is proportional to enzyme concentration in the range employed. Techniques frequently used for the determination of enzyme activity are spectrophotometry (Minakami et al., 1962), manometry (Wellner and Meister, 1960), chemical assay (Davis and Metzler, 1962), fluorescence (Dalziel, 1962a) and radioisotope analysis (Ochoa and Mii, 1961).

The other determination to be made during the course of a purification is the protein content of the sample. This is most conveniently obtained by the Biuret method (Gornall et al., 1949). However, this is an insensitive assay and when material is scarce alternative methods may be employed. The two popular methods are the Folin-Ciocalteu method (Lowry et al., 1951) and determination of the ultra-violet absorption at 280 mμ (Grimm and Doherty, 1961). The increased sensitivity of the recently reported modified biuret reaction (Ellman, 1962) may also be helpful.

From these two assays one can calculate the total activity (units/ml. x volume) and specific activity (units/mg. protein) of any fraction. The aim of any purification step is to obtain a large increase in specific activity with as little loss as possible in total activity.

Choice of Starting Material: The next consideration should be the choice of starting material. The source of choice should have a relatively high content of enzyme thus minimizing the amount of work necessary to obtain the pure product, and should be readily available. Thus the liver containing 1% of a hypothetical enzyme would be a better source than the hypothalamus containing 5% enzyme. A further factor is the reproducibility of the starting material. Bacteria and standardized experimental animals (cf., Czok and Bücher, 1960) commend themselves in this regard.

Extraction: Once the source is available the liberation of the enzyme is the next step. This can be achieved in a variety of ways, e.g., aqueous extraction, homogenization, use of pH, organic solvents, enzymes etc. A detailed account of these techniques has been given by Morton (1955). It should be noted that many enzymes, by virtue of their attachment to subcellular particles, e.g., mitochondria, can be purified to a great extent by isolation of their parent particle as described earlier in this chapter.

Working Conditions: Wherever possible, all routine manipulations in enzyme purification should be carried out at about 0° C. This requires the use of refrigerators, cold rooms, refrigerated centrifuges and receptacles for crushed ice. Furthermore, it is usual to work around pH 7 although enzymes are purified at pH's both more acid and more alkaline than this. Reagents should be of as high a quality as is possible and glass distilled water is to be preferred. These precautions are taken to eliminate the deleterious effect of heavy metals and other contaminants. Throughout the preparation scrupulous attention should be paid to cleanliness.

Stability: Once the enzyme is in solution it is wise to check its stability by incubating it at a variety of pH's and temperatures in the presence of such reagents as EDTA, glutathione, mercaptoethanol and the enzyme's substrate (or product). The results of such an experiment will throw much light on the stability of the enzyme and will indicate the best working conditions.

Salt Fractionation: One popular method of purification is fractional precipitation of the enzyme by salt. Ammonium sulfate is frequently used for this purpose. However, ammonium acetate often proves more useful for those proteins which precipitate at low salt concentrations. The method of approach is described by Dixon and Webb (1958). In view of the variety of ways employed in determining % saturation and also the importance of temperature it is recommended that the quantity of salt added be calculated on a basis of gms. ammonium sulfate/volume of material (and hence molarity) (cf., table 18, page 158).

Solvent Precipitation: A second method of achieving fractional precipitation is by the controlled addition of organic solvents. A thorough study (Askonas, 1951) of this technique in rabbit muscle extracts revealed the following critical features:

1. Subzero temperatures are important.
2. Nature and concentration of salts, and pH have profound influence.
3. Acetone > ethanol > propanol in efficacy. It is recommended that 95% (v/v) solvents be used to minimize heating on mixing solvent and enzyme. A good example is provided by Kuby et al. (1954a).

Heat Treatment: This relies on the controlled heating of the sample at a temperature which will denature much of the protein without destroying any of the enzyme. The important aspects of this technique are:

1. Rapid heating and cooling. The use of stainless steel containers facilitates this.
2. The heating should be performed under controlled conditions of pH, protein concentration and salt.
3. The sample should be held at temperature as long as possible and at least 5 minutes.

Note that the variables time, temperature, pH, protein concentration and salt should be investigated to determine the optimum conditions.

Dialysis: Most purifications require at least one dialysis step, either to lower the ionic strength prior to chromatography or to achieve a controlled ionic composition of the enzyme fraction. Prior to use the dialysis tubing should be cleaned to eliminate heavy metal impurities: we prefer boiling for 5 min. in 1 mM EDTA, followed by thorough rinsing with water and finally testing the tubing for leaks. A typical procedure takes 24 hours with several changes of dialysis medium, there being at least a ten fold excess of medium over enzyme. For small volumes of material the time consuming dialysis can be replaced by gel-filtration on Sephadex (Porath, 1960).

Adsorption Techniques: The use of adsorption has been a valuable technique in enzyme purification both in batch methods and by column techniques. The most common materials are calcium phosphate and an alumina c γ gel. A full discussion of these techniques is given by Colowick (1955). Due to their poor flow properties, column techniques require either special gels (Levin, 1962) or the use of bulking agents (Massey, 1960).

Ion Exchange Chromatography: This technique has until recently had limited application because of denaturation problems (cf., Dawson and Magee, 1957). However, with the advent of the cellulose ion-exchange materials it has become one of the most powerful tools in enzyme purification. Peterson and Sober (1962) have written an excellent article on the practical aspects of these methods.

Preparative Electrophoresis: With the development of the Porath apparatus for electrophoresis on columns of cellulose or starch (Porath, 1954; Flodin and Porath, 1954) the purification of enzymes by electrophoresis has become a common procedure. A commercial version capable of holding 20 gms. of protein has recently become available (LKB - Produkter AB, Stockholm 12, Sweden). Other techniques for preparative electrophoresis are discussed by Bier (1962).

Partition Techniques: Although not yet fully developed, this promises to be a powerful new tool in enzyme purification. A comprehensive treatise has been written by Albertson (1960).

Crystallization: The crystallization of an enzyme can often help during the final stages of purification, repeated crystallization being employed to remove residual contaminating impurities (Manning and Cambell, 1961).

Once the enzyme has been extracted from the tissue one must decide in what order to apply the methods just described. The guiding principle here is to try and do as much as possible before performing a salt fractionation (this is often followed by a dialysis and hence is a halt in the purification). Thus one can try pH precipitation, heating and batch treatments with gel and ion exchanger. Then the material is concentrated by solvent or salt fractionation and possibly dialyzed. The above steps may then be repeated if convenient. Column chromatography on any of the media discussed is usually attempted when one has about a gram of protein and the electrophoresis stage can be applied to the column effluent.

Finally, crystallization can be attempted and residual impurities removed.

Storage of Enzyme: Because enzymes vary enormously in their properties no hard and fast rules can be given. However, the "average" enzyme is probably best kept frozen, at neutral pH at a protein concentration around 20 mg/ml.

G. A. PALMER

BUFFERS

It is assumed that the reader is familiar with the concept of pH. We wish here merely to develop the "pKa" concept and to show its usefulness.

Any acid, capable of ionization, when placed in an aqueous solution will liberate hydrogen ions according to the following equation:

$$HA \rightleftharpoons H^+ + A^-$$

or

$$(H^+)(A^-)/HA = K$$

If one takes the logarithms of both sides of the equation one has,

$$\log (H^+)(A^-)/HA = \log K$$

$$\log H^+ + \log A^- - \log HA = \log K$$

$$\log H^+ = \log K + \log HA - \log A^-$$

$$-\log H^+ = -\log K + \log A^-/HA$$

Under practical circumstances, any salt of the acid present will contribute A^- ions, hence

$$pH = -\log K + \left(\log \frac{salt}{acid} \right)$$

The term $-\log K$ may be expressed as pKa (Equation 47):

$$pH = pKa + \left(\log \frac{salt}{acid} \right) \qquad 47$$

It is evident from equation (47) that when the acid is half neutralized, the pH of the solution is pKa. When 10% of the acid is neutralized, (pH = pKa + log 1/10 = pKa -1) the pH is about 1 unit lower than the pKa; when 90% is neutralized, the pH is roughly 1 unit higher than the pKa. Based on their pKa one can thus pick buffers which will maintain the pH relatively constant in the desired range.

A base will dissociate as follows:

$$BOH \rightleftharpoons B^+ + OH^-$$

or

$$K_b = \frac{(B^+)\ (OH^-)}{BOH}$$

taking the logarithm of both sides:

$$\log K_b = \log B^+ + \log OH^- - \log BOH$$

$$-\log OH^- = -\log K_b + \log \frac{B^+}{BOH}$$

$$= -\log K_b + \log \frac{salt}{base}$$

-log OH may be expressed as pOH.

But since the dissociation constant of water is 1×10^{-14},

$$pH = 14 - pOH, \qquad \text{hence } pOH = 14 - pH$$

$$14 - pH = -\log K_b + \log \frac{salt}{base}$$

$$pH = 14 + \log K_b - \log \frac{salt}{base}$$

$- \log K_b$ can be designated as pK_b, hence this equation may be expressed as:

$$pH = 14 - pK_b - \log \frac{salt}{base}, \qquad \text{or}$$

$$pOH = pK_b + \log \frac{salt}{base}$$

Some examples of the use of the pK_a and pK_b relationship are as follows:

1. Acetic acid: $K = 1.86 \times 10^{-5}$ and $pK_a = 4.73$; hence acetate-acetic acid mixtures would be suitable as buffers over the range 3.7 - 5.7 (representing 10 - 90% neutralization).

2. Similarly, for phosphoric acid:
    $H_3 PO_4 \rightleftharpoons KH_2 PO_4$; $K_1 = 1.1 \times 10^{-2}$; $pK_a = 1.959$; pH range, 1-3.
    $KH_2 PO_4 \rightleftharpoons K_2 HPO_4$; $K_2 = 2 \times 10^{-7}$; $pK_a = 6.7$; pH range, 5.7 - 7.7.
    $K_2 HPO_4 \rightleftharpoons K_3 PO_4$; $K_3 = 3.6 \times 10^{-13}$; $pK_a = 12.44$; pH range, 11.4 - 13.4.

3. For bases ammonium hydroxide has a basic dissociation constant of 1.8×10^{-5} and a pK_b of 4.74. Ammonium hydroxide - ammonium salt mixtures would serve as buffers over the range 8.3 (14 - 5.74) to 10.3 (14 - 3.74). In the case of bases, the lower the numerical value of the dissociation constant, the lower the pH at which they serve as buffers.

Table 17

Properties of Acids and Bases Suitable for Buffers

Acid or base (indented)	Dissociation Constant		pK_a	pK_b	Buffer at pH
Pyrophosphoric	K_1	1.4×10^{-1}	0.854	–	1
"	K_2	1.1×10^{-2}	1.959	–	2
Phosphoric	K_1	1.1×10^{-2}	1.959	–	2
o-Aminobenzoic		1.4×10^{-12}	–	11.854	2.1
Glycine		4.4×10^{-12}	–	11.647	2.3
α-Alanine		5.1×10^{-12}	–	11.293	2.7
Malonic	K_1	1.6×10^{-3}	2.88	–	3
Phthalic	K_1	1.26×10^{-3}	2.90	–	3
Tartaric	K_1	1.1×10^{-3}	2.96	–	3
Salicylic	K_1	1.06×10^{-3}	2.98	–	3
Fumaric	K_1	1×10^{-3}	3.0	–	3
Citric	K_1	8.0×10^{-4}	3.1	–	3
Sulfanilic		6.2×10^{-4}	3.22	–	3
Glycylglycine		8.71×10^{-4}	3.06	–	3.1
Brucine	K_2	2.5×10^{-11}	–	10.602	3.5
Mandelic		4.29×10^{-4}	3.36	–	3.5
Malic		4.0×10^{-4}	3.39	–	3.5
Hippuric		2.3×10^{-4}	3.64	–	3.5
Formic		1.76×10^{-4}	3.76	–	4
Lactic		1.38×10^{-4}	3.86	–	4
Barbituric		1.05×10^{-4}	3.98	–	4
Tartaric	K_2	6.9×10^{-5}	4.16	–	4.2
Succinic	K_1	6.6×10^{-5}	4.18	–	4.2
Oxalic	K_2	6.1×10^{-5}	4.21	–	4.2
Quinine	K_2	3.3×10^{-10}	–	9.481	4.5
Fumaric	K_2	3×10^{-5}	4.52	–	4.5
Acetic		1.86×10^{-5}	4.73	–	4.7
Citric	K_2	1.8×10^{-5}	4.75	–	4.7
Aniline		4.6×10^{-10}	–	9.337	4.8
Valeric		1.6×10^{-5}	4.80	–	4.8
Butyric (n-, iso-)		1.48×10^{-5}	4.83	–	4.8
Propionic		1.4×10^{-5}	4.86	–	4.9
Methylamine		1×10^{-5}	–	9.0	5.0
Quinoline		1×10^{-5}	–	9.0	5
Malic	K_2	9×10^{-6}	5.05	–	5.1
Benzoic		6.3×10^{-6}	5.21	–	5.2
p-Toluidine		2×10^{-9}	–	8.70	5.3
Pyridine		2.19×10^{-9}	–	8.66	5.3
Citric	K_3	4×10^{-6}	5.40	–	5.4
Phthalic	K_2	3.1×10^{-6}	5.51	–	5.5
Succinic	K_2	2.8×10^{-6}	5.56	–	5.6
Malonic	K_2	2.1×10^{-6}	5.68	–	5.7
Uric		1.5×10^{-6}	5.83	–	5.8
Histidine		1.26×10^{-8}	–	7.90	6.1
Carbonic	K_1	3×10^{-7}	6.53	–	6.5
Pyrophosphoric	K_3	2.9×10^{-7}	6.54	–	6.5
Maleic	K_2	2.6×10^{-7}	6.58	–	6.6
"Veronal"		3.7×10^{-8}	–	7.43	6.6
Phosphoric	K_2	2×10^{-7}	6.7	–	6.7
Strychnine		1×10^{-7}	–	7.0	7.0
Imidazol		1.2×10^{-7}	–	6.92	7.1
Quinine	K_1	2.2×10^{-7}	–	6.6	7.3
Tris (hydroxymethyl)-aminomethane		1.2×10^{-6}	–	5.92	8.1
Glycylglycine		1.36×10^{-6}	–	5.87	8.1
Pyrophosphoric	K_4	3.6×10^{-9}	8.44	–	8.4
α-Alanine		9×10^{-10}	9.10	–	9.1
Boric	K_3	6.4×10^{-10}	9.20	–	9.2
Histidine		6.6×10^{-10}	9.18	–	9.2
Glycine		1.66×10^{-10}	9.78	–	9.8
Phenol		1.3×10^{-10}	9.89	–	9.9
Ammonium hydroxide		1.8×10^{-5}	–	4.74	9.3
Dimethylamine		3.6×10^{-5}	–	4.44	9.6
Butylamine (sec.)		4.4×10^{-4}	–	3.36	10.6
Methylamine		5×10^{-4}	–	3.30	10.7
Dimethylamine		5.2×10^{-4}	–	3.29	10.7
Ethylamine		5.6×10^{-4}	–	3.25	10.7
Brucine	K_1	7.2×10^{-4}	–	3.14	10.8
Phosphoric	K_3	3.6×10^{-13}	12.44	–	12.4
Salicylic	K_2	1×10^{-13}	13.0	–	13.0

In Table 17 are collected the dissociation constants, pK_a and pK_b values, for a variety of acids and bases and the pH at which they serve as buffers. This table should aid in the search for some material, other than the usual type of buffer, suitable for obtaining a particular pH.

The pK_b concept outlined above always has seemed entirely adequate to us, and we are not disturbed at finding a "base" (e.g., brucine, table 17) buffering at pH 3.5. However, there is an alternative way of looking at this matter which may be clearer to some individuals. It is possible to consider the NH_4^+-NH_4OH pair as a material with a pK_a of 9.3 rather than a pK_b of 4.7, and the pK_a may be substituted in the table. This notation would simplify table 17, but as it might be disturbing to some, we have retained the pK_b concept in constructing table 17.

Common buffers are shown in figure 50; the data taken from Clark (1920) have been corrected to the currently accepted values for pH. The use of this chart is obvious but a few examples will serve to clarify the working details.

1. Desired: 0.05 M buffer of pH 3. Take 50 ml. of 0.2 M phthalate plus 21.5 ml. of 0.2 M HCl and dilute to 200 ml.

2. Desired: 0.05 M buffer of pH 5. Take 50 ml. of 0.2 M phthalate plus 22.5 ml. of 0.2 M NaOH and dilute to 200 ml.

3. Desired: 0.067 M phosphate buffer of pH 6.7. Take 6.0 ml. of 0.067 M KH_2PO_4 plus 4 ml. 0.067 M Na_2HPO_4.

4. Desired: 0.05 M buffer of pH 9. Take 50 ml. borate-KCl mixture plus 20 ml. 0.2 M NaOH and dilute to 200 ml.

One note of caution should be emphasized. The composition of the buffer is not to be disregarded in physiological experiments. One must take care that effects observed by altering the pH are due to change in hydrogen ion concentration and not to other alterations of the buffer.

W. W. UMBREIT

SOLUTIONS OF AMMONIUM SULFATE

Despite the extensive use of ammonium sulfate in the preparation of enzymes, there is a disconcerting lack of uniformity in designating the actual concentration of the salt employed. For example, data often are reported in terms of per cent saturation with no mention of the temperature. McGilvery has suggested that this ambiguity be eliminated by designating ammonium sulfate concentration in terms of its final molarity. Table 18, furnished by R. W. McGilvery, indicates how much ammonium sulfate is required under specific conditions to obtain the final molarity desired. The equations from which the values in this table were derived are described by Pogell and McGilvery (1954).

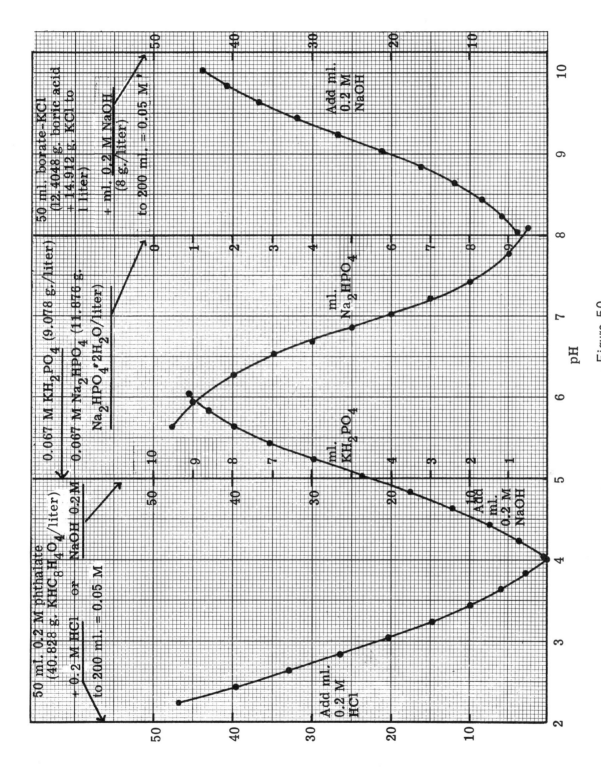

Figure 50
Graph indicating composition of buffers

Table 18

Data for Determining the Molarity of Ammonium Sulfate Solutions

AMMONIUM SULFATE AT 0°

M'−M =			0.1		0.2		0.3		0.4		0.5		0.6		0.7		0.8		0.9		1.0		1.1		1.2		1.3		1.4		1.5		1.6		1.7	
M	W	G	g	V	g	V	g	V	g	V	g	V	g	V	g	V	g	V	g	V	g	V	g	V	g	V	g	V	g	V	g	V	g	V	g	V
0.0	1000	0	13	27	26	56	40	88	54	120	68	153	82	189	96	226	110	268	125	313	140	360	155	409	170	459	185	517	201	581	217	650	233	723	250	806
0.1	996	13	13	28	27	58	41	90	55	123	69	158	83	195	97	234	112	276	127	323	142	371	157	422	172	478	188	540	204	607	220	681	237	762	254	849
0.2	991	26	14	29	28	60	42	92	56	127	70	162	84	201	99	242	114	286	129	334	145	384	159	439	175	500	191	565	207	638	224	714	241	801	258	897
0.3	986	40	14	30	28	61	42	94	56	130	70	168	85	208	100	251	115	296	130	346	147	400	161	457	177	522	193	592	210	670	227	751	244	844	261	946
0.4	980	54	14	31	28	63	42	97	57	133	71	173	86	216	101	260	116	307	131	359	147	416	163	477	179	546	196	621	213	703	230	790	247	890	265	1007
0.5	974	68	14	32	28	65	42	100	58	137	72	179	87	223	102	271	118	318	133	373	151	435	165	498	182	572	199	651	216	741	233	834	251	948	269	1071
0.6	968	82	14	33	28	67	43	103	59	142	73	186	88	231	103	281	119	332	135	388	154	456	168	523	185	601	202	685	219	783	237	886	255	1008	273	1140
0.7	962	96	14	34	29	70	44	106	60	147	74	192	89	240	105	292	121	346	137	408	157	478	171	551	188	633	205	725	223	832	241	945	259	1073	277	1218
0.8	956	110	15	35	29	72	45	110	61	153	75	200	91	250	107	306	123	363	140	428	159	503	174	581	191	671	209	771	227	882	245	1008	263	1148	282	1315
0.9	949	125	15	36	30	75	45	115	62	159	76	208	92	261	108	320	124	380	142	451	161	528	176	615	194	713	212	822	230	938	248	1074	267	1237	286	1422
1.0	943	140	15	38	30	77	45	121	63	166	77	217	93	274	110	335	127	401	144	478	164	558	179	652	197	760	215	874	233	1004	252	1158	271	1340	291	1552
1.1	937	155	15	39	31	80	46	126	65	174	78	229	95	288	112	352	129	424	146	505	167	592	182	693	200	809	218	932	237	1081	256	1254	276	1462	296	1710
1.2	930	170	15	40	31	84	47	132	66	182	80	240	97	304	114	372	131	449	149	538	170	632	185	741	203	862	222	1007	241	1170	261	1371	281	1612	302	1925
1.3	924	185	16	42	32	88	48	138	67	192	82	254	99	321	116	395	134	478	152	573	172	675	188	793	207	929	226	1093	246	1284	266	1517	287	1816	308	2192
1.4	918	201	16	44	32	92	49	145	68	203	83	268	100	339	118	419	136	509	154	605	175	721	191	853	210	1007	230	1193	250	1418	271	1707	292	2062		
1.5	912	217	16	46	33	97	50	153	69	214	84	288	102	359	120	445	138	541	156	649	178	778	194	927	214	1100	234	1317	255	1592	276	1936				
1.6	905	233	16	48	33	101	51	162	70	226	86	301	104	380	122	475	140	578	159	700	181	840	198	1017	218	1218	239	1482	260	1809						
1.7	898	250	17	50	34	107	51	171	71	240	87	319	105	405	123	507	142	621	161	758	184	916	201	1117	222	1373	243	1681								
1.8	891	267	17	53	34	113	52	180	72	247	88	338	106	432	125	543	144	672	164	826	188	1010	205	1255	226	1549										
1.9	884	284	17	56	35	120	53	191	73	270	89	360	108	466	127	588	147	732	167	912	192	1136	209	1417												
2.0	877	301	18	59	36	127	54	202	74	288	92	381	110	504	130	645	150	810	171	1024	192	1296														
2.1	869	319	18	63	36	135	55	215	76	309	94	421	112	549	132	711	153	909	174	1164																
2.2	861	337	18	67	37	145	56	231	78	334	96	460	114	606	135	794	156	1032																		
2.3	853	355	19	72	38	156	58	251	80	366	99	510	117	684	138	906																				
2.4	845	373	19	78	39	168	59	276	82	409	101	573	120	783																						
2.5	838	392	19	84	40	184	61	305	82	459	101	651																								
2.6	831	411	20	93	41	205	62	343	82	525																										
2.7	823	431	20	103	42	231	62	396																												
2.8	816	451	21	117	42	264																														
2.9	808	472	21	132																																
3.0	800	493																																		

Values of V when M = 0:

M'−M =	1.8	1.9	2.0	2.1	2.2	2.3	2.4	2.5
V =	896	997	1110	1235	1375	1533	1712	1915

M = initial molarity
M' = desired molarity
W = ml. of water per liter of solution at M
G = gm. of ammonium sulfate per liter of water
g = gm. of ammonium sulfate to add per liter of water at M to raise solution to M'
V = ml. of 3.75 M ammonium sulfate to add per liter of solution at M to raise it to M'

see J. Biol. Chem. 208: 149 (1954) for equations

EXAMPLES: To find amount of solid ammonium sulfate to raise 1 liter of 1.1 M ammonium sulfate to 2.0 M (0.9). Then the amount is 0.937 x 146 gm.

To find volume of 3.75 M ammonium sulfate to raise 1 liter of 1.6 M ammonium sulfate to 2.2 M (M' − M = 0.6), read V directly from table (380 ml.).

ADJUSTMENT OF pH: If pH is measured on an aliquot diluted to 0.2 M ammonium sulfate with the glass electrode at 25°, the following equation applies: pH = 7.29 − log M + log n. M = molarity of ammonium sulfate, and n = ml. of 15 N ammonium hydroxide added per liter.

Chapter 9
THE HOMOGENATE TECHNIQUE

INTRODUCTION

The use of homogenates assumes for purposes of methodology that any chemical reaction which occurs in living cells will also occur in cell-free preparations of protoplasm provided the conditions are right. That this assumption is a valid one has been shown again and again since the first publication on the general principles of the approach (Potter and Elvehjem, 1936). In the earliest studies, dilute phosphate buffer or water was the fluid used for homogenization media; at the time of the second edition of this book in 1949 isotonic KCl was used for certain studies, and soon after that the sucrose medium was shown to be excellent for the preparation of homogenates with mitochondria whose condition appeared to approach that of the intracellular state (Hogeboom, Schneider, and Palade, 1948; Schneider and Hogeboom, 1950a). At this writing 0.25 M sucrose is the medium used for preparation of homogenates for most studies in which the maintenance of ATP is one of the probable requirements.

It should be emphasized that all of the studies with homogenates are but stepping stones to further studies with cell fractions. The chapter on the preparation of cell fractions is an important aspect of the homogenate technique, for the reaction conditions useful or suitable with homogenates are likely to be useful with cell fractions, and generally have been so employed. This is not true of tissue slice techniques which employ a medium modeled after intracellular fluid with its sodium, chloride and calcium ions, whereas the media used with cell fractions and homogenates generally avoid these three ions or include them only in very small amounts.

This close relationship between studies of homogenates and cell fractions arises because the homogenates are in reality suspensions of the formed elements of the cells, and in most current studies an attempt is made to obtain homogenates with a maximum of cell breakage and a minimum of damage to the cell contents. These include nuclei, mitochondria, what was formerly called microsomes or submicroscopic particles, soluble enzymes, cell membranes, and other parts of the cell (see Chapter 10). At present the status of the submicroscopic particles is somewhat ambiguous, since the fraction appears to include the lamellae of the endoplasmic reticulum together with the "small particles" or "ribosomes" that are associated with the lamellae (Palade, 1955). It appears that the reticulum can be destroyed during homogenization and that it will reconstitute itself into units that maintain their association with the ribosomes. The following quotations from Palade and Siekevitz (1955) give some indication of the present status of this fraction in rat liver homogenates. "It was found that the microsomes are morphologically identical with the vesicular and tubular elements of the endoplasmic reticulum (ER) of intact cells. The 3 structural components of the ER, i.e. (a) the small dense particles (100-150 Å dia.) associated with (b) its membrane (60 Å thick) which bounds (c) a homogeneous content are clearly recognizable in isolated microsomes. The membrane of the microsomes appears to be continuous, and the content is noticeably dense. In solutions of various concentrations they behave like osmometers. These findings suggest that they derive from the ER by pinching off rather than by mechanical tearing."

At present the homogenate technique, in conjunction with the preparation of cell fractions, has two main functions. One is the assay of enzyme activity under conditions in which enzyme activity (A) is a function of enzyme concentration (C). In other words, if A can be measured under conditions in which minor variations in the concentration of substrates, coenzymes, inhibitors, hydrogen ions, and electrolytes do not affect the results, we can arrive at the situation where C = kA and where k is probably constant from one tissue to another. In the course of establishing these conditions, the effect of the various factors on A are learned, and if in a standard reaction system all of the factors are known and understood, the result for the whole homogenate will be the same as the sum of the activities in each cell fraction. In assay procedures, it is essential that all of the tissue be used since if extracts are employed one can never be sure how much activity remains unextracted. Thus the goal of the homogenate procedure is to isolate the reaction, rather than the enzyme.

In addition to the assay methods, the homogenate technique lends itself to the study of reaction mechanisms which involve a number of coordinated enzyme systems, and to the development of procedures for the testing and fractionation of new enzymes. By adding certain cofactors and substrates and omitting others, it is possible to effect a reconstruction and integration of particular enzyme organizations which represent segments of cell function (see Chapter 10).

CONSTRUCTION OF THE HOMOGENIZER

The apparatus consists of a test tube and a close-fitting power-driven pestle (see fig. 51). The original homogenizer consisted of a 16 x 150 mm. pyrex test tube and a pestle which was made by sealing off one end of a 220 mm. length of 6 mm. capillary tubing and blowing a thick-walled cylindrical bulb about 20 mm. long, using a slightly larger test-tube for a mold. Later it was found advantageous to form the bulb from a piece of thick-walled glass tubing whose outside diameter is that of the inside of the test-tubes. The large tubing is sealed to the capillary tubing, then constricted and sealed off at a length of about 20 mm., and molded in the test tube as before. For working with extremely small tissue samples, it is convenient to use small homogenizers; 13 x 100 mm. Pyrex tubes can be used, and the pestles can be blown from 6 mm. capillary tubing as in the original method. The final operation is the sealing of 6 or 7 small beads of about 2 mm. diameter to the bottom of the pestle to form cutting teeth. The device is then ready to grind. The beads are ground down on emery cloth so that each one has a flat surface which will approximate the inside of the bottom of the test tubes. This gives them a right-angled cutting edge which remains until the teeth disappear with continued use. Pestles with teeth less than 1 mm. high are best. It is desirable to have five or ten outfits on hand and to have a number of test tubes for each pestle. The sides of the pestles are ground with a few moments operation in an over-size test-tube containing a light suspension of fine carborundum powder in water. The tubes are ground similarly, using an under-size pestle. The object is not to produce a ground glass surface over the entire area of the grinding surfaces, but rather to eliminate all of the irregularities from both the tubes and the pestles. When the grinding is completed, pestles and tubes are matched by testing them with water in the tubes: the tubes should fall off the pestles very slowly when

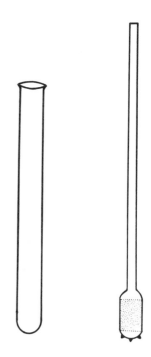

Figure 51
Tissue Homogenizer

not supported. The clearance is then 0.10 - 0.12 mm. For any given pestle, it is well to have both tight-fitting and loose tubes, and as wear takes place, new tubes can be fitted to the pestle. The pestles should not be permitted to grind glass to glass because powdered glass breaks nuclei and other cell structures, and will also interfere with dry weight determinations which are sometimes made with homogenates prepared in water.

The homogenizer is powered by a cone-driven stirring motor of the Cenco or Sargent type, operated at a speed of about 1000 r.p.m. The use of a cone-drive motor prevents breakage because when a piece of connective tissue or muscle jams between the pestle and the tube, the friction drive slips instead of breaking the pestle.

Unground glass pestles may be obtained from Erway Glassblowing Company, Oregon, Wisconsin. Plastic (Teflon) pestles are satisfactory (see page 181) though considerably more expensive.

THE USE OF THE HOMOGENIZER

Homogenates usually are not prepared until the reaction mixtures have been added to all of the vessels. The animal normally is killed by decapitation, and the desired organ is quickly excised and placed in cold isotonic medium in a small beaker surrounded by cracked ice. For assay purposes, a representative tissue sample should be taken. This is no problem with most organs such as liver or muscle, but in the case of kidney and brain it is best solved by using one whole kidney or a specified lobe of the brain. Unless the amount of tissue is limited, it is well to take a sample weighing between 500 and 800 milligrams wet weight. The tissue can be weighed accurately and speedily on a torsion balance of one gram capacity graduated in fifths of a milligram, such as is made by the Roller-Smith Company.

The weighed tissue is dropped into a homogenizer tube which contains the calculated amount of medium, which may be distilled water, isotonic KCl, isotonic sucrose or some other solution that will be determined by the needs of the assay. Lardy has advised the use of boiled redistilled water for the preparation of isotonic sucrose that is completely neutral, since dissolved CO_2 can lower the pH appreciably. Formerly alkaline isotonic KCl was used. This consists of 0.154 M KCl plus 8 ml. of 0.04 M $KHCO_3$ per liter. The final homogenate should have a pH of about 7.0. To make a ten per cent homogenate, it is simplest merely to add 9 times the weight of the tissue. Very often more dilute homogenates are used. These are conveniently made by diluting an appropriate amount of 10 per cent homogenate, without further grinding. For some work it is unnecessary to chill the tissue, the homogenizer and the medium. However, it is desirable in many cases, and we find it convenient to keep the motor in the cold room and the homogenizer tube in cracked ice when the tissue is being weighed and the calculations are being made.

The homogenizer functions by tearing up the tissue with the cutting teeth and then grinding it between the walls of the tube and the walls of the pestle. Accordingly, the tube is moved up and down rapidly in order to force the tissue back and forth past the grinding walls. The pestle is supported rigidly in a chuck on the drive shaft of the stirrer. Various investigators have used a short length of pressure tubing to affect a universal joint between the drive shaft and the pestle. This is not satisfactory for the production of cell-free homogenates unless the homogenizer tubes and pestles are almost perfectly matched. On the other hand, imperfectly fitting tubes and pestles can be used quite successfully when the pestle is supported rigidly, if the operator pushes the tube laterally while working it up and down so that the clearance between pestle and tube is nearly zero on one side. One has to avoid breaking the pestle, of course.

The completed homogenate will be relatively cell-free but will contain shreds of connective tissue which tend to clog ordinary pipettes. It is advisable to use pipettes that have slightly enlarged openings at the end for pipetting homogenates. These are easily prepared when the tips are drawn out, an operation which should be done with all pipettes used for this type of work anyway. Mohr pipettes are preferred.

Homogenates should not be stored and used later on in the same day unless this fact is recorded with the data. Many enzymes which have been too labile to study thus far by other techniques can be studied by means of fresh homogenates. All comments on homogenization that are applicable to cell fractions (Chapter 10) are also applicable to the preparation of whole homogenates. All additions except the homogenate are combined into one "master mix" for each experiment whenever possible.

RESPIRATORY ENZYMES

<u>Succinic</u> <u>dehydrogenase</u> <u>and</u> <u>cytochrome</u> <u>oxidase</u>: The technique for assaying animal tissues for these two enzymes was described by Schneider and Potter (1943). The assay for cytochrome oxidase was carried out on the same tissue samples as the assay for succinic dehydrogenase, and it was found that in all cases the oxidase was present in great excess over the dehydrogenase. This means that when succinate is the substrate the limiting factor is the enzyme which oxidizes succinate, that is, succinic dehydrogenase. The SC factor, or Slater factor, which connects succinic dehydrogenase to cytochrome c, is probably not limiting in this system. On the other hand, when cytochrome c is reduced chemically, the limiting factor is the enzyme (or enzymes) which brings about the reaction between cytochrome c and oxygen, that is, cytochrome oxidase. The sequence of reactants in the two cases shows the relation of the two assays.

<u>Succinic Dehydrogenase</u> <u>assay</u>: (Rat Liver Q_{O_2} = 88)

$$Succinate \longrightarrow Succinic\ Dehydrogenase \longrightarrow SC\ Factor \longrightarrow$$

$$Cytochrome\ c \longrightarrow Cytochrome\ Oxidase \longrightarrow O_2$$

<u>Cytochrome Oxidase</u> <u>assay</u>: (Rat Liver Q_{O_2} = 392)

$$Ascorbate \longrightarrow Cytochrome\ c \longrightarrow Cytochrome\ Oxidase \longrightarrow O_2$$

In every tissue thus far examined, the preponderance of cytochrome oxidase over succinic dehydrogenase has been great enough to make the succinic dehydrogenase assay a valid one. One would expect the cytochrome oxidase system to have a greater capacity for electron transfer than any one of the systems which funnel into it, and the fact that such is the case makes it technically possible to measure the capacity of the component systems. The assay has been arranged (rat liver is used as an example) so that one sample of tissue can be assayed for both enzymes with six flasks and manometers set up as follows (Table 19):

Table 19

Reaction Mixtures and Results in the
Succinic Dehydrogenase–Cytochrome Oxidase Assay (37°C.)

The center cups contained 0.2 ml. 2N NaOH + 3 sq. cm. folded filter paper; Warburg flasks without sidearms; 10 minutes equilibration. Reactants and homogenates at room temperature prior to assay.						
Flask No.	1 ml.	2 ml.	3 ml.	4 ml.	5 ml.	6 ml.
H_2O (to make 3.0 ml.)	0.6	0.5	0.9	0.3	0.25	0.20
0.1 M PO_4 pH 7.4 with NaOH	1.0	1.0	1.0	1.0	1.0	1.0
0.5 M Na-Succinate pH 7.4	0.3	0.3	0.3	--	--	--
1×10^{-4} M Cytochrome c	0.4	0.4	--	--	--	--
2.4×10^{-4} M Chtochrome c	--	--	--	1.0	1.0	1.0
4×10^{-3} M $CaCl_2$	0.3	0.3	0.3	--	--	--
4×10^{-3} M $AlCl_3$	0.3	0.3	0.3	0.3	0.3	0.3
0.114 M Na-ascorbate pH 7.0*	--	--	--	0.3	0.3	0.3
1% rat liver homogenate in water**	--	--	--	0.10	0.15	0.20
5% rat liver homogenate in water**	0.1	0.2	0.2	--	--	--
μl. O_2 uptake per 10 min. (average of four 10 minute periods)	20.0	42.0	8.0	30.4	43.2	56.0

*Prepared by adding 1 ml. of 0.1 N NaOH to 20 mg. of ascorbic acid just before use.
**Diluted from 10 per cent homogenate.

The plan does not include a measurement of the endogenous oxygen uptake of the liver because experience has shown that this is insignificant. However, it is well to establish this point in any new work, especially if larger amounts of tissue are used. The amount of tissue is usually chosen so as to give oxygen uptake values in approximately the range indicated. The treatment of the data will now be described:

Succinic dehydrogenase: The necessary data are given by flasks 1 and 2. The assay is always run at two levels of tissue rather than with duplicates at the same level, because this technique has the advantage of providing continual proof that the uptake is proportional to the tissue concentration. The data are reported finally as Q_{O_2}, that is, the microliters of oxygen taken up per hour per milligram of dry weight. However, the data are first converted to the 10/20 ratio, which is the average oxygen uptake per 20 mg. of fresh tissue per 10 minutes (or 10 mg. fresh tissue per 20 minutes). Since the readings are taken at 10-minute intervals and the homogenates are prepared in strengths of 1, 5, or 10% the 10/20 ratio can usually be calculated mentally, and its usefulness lies in the fact that it is identical with the Q_{O_2} when the per cent dry weight of the tissue is 30%. This is the value most frequently found for rat liver. To illustrate, the data from flasks 1 and 2 are used to obtain the 10/20 ratio and to calculate the Q_{O_2}:

The 10/20 ratio = (4 x 20) + (2 x 42) / 2 = 82
The Q_{O_2} = 82 x 6 x 1/20 x 100/30 = 82

When the per cent dry weight is not 30, the 10/20 ratio is multiplied by $\dfrac{30}{\text{Obs. \% Dry Weight}}$ to give Q_{O_2}. The Q_{O_2} should be defined according to the substrate which is used. The data from flasks 1 and 2 therefore give the <u>succinate</u> Q_{O_2}.

It is of some interest to note that the basis for adding calcium and aluminum ions to the reaction mixture has been the object of considerable study and that most of the consequences of adding calcium are now discernible. The calcium effect was originally studied by Axelrod, Swingle, and Elvehjem (1941) and by Potter and Schneider (1942) who discussed the relevant literature and showed the effect of calcium and aluminum ions. Swingle, Axelrod, and Elvehjem (1942) suggested that calcium accelerated DPN breakdown and Pardee and Potter (1948) showed that the calcium effect was correlated with the production of oxalacetate which is toxic to the succinic dehydrogenase, and showed that additions of DPN to the succinoxidase system produced marked inhibition that was directly proportional to the production of oxalacetate. Potter, Siekevitz and Simonson (1953) showed that calcium ions stimulated the respiration of "resting" mitochondria and Siekevitz and Potter (1953a) showed that calcium uncoupled phosphorylation from oxidation. Finally Ernster, Lindberg, and Löw (1955a) have shown that the uncoupled phosphorylation in mitochondria could be restored with ATP and manganese ions for succinate oxidation, whereas DPN had to be added for substrates requiring this cofactor (Lindberg & Ernster, 1954). It now appears that the succinoxidase assay in the absence of added calcium is inadequate because the homogenate contains enough DPN in the mitochondria to give oxalacetate but cannot generate enough ATP to maintain oxalacetate disappearance in the Krebs cycle. Addition of calcium ions, discharges the mitochondrial ATP (Siekevitz and Potter, 1953b), permits the DPN to leak out and be destroyed, uncouples succinate oxidation from phosphorylation, and permits the system to oxidize succinate to fumarate at a maximal rate.

<u>Cytochrome oxidase</u>: The cytochrome oxidase assay is complicated by the fact that the substrates are all more or less autoxidizable and are generally affected by traces of copper or catalysts other than the cytochrome system. We selected ascorbic acid as the best reductant for the system, but it also has some autoxidation, the measurement of which cannot be made simply by putting the substrate in a flask with the buffer and measuring the rate of oxidation. We have found that the best way to measure the autoxidation rate is to extrapolate to zero tissue concentration from a series of three different tissue concentrations as in the table, in which flasks 4, 5 and 6 contain 1.0, 1.5 and 2.0 mg. of fresh liver, respectively. The autoxidation rate is obtained <u>in this case</u> by subtracting the increments in the last two flasks from the value of the first flask:

$$30.4 - (12.8 + 12.8) = 4.8$$

This value is then subtracted from all the values, and the 10/20 ratios are calculated. The oxygen uptakes corrected for autoxidation are then, respectively, 25.6, 38.4 and 51.2 and the 10/20 ratios are 256, 256 and 256 and the ascorbate Q_{O_2} is therefore 512.

In the paper by Schneider and Potter (1943) this figure was accompanied by a correction factor that was based on what is now referred to as a "cytochrome quotient" (see Schneider, Claude and Hogeboom, 1948). The correction was based upon the observation that the oxidation of ascorbate was more rapid under the conditions which decreased the oxidation rate on succinate in the absence of cytochrome c. Such conditions appear to cause the disruption of the mitochondria and the phenomenon may mean that the cytochrome oxidase in intact mitochondria is less available to ascorbate and cytochrome c than is the oxidase in disrupted mitochondria. It is probably appropriate to use the technique that gives the maximum rate and to apply no correction.

Various workers have encountered difficulty with this system as a result of metal-catalyzed autooxidation of ascorbic acid. However, Maley and Lardy (1954) have reported that when glass-distilled water was used for all reagents the oxidation of ascorbic acid was negligible in the absence of cytochrome c or in the presence of cytochrome c without tissue. Lehninger, Ul Hassan and Sudduth (1954) have also commented on autooxidation with 2 out of 3 commercial cytochrome c preparations. It is obvious that each investigator should make routine tests for autooxidation in the absence of tissue. Lehninger et al. also noted the effect of tonicity on mitochondria and supported the above conclusion that in intact mitochondria the cytochrome oxidase is not fully available to ascorbate. The water homogenate permits maximum oxidation rates but uncouples oxidative phosphorylation. Therefore, it is used for the cytochrome oxidase assay.

The conditions which have been described as optimum for liver probably apply to other tissues as well, but should not be assumed to do so.

Malic dehydrogenase and DPN-Cytochrome C-reductase: It appears likely that these two enzyme systems can be assayed by utilizing the cytochrome system as the terminal connection with oxygen, since the cytochrome oxidase seems to be present in considerable excess (see preceding section). Handler and Klein (1942) showed that DPN is rapidly broken down in homogenates and one might expect that the study of coenzyme systems might be impossible in homogenates. However, they also showed that the breakdown is inhibited by nicotinamide, as had been reported by Mann and Quastel (1941). Oxalacetate, the product of malate oxidation powerfully inhibits the reaction, and unless it is removed the system cannot be studied. Its oxidative removal, besides being difficult to accomplish, would complicate the results. The oxalacetic acid is therefore removed by means of the transamination reaction, which Straub (1941) utilized for this purpose. Transaminase is present in the homogenate. The reaction sequence is:

$$\text{Malate} \longrightarrow \text{malic dehydrogenase} \longrightarrow \text{DPN} \longrightarrow \text{DPN-cytochrome-c-reductase} \longrightarrow \text{cytochrome c} \longrightarrow \text{cytochrome oxidase} \longrightarrow \text{oxygen.}$$

The underlined reagents are added in excess; the side reactions are controlled by adding nicotinamide and glutamate; the limiting factor is malic dehydrogenase when the cytochrome reductase is present in excess. In order to assay for the reductase, one must add malic dehydrogenase in excess; this can be done by adding a Meyerhof extract.

The system appears to require a higher concentration of cytochrome c than does the succinate system. An assay can be carried out for both enzymes in duplicate using 4 flasks and manometers (Table 20); no controls are described. The removal of oxalacetate is still not 100% efficient and this probably accounts for the rapid slowing of the reaction. The data are therefore based on the first two five-minute readings, while a third reading is taken to show that the reaction has not slowed appreciably in the first fifteen minutes. The system has been studied in rat liver, and this is the only tissue for which an attempt has been made to describe optimum conditions (Potter, 1946). The system probably could be improved further by adding purified transaminase (Schlenk and Fisher, 1947) and malic dehydrogenase (Straub, 1942). With the development of the glycolytic reaction system (see later), a better cytochrome reductase system might be developed using this system to reduce DPN instead of the malic system. However Reif, Potter and LePage (1953) used glycolysis as a source of DPNH in sucrose homogenates and obtained Q_{O_2} values much lower than those obtained when water homogenates were employed, as in the earlier reports by Potter (1946, 1947). Further studies are needed to develop a DPN-cytochrome c reductase based on a glycolytic system in a water homogenate. A complete understanding of the relationship between this enzyme and oxidative phosphorylation is still lacking, but at present it appears that maximal rates of oxidation for assay purposes cannot be obtained in systems that remain coupled to phosphate uptake. It seems likely that fully supplemented water homogenates with additional uncoupling by means of dinitrophenol might give valid measures of oxidative capacity. A spectrophotometric method for DPN-cytochrome c reductase has been used by Potter and Albaum (1943) but has not been developed as an assay.

Table 20

Reaction Mixtures in the Malic Dehydrogenase and
DPN-Cytochrome c Reductase Assay (37°C.)

(0. 2 ml. 2N NaOH + 3 sq. cm. filter paper in center cup)

Flask No.	1 ml.	2 ml.	3 ml.	4 ml.
H_2O	0.7	0.6	0.1	--
0.1 M PO_4 pH 7.4 with NaOH	0.8	0.8	0.8	0.8
0.1 M Nicotinamide	0.3	0.3	0.3	0.3
0.5 M Na-malate	0.3	0.3	0.3	0.3
0.5 M Na-glutamate	0.3	0.3	0.3	0.3
0.5% DPN (sidearm; added after equilibration)	0.2	0.2	0.2	0.2
4 x 10^{-4} M cytochrome c	0.3	0.3	0.3	0.3
Meyerhof extract, excess	--	--	0.6	0.6
5% rat liver homogenate	0.1	0.2	0.1	0.2

The malate Q_{O_2} is calculated from flasks 1 and 2 and the DPN Q_{O_2} is calculated from flasks 3 and 4; the 10/20 ratio is based on the first ten minutes of oxygen uptake.

OXIDATIVE PHOSPHORYLATION

In the previous edition a section on keto-acid oxidases was included under respiratory enzymes, but it now seems desirable to include them with the operation of the Krebs citric acid cycle. The conditions that are suitable for the oxidation of pyruvate or α-ketoglutarate are also suitable for any member of the cycle, at least in a general way, because the oxidation of these keto acids or of any other member of the cycle rapidly leads to the production of all the other members. Moreover, the enzymes considered up to this point, although certainly involved in oxidative phosphorylation, do not appear to require the maintenance of ATP in the medium.

Earlier studies were carried out in water homogenates fortified with ATP, while later studies were carried out with isotonic KCl homogenates, and finally isotonic sucrose homogenates (cf. Potter and Siekevitz, 1952). It became evident that optimal rates of oxidation require a certain balance between the relative amounts of ATP, ADP, and AMP, and that while ATP is needed for the maintenance of the oxidative systems, ADP and AMP are needed as phosphate acceptors. Maximal rates of oxygen uptake are prevented in sucrose homogenates of some tissues, notably liver, because of a lack of phosphate acceptors. In such a tissue, additions of hexokinase (Lardy and Wellman, 1952) or of dinitrophenol (DNP) (Siekevitz and Potter, 1953c) will give higher rates of oxidation, and fluoride will give decreased rates of oxidation probably because of a decreased rate of ATP breakdown. Siekevitz and Potter also showed that in some tissues both fluoride and DNP decreased the oxidative rate, while in others fluoride prevented a progressive lowering in rate and DNP accelerated the decrease. All of these findings reflect the fact that the balance between phosphorylation and dephosphorylation in homogenates varies considerably from one tissue to another. Moreover, even the maximal rates attained with hexokinase or DNP probably do not reveal the potential hydrogen transport capacity of the oxidative system due to the permeability barriers between the mitochondrial components and the other enzymes in the cell. Siekevitz and Potter (1955) have shown that fresh rat liver mitochondria contain a complement of nucleotides that do not diffuse into the medium during the course of isolation at 0° in isotonic sucrose and diffuse but slowly on storage at 0°. However, they are rapidly lost to the medium at 30° or 37° if ATP is not maintained, e.g., by oxidative phosphorylation. The demonstration that oxidative rates with ascorbate or DPNH are increased by hypotonic conditions (Maley and Lardy, 1954; Lehninger, 1951; Lehninger, Ul Hassan and Sudduth, 1954) is further evidence that the permeability of the mitochondria is very important in determining oxidative rates, and a comparison of the rate obtained in a DPN-system based on a water homogenate (Potter, 1946) with rates obtained with the more recent sucrose homogenates shows that the latter never attain the magnitude of the rates with the water system.

The above considerations lead to the realization that we are still a long way from a complete knowledge of the interplay between the oxidative mechanisms in various parts of the cell (cf. Schneider and Potter, 1949; Potter, Lyle, and Schneider, 1951; Potter, Recknagel, and Hurlbert, 1951) and to a realization that no single technique can be relied upon to provide decisive information about the balance between alternative metabolic pathways in animal tissues. Evidence from several approaches, including experiments with whole animals, must be used to arrive at the final conclusion (cf. Potter, 1951). Moreover, as pointed out by Schmitz, Potter, and Hurlbert (1954), the intact animal must be the court of final inquiry. With these conclusions in mind, the studies with homogenates must be looked upon as supplementary to experiments with slices, cell fractions and whole animals, and in general the homogenate may be expected to give ground to the more sophisticated use of individual and recombined cell fractions. The following reaction systems cannot be regarded as the final or optimal combination, but are mainly useful for the demonstration of relative levels of oxidative and phosphorylative capacity, and for the maintenance of reservoirs of phosphate bond energy. As such they make excellent basic systems for localizing the biochemical mechanism of drug action.

Krebs cycle systems! With most tissues, the oxidation of pyruvate in homogenates proceeds rather poorly unless a continuing supply of oxalacetate is available for the condensation reaction that leads to citrate (Pardee and Potter, 1949). Oxalacetate per se has several disadvantages, and of the various possible compounds, fumarate is preferred; it is readily available, stable, and it quickly yields malate and oxalacetate. A study by Aisenberg and Potter (1955) illustrates the maximal loading of the oxidative system by substrate combinations, while pyruvate alone or fumarate alone were unable to establish comparable rates (see Table 21).

Table 21

Total Oxygen Uptake by Rat Kidney Homogenate (Krebs Cycle)

Micromoles of Substrate *		Oxygen Uptake
Pyruvate	Fumarate	μl. per 40 min.
-	-	18
-	3	87
-	6	183
-	12	182
3	-	68
6	-	59
3	3	276**
6	6	332

*Six micromoles of acetate were added in each case.
**Three micromoles of glutamate raised this figure to 319.

In the above experiment the following reaction mixture was used in the most active system (acetate not shown):

Table 22

Reaction System for Krebs Cycle Oxidations in Rat Kidney Homogenates

Addition	Final Molarity	Total μ-moles per 3 ml.	Osmotic Equivalents per 3 ml.
0.3 ml. 0.1 M KH_2PO_4 (to pH 7.3 with KOH)	0.01 M	30	90
0.06 ml. 0.1 M K-fumarate	0.002 M	6	18
0.06 ml. 0.1 M K-pyruvate	0.002 M	6	12
0.4 ml. of 0.03 M $MgCl_2$	0.004 M	12	36
0.3 ml. of 0.01 M K–ATP	0.001 M	3	9
0.51 ml. H_2O	-	-	-
0.97 ml. of 0.50 M Sucrose	-	485	485
0.4 ml. of 10% kidney in 0.25 M Sucrose	-	100	100
Total osmotic equivalents			750

In the above calculation of osmotic equivalents the electrolytes are weighted according to the number of ions they yield, and inaccuracies at this point tend to make the medium hypotonic with respect to 0.25 M sucrose. However, considerable latitude is permitted in this respect (Potter and Recknagel, 1951).

With kidney homogenates, no additional phosphate turnover is needed for maximal oxygen uptake, but in the case of liver homogenates, a considerable increase can be obtained with 3×10^{-5} M DNP (Siekevitz and Potter, 1953b) or with hexokinase and glucose (Lardy and Wellman, 1952; Siekevitz and Potter, 1953a). The use of DNP to determine the status of the phosphate balance can be recommended, as it appears to permit the adjustment of the system to a maximum rate of oxygen uptake — if it inhibits, the rate of phosphate breakdown is already excessive.

The system described will prove adequate for most of the substrates of the Krebs cycle without additional supplementation in most tissues. However, it cannot be predicted whether under certain conditions DPN, TPN, Co A or additional cofactors may be needed, and they should be tested in new situations, using the basic system as a control. Aisenberg and Potter (1956) found that certain tumor homogenates that had previously been devoid of the ability to activate acetate were able to do so when both fluoride and Co A were added to the test system.

P:O Ratios - The measurement of P:O ratios in homogenates is of significance only insofar as it shows the balance between dephosphorylating reactions and oxidative or glycolytic phosphorylation. Maximum yields cannot be expected because of the activity of phosphate "leaks", for example, in the presence of microsomes the glucose-6-phosphate formed when glucose and hexokinase are added will be converted back to glucose and inorganic phosphate.

Thus the use of hexokinase and glucose is not recommended for studies on whole homogenates. Potter (1945a,b) and Potter, LePage, and Klug (1948) utilized creatine and a crude creatine kinase to trap the esterified phosphate, and later Lardy and Wellman (1952) reported tests with this acceptor system. The preparation of crystalline creatine kinase by Kuby, Noda, and Lardy (1954a, b) should make reinvestigation of this system worthwhile, using the purified creatine kinase in place of glucose and hexokinase and noting the precautions for determining inorganic phosphate in the presence of creatine phosphate.

In the whole homogenate, fluoride will raise the P:O ratio either with or without added hexokinase (cf. Potter and Siekevitz, 1952). In the whole homogenate the occurrence of ATP breakdown, and the dephosphorylation and deamination of AMP all combine to decrease the yield of esterified phosphate and to lower the ratio. The measurement of maximum yields appears to be facilitated by the use of isolated mitochondria. Lardy and coworkers have repeatedly reported the occurrence of P:O ratios with an average near 4.0 in the α-ketoglutarate system, where short time periods combined with a malonate block were used to minimize the influence of the further oxidation of the succinate derived from α-ketoglutarate (Maley and Lardy, 1953, 1954; Lardy and Wellman, 1952; Copenhaver and Lardy, 1952). They have emphasized the use of glass-distilled water for all reagents and glassware. It would appear that the measurement of ascorbic acid oxidation with the reagents plus cytochrome c and with the mitochondria and reagents minus cytochrome c would be a logical way to determine the quality of the system before proceeding to the measurement of P:O ratios and the effect of drugs thereon. Secondly, the measurement of the oxidative rate with and without phosphate acceptors or uncoupling agents, e.g., 3×10^{-5} M DNP, should provide another measure of the quality of the system. Finally, the purity of the mitochondria in terms of contaminating nuclei and microsomes should be emphasized. Table 23 gives the preferred reaction system for maximal P:O ratios (Maley and Lardy, 1953, and personal communication). As in all reaction systems involving ATP, all reactants and flasks are kept in an ice bath prior to addition of homogenates or cell fractions.

Table 23

Reaction System for Maximal P:O Ratios at 30° C.

(Rat Liver Mitochondria)

Addition	Final Molarity	Total μ Moles per 3 ml.
1.0 ml. 0.25 M Sucrose*	-	250
0.3 ml. 0.1 M K-malonate**	0.01 M	30
0.3 ml. 0.1 M K-α-ketoglutarate	0.01 M	30
0.1 ml. 3 x 10^{-4} M cytochrome c***	1 x 10^{-5} M	0.03
0.4 ml. 0.1 M KH$_2$PO$_4$	0.0133 M	40
0.1 ml. 0.06 M K-ATP	0.002 M	6
0.1 ml. 0.015 M MgSO$_4$ (added last)	0.0005 M	15
0.5 ml. mitochondria from 500 mg. rat liver in 0.25 M sucrose (equivalent to 2-3 mg. N, stressing purity rather than yield).		
Sidearm: 0.2 ml. 0.25 M glucose with dissolved hexokinase just sufficient to give optimum rate of P transfer. ****	0.0166 M	50

   *The sucrose is dissolved in glass-redistilled water that is boiled to expel CO_2. It is refrigerated and prepared once a week or oftener. The other reagents are also prepared in glass re-distilled water and are neutralized to pH 7.4 with KOH if necessary.
  **0.1 ml. malonate is used in some other systems.
 ***The inclusion of cytochrome c does not appear to be essential.
****Determined for each lot of hexokinase, using the P:O ratio as a measure of activity.

In this reaction system, the glucose and hexokinase are added from the sidearm after 7-10 minutes of temperature equilibration, and "zero-time" flasks are immediately taken off, chilled, and deproteinized with 0.2 ml. of 10 per cent TCA. Inorganic phosphate is determined on these flasks, and the P:O ratio is determined on the basis of this figure and the inorganic phosphate level at the end of a short period of measured oxygen uptake.

With essentially the same system, P:O ratios have been determined for a variety of substrates in the Krebs cycle and peripheral to it, by Lardy and associates, and efforts to determine the P:O ratio for the H-transport stages from reduced DPN and reduced cytochrome c have been made by Lardy and by Lehninger (loc. cit.). In all of these studies permeability plays an important role, and it seems likely that much future work will be required to determine how the passage of material into and out of the cell compartments is controlled. At this point, it may be stated that the observed activity of the respiratory enzymes is dependent upon three factors: (1) The amount of enzyme, (2) the rate of phosphate turnover, and (3) the accessibility of the enzymes.

The system in Table 23 could probably be used without modification to study acetoacetate formation in liver by simply substituting pyruvate for α-ketoglutarate and retaining malonate. This would be essentially the same system used by Recknagel and Potter (1951) to study acetoacetate formation except that they used KCl instead of sucrose. The variable should of course be checked.

Glycolytic Enzymes: Glycolysis has been studied extensively in tissue slices and in tissue extracts, but in neither instance does one obtain a measure of the glycolytic enzyme content of the tissue sample. In slices, the aerobic enzymes mask the results of glycolysis when oxygen is present, and the glycolytic systems in many normal tissues appear to be unable to keep pace with ATP breakdown when oxygen is absent. Whatever the explanation, anaerobic glycolysis is very low in slices of such tissues (cf. Burk, 1939). On the other hand, in extracts one cannot be assured that the enzyme content of the extract is an adequate measure of the enzymes in the original tissue. Extracts played a decisive role in the elucidation of the nature of glycolysis, but they have never been proposed as the basis for tissue assays.

Homogenates were used originally for the study of glycolysis in brain. Further studies on the development of assay techniques have been made by LePage (1948) who reported on studies with cancer tissue, and by LePage and Schneider (1948) who measured glycolysis in fractions obtained by the centrifugation of homogenates. References to the earlier papers are given in these papers. The latter studies revealed that no fraction, including the final supernatant extract, was as active as the whole homogenate.

The optimum conditions for tumor homogenates are reported by LePage (1948) and for liver homogenates by Stoesz and LePage (1949). These reaction systems are given in Table 24.

Table 24

Reaction Mixture for Glycolysis in Homogenates (37° C).

Figures in parentheses were developed for liver homogenates
Figures not in parentheses were developed for tumor homogenates

Addition	Final Molarity		Total μ moles per 3 ml.	
(0.55) 0.75 ml. H_2O	-		-	
(0.20) 0.30 ml. 0.024 M K-PO_4 pH 7.6	0.0024	(0.0016)	7.2	(4.8)
(0.30) 0.15 ml. 0.5 M $KHCO_3$	0.025	(0.05)	75	(150)
(0.30) 0.30 ml. 0.4 M Nicotinamide	0.04	(0.04)	120	(120)
(0.30) 0.10 ml. 0.01 M K-ATP	0.00033	(0.001)	1	(3)
(0.30) 0.20 ml. 0.003 M K-DPN	0.0002	(0.0003)	0.6	(0.9)
(0.45) 0.15 ml. 0.04 M K-HDP	0.002	(0.006)	6	(18)
- 0.30 ml. 0.10 M glucose	0.01	-	30	-
(0.30) 0.20 ml. 0.10 M $MgCl_2$	0.0067	(0.01)	20	(30)
(0.15) 0.10 ml. 0.15 M K-pyruvate	0.005	(0.0075)	15	(22.5)
(0.15) 0.15 ml. 0.20 M KF	0.01	(0.01)	30	(30)
(0.20) 0.30 ml. 10% homogenate in .154 M KCl	0.0154	(0.01)	46	(30)

Table 24 serves to illustrate the fact that the optimum conditions for one tissue are not necessarily the best for other tissues. However the differences are not great (cf. the original papers), and the system was applied by LePage (1950) to heart, skeletal muscle, diaphragm, kidney, liver, brain, and 3 types of tumors with only minor modifications. The mixture was the same as that for tumor shown above, except that 22.5 μ moles of pyruvate were present instead of 15.

Thus far the studies on the glycolytic enzyme system have not established one enzyme as the rate-limiting factor. Under the conditions employed, there may be an initial rate-limiting step below hexose diphosphate which may later shift to the reactions involved in the conversion of glucose to hexose diphosphate. By carrying out analyses at various time intervals, considerable information can be obtained regarding the relative amounts of the enzymes that are involved in glycolysis. Future studies on homogenates supplemented with individual enzymes may make it possible to establish the identity of rate-limiting steps, while alterations in the reaction mixture, such as increasing the HDP, may serve to eliminate certain steps. In all such studies the determination of inorganic phosphate and lactic acid as carried out by LePage is preferable to the measurement of CO_2 output alone.

Further discussion of glycolytic systems and reference to studies by Meyerhof and co-workers is given elsewhere (Potter and Siekevitz, 1952).

The largest proportion of the glycolytic enzymes is in the soluble supernatant of the cell, and this fraction can be used as a glycolytic system for some purposes; when the supernatant is prepared from brain or tumor homogenates, hexokinase is present and active (LePage, 1950) while with other tissues this does not seem to be the case.

Phosphorylation of non-adenine nucleotides: Recent work has shown that homogenates of rat liver, under conditions similar to those described in Table 25, are able to phosphorylate not only AMP and ADP, but also the mono- and diphosphates of uridine (Herbert, Potter, and Takagi, 1955) and of cytidine and guanosine (Herbert and Potter, 1956). It was shown that the mitochondria are unable to phosphorylate the monophosphates other than AMP, but are able to phosphorylate all of the diphosphates. The monophosphates could be phosphorylated by the mitochondrial supernatant. Thus, it was found useful to utilize the cell fraction obtained by removing the nuclei from the whole homogenate, at a level equivalent to 160 mg. of liver per 3.0 ml. reaction mixture. In order to maintain the oxidation rate at a high level, 3 Krebs cycle substrates were supplied, as shown in Table 25. This reaction mixture is adapted from the references given.

Table 25

Reaction Systems for Phosphorylation of Nucleotide Mixtures

Additions		Final Molarity	Total μ Moles per 3 ml.
0.15 ml	0.1 M KH_2PO_4 to pH 7.2	0.005 M	15
0.15 ml	0.1 M K-glutamate	0.005 M	15
0.15 ml	0.1 M K-pyruvate	0.005 M	15
0.06 ml	0.1 M K-fumarate	0.002 M	6
0.30 ml	0.03 M $MgCl_2$	0.003 M	9
0.30 ml	of 0.01 M K-AMP	0.001 M	3
0.30 ml	of 0.01 M K-UMP, CMP or GMP	0.001 M	3
0.24 ml	of H_2O		
0.55 ml	of 1.0 M Sucrose		
0.80 ml	of cytoplasmic fraction equivalent to a 20% homogenate in 0.25 M Sucrose	0.25 M	750

The use of this reaction system depends upon the availability of chromatographic methods for separating the various nucleotides. By using a combination of the Type I and Type II columns worked out by Hurlbert, Schmitz, Brumm and Potter (1954) it was possible to separate the adenine nucleotides from any one series of non-adenine nucleotides on Dowex 1 formate columns 1 cm. in diameter and 3 cm. in height. Each column is made by sealing a 15 x 1 cm. glass tube to the bottom of a 125 ml. Erlenmeyer flask which acts as a reservoir for the eluent solutions. A constriction near the bottom of the column supports the glass wool on which the resin rests. Each eluent solution was placed on the column 5 or 10 ml. at a time, and the columns were operated at the appropriate rate by gravity, without running dry when the eluent had run through. Each eluent was used in 5 to 10 additions to give as many fractions, the number being chosen such that the final fraction for each eluent yielded no further products. The following tables give the schedules of eluents employed and may serve as guides to the development of other schedules for particular purposes.

Table 26

Eluent Schedules for Separating Adenine and Non Adenine Nucleotides

Type III Uridine Phosphates		Type IV Cytidine Phosphates		Type V Guanosine Phosphates	
Eluent*	Compound	Eluent*	Compound	Eluent*	Compound
H$_2$O		H$_2$O		H$_2$O	
0.05 M FA		0.05 M FA	CMP	0.05 M FA	–
0.20 M FA	AMP	0.20 M FA	AMP	0.20 M FA	AMP
0.10 M AF	UMP + IP	0.10 M AF	IP	1.5 M FA x 6** ⎫	GMP
2.5 M FA	ADP			1.7 M FA x 6 ⎭	
0.3 M AF	UDPX*	0.25 M AF	CDP	2.5 M FA x 6 ⎫	ADP
0.4 M AF	UDP	2.5 M FA	?	3.0 M FA x 6 ⎭	
0.7 M AF	UTP	3.0 M FA	ADP	4.0 M FA ⎫ x 10	GDP
1.25 M AF	ATP	0.4 M AF	?	+0.15 M AF ⎭	
		0.5 M AF	CTP	4.0 M FA ⎫ x 8	ATP
		0.7 M AF	X	+0.3 M AF ⎭	
		1.0 M AF	ATP	4.0 M FA ⎫ x6 ⎫	
				+0.4 M AF ⎭ ⎬	GTP
				4.0 M FA ⎫ x 6 ⎭	
				+0.6 M AF ⎭	

* Abbreviations: FA = formic acid; AF = ammonium formate;   UDPX = unknown derivative of uridinediphospate ** Number of 5 ml. portions of eluent

In the previous applications of these schedules, a balance sheet was kept for each reaction mixture, so that it could be shown that the sum of all the adenine nucleotide fractions and all the non-adenine nucleotide fractions remained constant throughout the experimental period. In experiments with radioactive phosphate or other compounds, similar balance sheets are essential in order to show that all radioactivity at any time is equal to the amount added originally.

Reconstituted Glycolytic Plus Oxidative Systems: In the study of metabolic reactions
against an overall metabolic background, it may be useful to have a system that contains
active hexokinase and a controlled amount of mitochondria. Based on LePage's work described earlier, the supernatant from high speed centrifugation of a brain homogenate
provides an active glycolytic system with hexokinase activity. To this may be added
graded levels of mitochondria to provide any balance between oxidation and glycolysis.
The microsomes and nuclei from both brain and liver are eliminated and may be added
back for particular purposes. The following reaction system (Table 27) has been used
by Aisenberg, Reynafarje, and Potter (1956) for studies on the Pasteur effect. Under the
conditions given, lactic acid accumulation will be 80-100% suppressed by the liver mitochondria.

Table 27

Reaction Mixture for Glycolysis Plus Oxidation

Addition	Final Molarity	μ Moles per 3.0 ml.
0.3 ml 0.01M K-ATP	0.001	3
0.2 ml 0.003 M K-DPN	0.0002	0.6
0.3 ml 0.4 M Nicotinamide	0.04	120
0.15 ml 0.04 M K-HDP	0.002	6
0.3 ml 0.10 Glucose	0.01	30
0.15 ml 0.50 M KHCO$_3$	0.025	75
0.30 ml 0.02 M K-PO$_4$ pH 7.4	0.002	6
0.1 ml 0.12 M MgCl$_2$ (added last)	0.004	12
0.4 ml H$_2$O or other addition, plus 175 μ moles sucrose		
0.4 ml Soluble Supernatant from 120 mg Brain (30% Homogenate in 0.25 M Sucrose)		
0.4 ml Mitochondria from 500 mg Liver (10% Homogenate in 0.25 M Sucrose)		
Gas phase 95% O$_2$; 5% CO$_2$. Temperature 30°.		

In the above reaction mixture, the omission of the mitochondria will result in a system
that will produce lactic acid, while the addition of graded amounts of mitochondria will
result in a progressive decrease in the amount of lactic acid produced. This effect is
independent of added cytochrome c, since the mitochondria of rat liver contain sufficient
cytochrome c to mediate DPNH oxidation.

Adenosine triphosphatase: The whole problem of oxidative phosphorylation and maintenance of energy production in cell-free systems is intimately connected with the activity
of an enzyme system that is still poorly understood, although steady advances are being
made. Kielley and Kielley (1951) showed the presence of latent ATP-ase in rat liver
mitochondria and its activation by ageing. Potter, Siekevitz, and Simonson (1953) showed
that latent ATP-ase could be immediately and maximally activated by adding calcium ions
in the presence of magnesium ions. Kielley and Kielley (1953) isolated a mitochondrial
ATP-ase that is activated by magnesium ions, but not by calcium ions, and is strongly
inhibited by ADP, which in the whole mitochondria will be removed by adenylate kinase
activity. Siekevitz and Potter (1953b) showed that calcium ions accelerate the discharge
of nucleotides from mitochondria, which has been correlated with mitochondrial swelling
(Brenner-Holzach and Raaflaub, 1954) and with inactivation of oxidative phosphorylation

(Siekevitz and Potter, 1955).   The loss of oxidative phosphorylation and its restoration have been studied by Hunter and Ford (1955) and also by Ernster and Löw (1955b) who suggested that tests of mitochondrial ATP-ase might be "foredoomed as inadequate due to the fact that both Mg^{++} and ATP may depress its activity by a reconstruction of mitochondrial integrity." Although reports of restoration of uncoupled mitochondria to the coupled state (in terms of P:O ratios), and from the translucent to the more opaque state (Beyer, Ernster, Löw, and Beyer, 1955b), there have been no reports of measurements to determine whether there was restoration of the bound nucleotide complement and/or latency of ATP-ase activity. However, Potter, Siekevitz, and Simonson (1953) have shown that aged mitochondria given ATP and Mg^{++} showed exactly the same activity as fresh mitochondria given ATP and Mg in the presence of calcium, which suggests that these two components alone do not restore latency and that they may permit adequate measurements of ATP-ase activity. Taken altogether, the above studies suggest that ATP-ase activity in mitochondria of rat liver is latent because of some kind of a combination with Mg^{++} and ATP. This combination is involved in maintaining mitochondrial integrity in terms of preventing leaks of nucleotides out or entrances of other substances into the mitochondria. This combination can be discharged by phosphate, calcium DNP, and probably many other agents. (The assumption that the combination contains calcium (Ernster and Löw, 1955) is not unreasonable, but does not appear to have experimental support.) Discharge of the mitochondrial ATP and Mg^{++} is accompanied by uncoupling of oxidative phosphorylation, loss of Mg^{++}, loss of adenine nucleotides and coenzymes, increased permeability, swelling, translucence, and development of maximal ATP-ase activity. All of these phenomena are profoundly modified by a variety of cations and anions.

The problem of measuring ATP-ase activity can probably best be met by the simultaneous addition of calcium and magnesium ions rather than by the addition of either ion alone, as formerly carried out by DuBois and Potter (1943). Further studies may be based on the reports by Potter, Siekevitz, and Simonson (1953), by Kielley and Kielley (1953) and by Plaut (1955). The reaction system recommended in Table 28 is based on the studies in this laboratory, and should be used with a careful consideration of the above discussion and references.

Table 28

Reaction Mixture for Measuring Potential ATP-ase Activity

Additions	Final Molarity	μMoles per 2 ml.
0.3 ml. of 0.02 M K-ATP pH 7.6	0.003	6
0.3 ml. of 0.02 M MgCl$_2$ *	0.003	6
0.3 ml. of 0.02 M CaCl$_2$ *	0.003	6
0.9 ml. of 0.25 M Sucrose		
0.1 to 0.2 ml. 5 per cent homogenate in 0.125 M Sucrose	0.125	250
0.1 ml. 0.125 M sucrose (when 0.1 ml homogenate is used)		
*Added together at time zero.		

The cold homogenate is added to cold sucrose in 13 x 100 mm. test tubes. The ATP is added to cold sucrose in 13 x 100 ml. test tubes. The ATP is added and the tubes are transferred to a bath at 37°, in the same order in which the calcium and magnesium are to be added. The calcium and magnesium additions are made at time zero. The reaction is stopped at 10 and 20 minutes by adding 1.0 ml. of 1.5 M TCA, and the flask contents are analysed for inorganic phosphate. The flask contents may also be used for ion exchange chromatography (Potter, Siekevitz, and Simonson, 1953) to show that the theoretical inorganic phosphate (IP) calculated from the equation:

$$\mu \text{Moles IP} = (2x \, \mu \text{moles AMP}) + \mu \text{moles ADP}$$

agrees with the observed production of inorganic phosphate. This test is desirable in applications to new material. Agreement was obtained when rat liver mitochondria were studied. Lack of agreement indicates occurrence of side reactions.

The results may be conveniently expressed in units of micrograms of IP produced per milligram of tissue per hour. Further studies are needed to establish the utility of this assay on whole homogenates and fractions other than mitochondria.

GENERAL

The reaction systems described are useful for studying new reactions in tissues and provide means for renewing the supply of ATP or other high energy phosphates by either aerobic or anaerobic systems. A point to be emphasized is that analytical methods or chromatographic separations should be used wherever possible to supplement manometric measurements. The principle of setting up a balance sheet to account for the disappearance of substrates in terms of products formed is always a sound procedure as it checks on methods as well as giving information on the system. The procedures described are at present being used to study biosynthetic reactions in the formation and utilization of nucleotides, and the action of various antimetabolites in these reactions. Similar studies with other biosynthetic reactions and drugs should also be facilitated by these procedures.

V. R. POTTER

Chapter 10
METHODS FOR THE ISOLATION
OF PARTICULATE COMPONENTS OF THE CELL

Since this chapter was first written, there has been a tremendous upsurge in the interest displayed by biochemists in the field of cytochemistry. Much of this interest stems from the findings that mitochondria could be isolated from liver tissue in a form and with the cytological properties displayed by mitochondria within the intact cell (Schneider, 1947; Hogeboom et al., 1948) and that these isolated mitochondria were the site of many important enzymatic reactions including those of the Krebs cycle (Schneider and Potter, 1949), fatty acid oxidation (Schneider, 1948; Kennedy and Lehninger, 1949), oxidative phosphorylation (Potter et al.,1951b) and synthesis (Kielley and Schneider, 1950).

As is usually the case when a great deal of activity takes place in a scientific field during a short period of time, a considerable amount of controversy and confusion ensues. This is perhaps even more true of cytochemistry than of other fields and extends not only to interpretation of results but also to methodology. An attempt will be made to point out in this chapter where such controversies exist with respect to the methods used and to suggest possible solutions.

GENERAL PRINCIPLES

Cells exhibit complex structures when viewed under the microscope either in the living state or after fixation. A number of discrete particulate components are visible within the cell including a nucleus, with its nucleolus and chromatin material, mitochondria, secretory granules, fat droplets, and the Golgi substance. The chromosomes are not visible as such in the resting nucleus of the cell, but make their appearance during the early stages of mitosis. In addition, particles below the resolving power of the microscope have been demonstrated to exist in the cytoplasm of the liver cell with the dark field microscope (Brenner, 1947). Soluble materials (proteins, salts, etc.) comprise the remainder of the cell. Whether these soluble materials exist as such within the living cell or whether they are normally present in subcellular structures and leak out during isolation is a question that cannot be answered at present, but must be kept in mind for future work.

Since cells are so complex, cytologically, it is rather obvious that the study of the intracellular distribution of enzymes must involve close collaboration between the cytologist and the biochemist. The cytologist must identify the structures isolated and the biochemist must study their enzymatic properties.

Since most tissues are composed of several different types of cells, it would appear that single cells and the particulate components isolated from single cells would be the ideal materials for the study of the intracellular distribution of enzymes. Linderstrøm-Lang, Holter and their associates (Linderstrøm-Lang, 1938; Holter, 1954) have in fact been able to make such studies on single cells. In general, however, the use of single cells has been distinctly limited both with respect to the types of cells and the enzymes that could be studied. An encouraging direction taken by more recent studies with this method has been the attempt to compare the results obtained by centrifuging intact single cells with those obtained from the differential centrifugation of homogenates of these cells (Holter and Pollock, 1952).

A method which permits fuller exploitation of current knowledge of enzymes was provided by the development of the homogenate technique (Chapter 9) and the so-called cell fractionation technique. The homogenate technique provided methods for the quantitative assay of enzymatic activity in cell-free preparations of tissues (homogenates). Subsequently, it was found that the morphological and cytological properties of the particulate components of the cell were preserved when the homogenates were made in appropriate media, and that the homogenates could be separated by means of differential centrifugation into a nuclear fraction, a mitochondrial fraction, a sub-microscopic particle fraction, and a soluble fraction (Hogeboom, Schneider and Palade, 1948; Schneider, 1948; Schneider and Hogeboom, 1950a).

In the study of the intracellular distribution of enzymes by the cell fractionation technique, several important principles must be followed (Schneider and Hogeboom, 1951). In the first place, the identity of the fractions must be established cytologically. Ideally, each fraction should consist of a single particulate component whose cytological and morphological properties closely approach those of the particulate component in the living cell. A corollary requirement is that the yeild of the isolated cell component must represent a large fraction of that present in the whole tissue. The need for this requirement becomes obvious when one considers the fact that none of the tissues used in cell fractionations are homogeneous populations of a single cell type. The ideal separation procedure, then, provides the isolated cell component in a high degree of purity <u>and</u> in a high yield. Secondly, the enzymatic activity of each fraction must be determined, and it must be demonstrated that the sum of the activity of all fractions equals the activity of the unfractionated homogenate. This is necessary because in enzyme assays, the possibility must be considered that inhibitors or activators are present in the homogenate and that the distribution of enzyme and of inhibitor or activator may be entirely different. Consequently the sum of the activities of the fractions will be either greater or less than the activity of the homogenate. Several instances will be cited later in which this is true. In these cases it is necessary to measure the activities of the fractions in various permutations and combinations as well as separately in order to determine the localization of the inhibitor or activator, as well as to eliminate the possibility of denaturation during the isolation procedure. The practice, which has been common in the past and continues at present, of isolating a cellular component and studying its properties to the exclusion of the rest of the cell cannot be considered to contribute to our cytochemical knowledge. The results of such studies must, from the cytochemical standpoint, be considered only as suggestive until they can be checked by complete studies on other cell fractions.

When the above requirements have been met, the localization of an enzyme in a cellular component is indicated in three ways: (a) a large percentage of the <u>total</u> activity of the homogenate is recovered in the fraction; (b) the <u>specific</u> activity of the fraction is several times as great as that of the homogenate; and (c) the specific activity of the fraction remains constant upon repeated sedimentation. These criteria have been met for very few enzymes (see Schneider, 1949; Schneider and Hogeboom, 1951; Schneider, 1953; Hogeboom <u>et al</u>.,1953).

The requirement of a balance sheet in studies of enzyme distribution in tissue fractions has met with some resistance despite the fact that it is merely an extension of a principle closely adhered to by enzyme chemists. In the purification of an enzyme from a tissue extract, for example, it is essential to determine both the total amount and the concentration of the enzyme in each fraction obtained during the isolation procedure for it is only in this manner that it is possible to determine both the degree of purification and the yield. Although purification of enzymes is not a primary objective of cell fractionation, purification of subcellular structures is. Consequently, in a study of enzymes associated with such subcellular elements, it is obvious that utilization of a balance sheet is also essential.

CYTOLOGICAL IDENTIFICATION OF PARTICULATE COMPONENTS
OF THE CELL

The identification of particulate components of the cell requires the collaboration of a cytologist thoroughly versed in the morphology of living cells as well as in the classical staining properties of fixed and unfixed cells and in the morphology of cells as seen under the electron microscope. It is especially important that the identification be made on unfixed and unstained material wherever possible, supplemented by observations employing staining methods and examination in the electron microscope. Only in this manner can the identification of cellular components be firmly established.

The study of cellular components in unfixed and unstained material has presented considerable difficulty in the past because of the slight difference between the index of refraction of the particulate components and the surrounding material. This difficulty can be eliminated largely by use of the dark field microscope and the recently developed phase and interference microscopes. The latter provide especially easy methods for the demonstration (in fresh preparations) of particulate components of the cell that are seen with great difficulty with the ordinary microscope.

During the past few years, the development of new fixation and thin sectioning techniques for use with the electron microscope has led to such startling clarification of the submicroscopic structure of mitochondria (Palade, 1952; Sjöstrand, 1953), the Golgi substance (Dalton and Felix, 1953), and the ground substance of the cytoplasm (Dalton et al., 1950; Palade and Porter, 1954; Sjöstrand and Rhodin, 1953) that the use of these techniques has become imperative in future cell fractionation work. Thus the characteristic substructure observed in mitochondria under the electron microscope has provided an entirely new method for the identification of these granules. Similarly the revelation that the cytoplasm contains many submicroscopic membranous lamellae with characteristically arranged granules (Palade, 1955) permits a new assessment of the composition of the microsome fraction (Palade and Siekevitz, 1955).

METHODS FOR THE COMPLETE FRACTIONATION OF RAT LIVER
HOMOGENATES BY DIFFERENTIAL CENTRIFUGATION

Choice of Tissue for Centrifugal Fractionation: Since most mammalian tissues consist of several types of cells rather than of a single type as required for centrifugal fractionation, the choice of tissues is exceedingly important. Rat liver has proved to be an excellent tissue for centrifugal fractionation, mainly because it is composed largely of one type of cell. In addition, liver cells are easily broken and contain a large variety of enzymes. As a result, liver tissue has been used in most of the studies on centrifugal fractionation. (Although parenchymal cells account for 85-90 per cent of the volume of the liver (Striebich et al., 1953), other cell types may account for as much as 40 per cent of the total number of cells in the liver (Wilson et al., 1953).) The fractionation methods described in this chapter have been devised for rat and mouse liver. Their application to other tissues may require some modification.

Centrifuges: In order to minimize autolytic processes during the centrifugal fractionation of tissues it is necessary to carry out all steps at as low a temperature as possible. For this reason the International Refrigerated Centrifuge PR-1 or PR-2 is the centrifuge of choice for most of the centrifugal procedures. This centrifuge permits the use of a variety of both horizontal and angle rotors in a refrigerated chamber which can be maintained at 32°F. ± 1° or at other selected temperatures. It is desirable to maintain the chamber at a temperature several degrees lower than required for the preparation, because the temperature of the rotor is usually several degrees above that of the surrounding air.

With the multispeed attachment and rotor No. 295 forces as great as 25,000 g can be obtained in this centrifuge. It is worthwhile to point out that the capacity of this rotor can be doubled by substituting 3/4" O.D. lusteroid tubes for the pyrex tubes and rubber jackets with which the rotor is supplied. If this is done, it is necessary to put 2 ml. of water in each rotor hole as a cushion because the rotor holes are larger than the lusteroid tubes and also because the rotor holes have a conical bottom rather than a round one. Rotor No. 296 is also useful, especially if fitted with Teflon inserts to accommodate 3/4" or 5/8" lusteroid tubes. Using 50 ml. lusteroid tubes cut off to an appropriate length, a total of 120 ml. can be spun in this rotor.

For centrifugal forces greater than those obtainable with the International centrifuge, the Spinco centrifuge (Model E or L, manufactured by the Specialized Instruments Corp., Belmont, California) is recommended. This centrifuge is electrically driven, and the rotor spins in a refrigerated evacuated chamber. The maximum force obtainable with the preparative rotors supplied with this machine is 210,000 g. In addition, the centrifuge can be obtained with the necessary optical equipment for analytical work.

Two formulae frequently used in centrifugal work merit inclusion in this discussion. The first deals with the determination of centrifugal force, and is given by the equation

$$F = \frac{S^2 r}{89500}$$

where F is the centrifugal force (in gravitational units, g), r is the radial distance in cm. from the center of rotation, and S is the speed in revolutions per minute. Another useful formula is that given by Pickels (1943) for roughly estimating particle size or for approximating the time required to sediment particles of known physical properties. According to this equation

$$T = \frac{D-L}{D+L} \left(\frac{N}{d^2 \, (g-p)S^2} \right)$$

where T is the time in minutes, D is the radial distance in cm. from the boundary (or outer edge of the tube for complete sedimentation) to the axis of rotation, L is the radial distance in cm. from the meniscus to the axis of rotation, N is the viscosity of the fluid in poises, g and p are the densities in grams per cubic centimeter of the particles and medium respectively, d is the average diameter of the particles in centimeters, and S is the rotational speed in R.P.M. A very useful discussion of the theory of differential centrifugation and of the most suitable methods for expressing the field strength used in centrifugal separation is given in the review of de Duve and Berthet (1954).

Density Gradient Centrifugation: A most useful adjunct to differential centrifugation, which has developed during the past few years is density gradient centrifugation. In this method separations are achieved by virtue of differences in the density of particles rather than in their size.

In practice density gradient separations can be performed in several different ways. The simplest application involves the use of a discontinuous density gradient in which solutions of decreasing density are layered one above the other in a centrifuge tube. The material to be separated is carefully introduced above the top layer and the tube is spun at high speed until equilibrium has been reached. Particles segregate at the interface of the layers corresponding to their density and can be separated by cutting the centrifuge tube into sections using the apparatus of Randolph and Ryan (1950).

The use of discontinuous gradients is somewhat limited in scope and can be extended by the use of linear density gradients. Such gradients can be prepared with specially designed mixing devices (Hogeboom and Kuff, 1954; de Duve et al., 1959) and can give sharper separations than discontinuous gradients.

In a still further application of density separations, the mixture to be separated is pipetted into the bottom of the centrifuge tube and a discontinuous or linear density gradient is introduced above the mixture. Upon centrifugation, lighter materials float into the gradient until they occupy a region of similar density.

Methods of Preparation of Homogenates: The most satisfactory method available for preparing cell-free tissue suspensions involves the use of the Potter-Elvehjem glass homogenizer (Chapter 9). When this apparatus is properly used practically all the cells are broken and the nuclei and other sub-cellular components remain unbroken. For the preparation of liver homogenates for cell fractionation, we have found that a modified homogenizer (Schneider and Hogeboom, 1952a) is useful. It consists of a plastic (Kel-F) pestle fitted to a smooth wall glass test tube. (Dounce, 1955) has suggested the use of a ball type glass pestle for homogenization. Because of the small surface of contact, this type pestle may have definite advantages for cell fractionation.) The pestle should fit the tube snugly, but not tightly. If the fit is tight, the number of up and down strokes of the tube is limited and the number of cells ruptured drops off markedly. There is the further danger of local heating and disruption of subcellular particles. With suitable Kel-F homogenizers and a homogenization time of two one-minute periods, rupture of over 90 per cent of the cells of liver tissue is routinely obtained. Both the mortar and pestle and the Waring blendor give either low yields of broken cells or breakage of nuclei and mitochondria. Use of the latter also may be accompanied by excessive frothing and heating.

Selection of Media for Homogenization: The medium in which the cells are disrupted has a profound effect on both the cytological and biochemical properties of the particulate components of the cell. The morphological and biochemical properties of mitochondria in different media have been studied most thoroughly. When homogenates of rat liver are made in distilled water, the mitochondria become swollen and the cytochrome c present in them is not active as shown by the succinoxidase test in the absence of added cytochrome c (Chapter 9). Cytochrome c is also associated with the submicroscopic particles isolated from water homogenates of rat liver (Schneider et al., 1948). It is apparently present in adsorbed form, because the cytochrome c is removed when these particles are washed in isotonic saline. In homogenates of rat liver made in isotonic saline or other salts, however, the mitochondria are strongly agglutinated, although the cytochrome c present in them is active in the succinoxidase system and the mitochondria are normal in size. As a result of this agglutination, the mitochondria sediment with the nuclei, and it is impossible to obtain an adequate separation of the two (Schneider, 1946a). The submicroscopic particles isolated from saline homogenates do not contain cytochrome c (Schneider, Claude and Hogeboom, 1948). Furthermore, the mitochondria in saline or water homogenates do not stain vitally with Janus Green B, the generally accepted stain specific for mitochondria. Homogenates prepared in isotonic or hypertonic sucrose have proved to be the most suitable for centrifugal fractionation of tissues (Hogeboom, Schneider and Palade, 1948; Schneider, 1948; Schneider and Hogeboom, 1950a). (Dounce et al. (1955) have proposed 0.44 M sucrose adjusted to pH 6-6.2 as a more suitable medium for isolation of both nuclei and mitochondria from liver, while Novikoff (1955) has reported that 0.25 M sucrose containing 7.5 per cent polyvinylpyrollidone (PVP) adjusted to pH 7.6-7.8 is an even better medium for the isolation of mitochondria and for the preservation of the lamellar structure of the cytoplasm. Both groups of workers reached their conclusions as a result of examination of ultra thin sections of their isolated fractions under the electron microscope.) In these solutions the mitochondria are normal in size, stain with Janus Green B, and are not agglutinated. Moreover, in hypertonic sucrose many of the mitochondria are elongated, a morphological property of mitochondria previously observed only within living cells. Mitochondria isolated from hypertonic sucrose homogenates also differ biochemically from those isolated from isotonic sucrose homogenates as shown by the succinoxidase test in the absence of added cytochrome c (Schneider and Hogeboom, 1950a). Although the morphological and cytological properties of liver mitochondria are best preserved in 0.88 M sucrose, the biochemical activity of the mitochondria is greater in some respects when isolated in 0.25 M sucrose. For this reason and because it is technically easier to work with 0.25 M sucrose, the latter has been accepted tentatively as the medium of choice in the fractionation of liver homogenates. Because of the valuable properties of 0.88 M sucrose from the cytological standpoint, it is desirable to use this medium for checking results obtained with homogenates in 0.25 M sucrose. The centrifugal fractionation of both isotonic and hypertonic sucrose homogenates will be described.

Sucrose solutions have not proved satisfactory for the isolation of all cell components, however. It has been found, for example, that nuclei agglutinate extensively in sucrose. The addition of very small amounts of $CaCl_2$, however, prevents this agglutination (Schneider and Petermann, 1950) and it has become possible to isolate nuclei from liver in 70-90 per cent yield with a calcium containing sucrose medium (Hogeboom et al., 1952). Nuclei isolated from calcium-sucrose solutions also exhibit the morphological appearance characteristic of those in intact cells. The presence of saline has been found necessary in the isolation of the Golgi substance from the epithelial cells of the epididymis (Schneider and Kuff, 1954; Dalton and Felix, 1954). Here saline serves two functions: (1) it is necessary for the cytological identification of the Golgi substance, and (2) it is required for the preservation of the Golgi substance outside the cell. The fact (Hogeboom et al., 1948) that some of the neutral red staining granules are broken in sucrose homogenates indicates that these solutions would be unsatisfactory for the isolation of these granules.

Centrifugal Fractionation of Rat Liver in 0.88 M Sucrose: (Schneider and Hogeboom, 1950a). Adult albino rats were fasted overnight to remove glycogen from the liver. The rats were killed by decapitation (if desired the livers may be perfused with cold 0.145 M saline and 0.88 M sucrose before removal from the animal.) The livers were cooled in a beaker placed in an ice bath and were passed through a tissue masher fitted with a screen containing holes 1 mm. in diameter. This procedure removed a large part of the connective tissue framework of the liver (Claude, 1946). (In more recent work, it has been found that 30 per cent of the liver nuclei may be damaged in the tissue masher (Hogeboom and Schneider, 1952).) The liver pulp was then weighed and homogenized in 9 volumes of ice cold 0.88 M sucrose (Merck, reagent grade) in the modification of the apparatus of Potter and Elvehjem (Schneider and Hogeboom, 1952a).

Ten ml. of homogenate were pipetted into each of two 30 ml. graduated test tubes and centrifuged for 10 minutes at 3000 r.p.m. (International rotor No. 269) to sediment the nuclei, unbroken liver cells, and erythrocytes. The sediment in each tube was washed once by suspending it in 4 ml. of 0.88 M sucrose with the aid of a loose Kel-F homogenizer pestle and recentrifuging as before. The final sediment was resuspended in 0.88 M sucrose and labeled the nuclear fraction, N_W. The complete recovery of nuclei in this fraction was indicated both by microscopical examination as well as by the fact that the entire DNA (desoxypentose nucleic acid, a specific nuclear constituent) of the homogenate was recovered in this fraction. A certain number of mitochondria are lost in the nuclear fraction, largely as a result of entrapment in the clumped nuclei. Succinoxidase determinations indicate that about 10 per cent of the mitochondria are lost in this fraction.

The supernatant and washing from the nuclear fraction are combined, transferred to a single 1-1/8" O.D. lusteroid tube, and centrifuged for 20 minutes at 19,000 r.p.m. (International rotor No. 295 or 296). The sediment was resuspended in 8 ml. 0.88 M sucrose and recentrifuged as before. At this point, the sediment consisted of three layers: (1) a small amount of brown material at the bottom of the tube, (2) a large intermediate layer of firmly packed tan material, and (3) a bulky layer of poorly sedimented pink-white material (light tan in perfused liver). (In the new medium of Novikoff (1955), the fluffy layer is absent.) The latter consisted mainly of submicroscopic particles and was removed together with the opalescent supernatant with a capillary pipette. The remainder of the pellet consisted of mitochondria and some submicroscopic material. The brown layer apparently contained mitochondria that were more firmly packed than in the bulkier tan layer. The sediment was resuspended in 0.88 M sucrose and was again centrifuged at 19,000 r.p.m. The supernatant at this point was clear and the surface of the pellet contained only a small amount of the poorly sedimented pink material. The latter was removed with the supernatant. The sediment was resuspended in 0.88 M sucrose (fraction M_W). This suspension was yellow-tan in color and showed pronounced birefringence of flow when stirred. The latter was considered to be caused by the rod-like shape of the majority of the isolated mitochondria in the suspension.

The supernatant and washings from the mitochondrial fraction were transferred to another lusteroid centrifuge tube and centrifuged for 60 minutes at 39,460 r.p.m. (Spinco rotor D) to sediment the submicroscopic particles. The supernatant, S_2, was removed with a capillary pipette. The sediment was transparent and reddish-brown in color (amber in perfused liver). It was resuspended in 0.88 M sucrose (Kel-F homogenizer; total volume, 12.5 ml.) and recentrifuged 60 min. at 50,740 r.p.m. (Spinco rotor A). The supernatant from this centrifugation was withdrawn and combined with S_2 and the sedimented submicroscopic particles were resuspended in 0.88 M sucrose (Fraction P_W). The latter fraction also exhibited strong birefringence of flow.

Centrifugal Fractionation of Isotonic (0.25 M) Sucrose Homogenates of Rat Liver: (Schneider, 1948; Schneider and Hogeboom, 1950a). Isotonic sucrose (0.25 M) possesses several advantages over hypertonic sucrose (0.88 M) as a medium for the centrifugal fractionation of liver. The activity of some complex enzyme systems, such as the system that oxidizes octanoic acid (octanoxidase), is much greater when the homogenates are made in isotonic sucrose than when made in hypertonic sucrose. Why this should be true is not at all clear, because other enzymes, such as those of the succinoxidase system, are only slightly affected by hypertonic sucrose. A further advantage in the use of isotonic sucrose is that greatly decreased centrifugal forces can be employed in the centrifugal fractionation, for isotonic sucrose has a much lower viscosity and specific gravity than hypertonic sucrose. As a result, the entire fractionation in isotonic sucrose can be made in the International centrifuge.

The preparation of the homogenate was similar to that described in preceding paragraphs for hypertonic sucrose. Ten ml. of a rat liver homogenate in 0.25 M sucrose was centrifuged for 10 min. at 2,000 r.p.m. (International Rotor No. 269) to sediment nuclei, unbroken liver cells, and red blood cells. The sediment was washed twice by rehomogenizing each time with 2.5 ml. of isotonic sucrose and centrifuging for 10 min. at the same speed. This treatment served to break up any intact cells as well as to reduce the number of mitochondria that have sedimented during the first centrifugation. The sediment remaining after the final centrifugation was resuspended in 0.25 M sucrose and labeled the nuclear fraction, N_W. This fraction contained all the nuclei of the homogenate as shown both by microscopic examination and analysis for DNA. The nuclei were agglutinated in large clumps and the fraction contained some free mitochondria and intact liver cells in addition to the nuclei and red blood cells. Recent determinations of the mitochondrial contamination of this fraction indicate that about 10 per cent of the total liver mitochondria, by actual count, are lost in this fraction. (Schneider and Hogeboom, 1952b).

The supernatant and washings obtained from the nuclear fraction were combined and centrifuged for 10 min. at 9,200 r.p.m. (International rotor No. 295 or 296) in a lusteroid tube to sediment the mitochondria. The appearance of the sediment was similar to that described for hypertonic sucrose. The sedimented mitochondria were washed twice by resuspending in 2.5 ml. of 0.25 M sucrose and recentrifuging at 9,200 r.p.m. The final sediment was resuspended in isotonic sucrose and labeled the mitochondrial fraction M_{W2}. Microscopic examination showed that this fraction contained only mitochondria. Absence of submicroscopic particles was further indicated by the low pentose nucleic acid phosphorus to nitrogen ratio (Schneider, 1948).

The supernatants from the mitochondrial fraction were combined and centrifuged 1 hr. at 25,980 r.p.m. (Spinco rotor D) in lusteroid tubes to sediment the submicroscopic particles. The sediment was transparent and red-brown in color as was noted in 0.88 M sucrose. The sediment was washed once by resuspending in 0.25 M sucrose (Kel-F homogenizer) and recentrifuging at 50,740 r.p.m. (Spinco rotor A) for 30 min. The final sediment was resuspended in 0.25 M sucrose and labeled the submicroscopic particle fraction P_W. Microscopic examination (dark field) revealed a large number of particles which could not be resolved because of their small size, but which were visible as pin points of light in rapid Brownian movement. The supernatant and washing from the submicroscopic particles were combined to form the soluble fraction, S_2.

Table 29 presents the results of the assay of liver fractions for three complex enzyme systems: the octanoxidase and oxalacetic oxidase systems (the enzyme systems that oxidize octanoic and oxalacetic acids, respectively) and the glycolytic system. In each case the sum of the activities of the four fractions (nuclear, N_W; mitochondria, M_W; submicroscopic particles, P_W; and supernatant, S_2) failed to equal that of the homogenate. This was especially true of the oxalacetic oxidase and glycolytic activities. However, when the fractions were recombined in various permutations and combinations and the activities determined, it was possible to obtain the full activity of the homogenate. Thus the possibility (mentioned in earlier paragraphs) that inhibitors or stimulators of enzymatic activity could be present in the homogenate and be distributed in various fractions was realized. In the case of the octanoxidase and oxalacetic oxidase systems, the main activity appeared to be associated with the mitochondria, whereas glycolytic activity was associated mainly with the supernatant. The fractions that contained the major activity of the homogenate were stimulated by other fractions that had little or no activity by themselves. Thus the octanoxidase activity of the mitochondria was increased by the submicroscopic particles, and the oxalacetic oxidase activity of the mitochondria was greatly augmented by the submicroscopic particles or the supernatant. Diphosphopyridine nucleotide-cytochrome c reductase (Hogeboom, 1949) and isocitric dehydrogenase (Hogeboom and Schneider, 1950) are apparently among the stimulating factors present in the latter fractions. The glycolytic activity of the supernatant was greatly increased by the addition of the mitochondria or the submicroscopic particles. Although these stimulatory effect are not fully understood, further investigations should provide useful and interesting information concerning the mechanisms by which the actions of the components of the cell are integrated to produce the enzymatic activity of the entire cell (Schneider, 1953; Hogeboom et al., 1953).

Additional comments on fractionation procedures: The presence of a poorly sedimented (fluffy) layer in the mitochondrial pellet has been mentioned above. (In the new medium of Novikoff (1955), the fluffy layer is absent.) This layer has been considered by us, on the basis of microscopic observations and biochemical determinations on the submicroscopic particle fraction, to consist mainly of submicroscopic particles (Schneider and Hogeboom, 1951). A similar conclusion was reached independently by Muntwyler et al. (1950). Additional evidence favoring this interpretation of the composition of the fluffy layer was presented by Potter et al. (1951b), by Jackson et al. (1953), by Novikoff et al. (1953), and by Smellie et al. (1953). Laird et al. (1953), however, have recently claimed to have identified the main component of the fluffy layer as small mitochondria and have found that the isolated "small mitochondria" resembled mitochondria in some respects and submicroscopic particles in other. Novikoff et al. (1953) using Laird's isolation procedure reported that the "small mitochondria" they isolated were in fact a mixture of small mitochondria and submicroscopic particles.

Table 29

Distribution of Octanoxidase and Oxalacetic Oxidase Activity in Rat Liver
Fractions and of Glycolytic Activity in Rabbit Liver Fractions

(from Schneider, 1948; Schneider and Potter, 1949; LePage and Schneider, 1948)

Fraction	Octanoxidase Activity		Oxalacetic oxidase Activity		Glycolytic Activity	
	Total*	% of H	Total*	% of H	Total*	% of H
H (homogenate)	4980	(100)	6180	(100)	313	(100)
N_W	138	2.8	648	10.5	39.5	12.6
M_W	4020	80.7	2750	44.5	0	0
P_W	0	0	0	0	8.5	2.7
S_2	0	0	31	0.5	165	52.7
$N_W + M_W$	4740	95.7	--	--	42	13.4
$N_W + P_W$	66	1.3	--	--	87	27.8
$N_W + S_2$	--	--	--	--	238	76.0
$M_W + P_W$	4730	95.0	5040	81.5	27.5	8.8
$M_W + S_2$	--	--	3830	62.0	215	68.6
$P_W + S_2$	--	--	53	0.9	297	94.9
$N_W + M_W + P_W$	5040	101	--	--	--	--
$M_W + P_W + S_2$	--	--	6060	98.0	--	--
$N_W + M_W + P_W + S_2$	--	--	--	--	328	104.8

* Cu. mm. O_2 per hr. per 10 ml. of 10 per cent homogenate or its equivalent.

** Micromoles lactic acid produced per hr. per 10 ml. of 10 per cent homogenate or its equivalent.

In spite of the fact that the bulk of the evidence favors the view that the fluffy layer is mainly submicroscopic in character, much work still remains to be done before a final conclusion on the nature of this material can be reached.

Recent experiments on the further fractionation of mitochondria isolated in the manner described above (fluffy layer removed) have revealed a considerable degree of heterogenetiy of the mitochondria with respect to certain biochemical properties (Schneider, 1953; Kuff and Schneider, 1954). Heterogeneity of the microsomes is also indicated (Novikoff et al., 1953; Barnum and Huseby, 1948). In the case of the mitochondrial fraction the results of de Duve and his coworkers indicate that the presence of as new type of particle, called lysosomes, are responsible for some of the heterogeneity observed (Appelmans et al., 1955; de Duve et al., 1955). The lysosomes, although constituting only a very small fraction of the liver, are exceedingly rich in hydrolytic enzymes such as acid phosphatase, ribonuclease, β-glucuronidase, and cathepsin and can be concentrated in a fraction intermediate between mitochondria and microsomes by altering the fractionation procedure in 0.25 M sucrose described above. It is not clear from the available evidence, however, whether these hydrolytic enzymes are exclusively localized in lysosomes and completely absent from mitochondria.

Isolation of nuclei: (The interested reader is referred to the review of Dounce (1955) for a further discussion of nuclear isolation techniques.) Although many methods have been proposed for the isolation of nuclei, from the cytochemical standpoint most of them suffer from one or more of the following deficiencies: low yields, morphological alterations, denaturation, and undetermined degree of contamination by other cell components.

Citric acid containing solutions have been among the most popular for the isolation of nuclei (Dounce, 1943). Nuclei isolated in these media show considerable morphological alterations, and, at the lower pH values at which the isolation is most successful, a number of enzymatic activities are undoubtedly inactivated.

Another method for the isolation of nuclei involves the use of non-aqueous solvents. This method was originally proposed by Behrens (1932) and consists of lyophilization or acetone dehydration of the tissue, grinding the dehydrated tissue in a ball mill, and isolating the nuclei by centrifugation of the tissue powders suspended in organic solvents of suitable density. Due to the fact that the density of the dehydrated nuclei is much greater than that of the rest of the cell, the nuclei can readily be separated. This method was recently revived and modified by Dounce et al. (1949) and Allfrey et al. (1952). The latter authors have claimed that aqueous media are unsuitable for the isolation of nuclei because (1) nuclear enzymes are extracted in these media, (2) as much as 50 per cent of the nuclear protein may be extracted under these conditions, and (3) adsorption of enzymes on nuclei may occur in these media. Hogeboom and Schneider (1952) have pointed out, however, that nuclei isolated in improved aqueous media do not show evidence of the tremendous loss of protein claimed by Allfrey et al., and that at least one water soluble enzyme was retained sufficiently well by nuclei in aqueous media to be recovered almost quantitatively in the isolated nuclei. Although it seems clear that the need for resorting exclusively to the non-aqueous methods for isolation of nuclei remains to be established, the usefulness of these methods in cytochemical work is apparent, and consequently their limitations should be clearly understood. One of the most serious drawbacks of the Behrens method is the fact that the amount of enzyme inactivation produced by the isolation procedure has not been determined. The use of controls consisting of whole dried tissue exposed to all of the solvent treatments does not satisfactorily answer this problem, since it is the relation to the whole, fresh tissue that is the important factor. Steps in this direction have been recently reported by Berenbom et al. (1952). The results of their studies suggest that it may be possible to study the distribution of a variety of enzymes (including the respiratory enzymes) with Behrens' procedure. Another limitation of the Behrens methods is that the cytoplasmic material is discarded and cytoplasmic activity must be obtained by difference from measurements of isolated nuclei and of the whole tissue. This procedure can hardly be considered as valid, at least in the study of enzymes (see earlier discussion). Another question which requires consideration is the fate of the cytoplasmic particles in the isolation procedure. Since these particles contain large amounts of lipids, one might expect that treatment with organic solvents would result in drastic alterations of these particles. However, Naora and Takeda (1954) have claimed that mitochondria could be isolated from lyophilized tissues using organic solvents.

The method of nuclear isolation which will be described in detail here involves the use of aqueous media. It is a modification of the methods of Schneider and Petermann (1950) and Wilbur and Anderson (1951). The procedure (Hogeboom et al., 1952) is as follows: The animals are killed by cervical dislocation and the livers perfused by way of the portal vein with cold 0.25 M sucrose containing 0.0018 M $CaCl_2$. All subsequent operations are carried out at 0-2° C. The livers are homogenized for 2 one-minute periods in 9 volumes of 0.25 M sucrose-0.0018 M $CaCl_2$ with a plastic homogenizing pestle of the Potter Elvehjem type. The homogenate is then filtered through a single layer of single napped flannelette (napped side up). This filtration effectively removes most of the intact liver cells remaining in the homogenate. A 10 ml. aliquot of the filtered homogenate is then layered over 20 ml. of 0.34 M sucrose-0.00018 M $CaCl_2$ and centrifuged at 2,000 r.p.m. for 10 min. The acceleration and deceleration of the rotor in this procedure must be very slow to prevent mixing of the layers that occurs in the transition of the tubes from the vertical to the horizontal position. In order to accomplish this, a rheostat is attached to the centrifuge to permit slow (30-60 secs.) starts and stops (the newer models of the International PR-1 centrifuge are equipped with such rheostats). The entire supernatant is removed and the sediment is rehomogenized for 15 secs. with 5 ml. of 0.25 M sucrose-0.00018 M $CaCl_2$. Ten ml. of 0.34 M sucrose-0.00018 M $CaCl_2$ are then slowly layered beneath the resuspended sediment and the mixture is recentrifuged as before. The procedure of homogenizing the pellet, relayering, and centrifuging is repeated twice more. The final sediment of nuclei is resuspended in 5 ml. of 0.25 M sucrose-0.00018 M $CaCl_2$. The mitochondria can be recovered by centrifuging the combined supermatants from the nuclei at 9,200 r.p.m. for 20 min. The sediment is resuspended in 0.25 M sucrose and resedimented at 18,000 r.p.m. for 10 min. and resuspended in 0.25 M sucrose. The supernatants from the mitochondrial fraction are combined and saved for analysis.

A somewhat simpler method for isolating liver nuclei described by Chaveau et al. (1956) should also be mentioned. In this procedure the tissue is homogenized in 2.2 M sucrose and centrifuged. Due to the high density of the medium, only nuclei sediment. Other subcellular elements and whole cells float and the nuclei can be obtained in one or two centrifugations.

Cytological studies of nuclei isolated by the latter procedures have shown that the isolated nuclei closely resemble those seen within living cells. The degree of contamination of these nuclei has been determined by quantitative methods and found to be low. The number of intact cells present, for example, represented less than 1 per cent of the total number of cells in the original tissue, whereas the number of mitochondria present in the isolated nuclei was less than 0.5 per cent of those present in the original homogenate. In terms of nitrogen, the amounts contributed to the nuclear fraction have been calculated to be 5.6 per cent for the intact cells and 1 per cent for the mitochondria. A contaminant which was present in the isolated nuclei and for which no quantitative correction could be made was a membranous structure resembling the cell membrane. Microscopic observations indicated that the presence of these structures would require a correction factor of small magnitude. DNA determinations on the isolated fraction indicated that 70-90 per cent of the nuclei were recovered from the original homogenate, and that the protein-DNA

ratio of the nuclei (corrected for contaminants) was close to that reported for nuclei isolated in non-aqueous media (Allfrey et al., 1952). The latter observation indicated that
little or no protein was lost from the nuclei during the isolation. This was also indicated
by the fact that almost the entire liver activity of the water soluble enzyme which synthe-
sizes DPN was recovered in nuclei isolated in the above manner. The association of the
enzyme with the nuclei was found to be under rather delicate control since the slight
amount of nuclear damage that occurred when the tissue was forced through a tissue
press was sufficient to cause a loss of 30 per cent of the total tissue activity from the
isolated nuclei.

Besides the obvious advantages of a high yield and quantitative information on the degree
of contamination by other cell constituents, this method has the further advantage of supplying the remainder of the tissue for analysis. Mitochondria isolated by this procedure
are not satisfactory, however, since they contain almost half of the tissue PNA, indicating a heavy contamination with submicroscopic particles. The presence of calcium ions
is undoubtedly responsible for the failure to obtain clean mitochondrial preparations,
since the ability of these cations to agglutinate submicroscopic particles is well known
(Schneider, 1946b). As a result, it is evident that just as the procedure described above
for isolating mitochondria and submicroscopic particles is unsuited for the isolation of
nuclei, so the procedure for the isolation of nuclei is unsuitable for the isolation of mitochondria and submicroscopic particles. It would seem that it might be possible to develop
a satisfactory method for the simultaneous isolation of nuclei, mitochondria and submicroscopic particles if the calcium ions could be eliminated after the nuclei have been
isolated. The addition of versene at this point might permit the desired separation.

Isolation of Golgi substance: The Golgi material has been a matter of considerable controversy since it was first discovered. This has been largely due to the fact that it was
first recognized in sections of fixed material, and that it has not been possible to identify
similar structures in all unfixed cells. Recently, however, Dalton and Felix (1953) were
able to observe, in the epithelial cells of the epididymis, a spherical structure as large
as the nucleus which closely resembled the Golgi substance as demonstrated in fixed sections by the classical techniques and possessed certain characteristic optical and staining
properties which permitted its extracellular identification.

The isolation of the Golgi substance was accomplished by centrifuging an epididymal homogenate layered over a density gradient. The Golgi substance has a characteristic
density which permits its separation from other cellular elements. The procedure is as
follows (Schneider and Kuff, 1954): a 20-25 per cent homogenate of rat epididymis in
0.25 M sucrose or 0.25 M sucrose-0.34 M NaCl was prepared, and 1.4 ml. was layered
over a density gradient consisting of 1.0 ml. layers of 0.335, 0.636, 0.957 and 1.11 M
sucrose, each of which contained 0.34 M NaCl in addition. The mixture (contained in
13 x 49 mm. lusteroid tubes) was spun in the Spinco SW 39 horizontal rotor for 60 min.
at 35,600 r.p.m. At the end of this time 3 bands of particulate material were observed
at the junctions of the sucrose layers. No particulate band was present at the boundary
between the homogenate and the uppermost (0.335 M) sucrose layer. The particulate
bands were separated by slicing the centrifuge tube at appropriate points in the apparatus
of Randolph and Ryan (1950). This was possible because the particulate bands were separated by fairly wide clear spaces, in which particulate material was absent. Cytological
examination revealed that the Golgi bodies were recovered largely in the second particulate band (juncture of 0.636 M and 0.957 M Sucrose layers) and had maintained their
characteristic cytological properties during the isolation. The first and third particulate
bands consisted mainly of submicroscopic material. In addition, a sediment, consisting
of the nuclei, unbroken cells, and mitochondria of the homogenate, was present at the
bottom of the centrifuge tube. The soluble materials remained in the layer occupied by
the original homogenate and a dense layer of fat had migrated to the top of this layer.

To reduce contamination of the Golgi layer by submicroscopic material Kuff and Dalton (1959) placed cytoplasmic extracts of the epididymis in 1.45 M sucrose containing 0.34 M NaCl at the bottom of the density gradient and floated the Golgi material to its equilibrium position by high speed centrifugation. This resulted in an efficient separation of the Golgi membranes from other cytoplasmic components.

METHODS FOR THE ISOLATION OF SINGLE PARTICULATE COMPONENTS OF THE CELL

The methods to be described in this section have concentrated on the isolation of a specific cell component. In general, these methods have not been concerned with studies of the remainder of the cell and are consequently subject to the criticisms made above.

Isolation of nuclei: The citric acid and Behrens' procedures have been discussed above. In addition, Lang and Siebert (1952) described the isolation of nuclei from homogenates in hypertonic sucrose solutions. The isolated nuclei appear to be well preserved from the cytological standpoint. The yield of nuclei was, however, low. The isolation of nuclei from the endosperm of the coconut has been reported by Cutter et al. (1952). Sucrose solutions are also used for this isolation, and the isolated nuclei are reported to be living and capable of maintenance in culture. The isolation of nuclei from onion root tips was described by Brown (1951). His method involves treatment of the tissue with pectinase to liberate the nuclei from the cells.

Isolation of nucleoli: Vincent (1952) has reported the isolation of nucleoli from starfish oocytes. The isolation was accomplished at pH 6.0 in water homogenates. Litt et al. (1952) have reported the isolation of nucleoli from isolated rat liver nuclei. The properties of the latter differ markedly in their nucleic acid composition from those of Vincent since they contain high concentrations of DNA. The latter was absent from the nucleoli isolated by Vincent.

Isolation of mitotic apparatus: The isolation of the mitotic apparatus from dividing cells of sea urchin eggs has been described by Mazia and Dan (1952). The procedure consists of the "fixation" of the cells in 30 per cent ethanol at -10°C., separation of the mitotic apparatus from the cytoplasm mechanically or preferably by solubilization, and isolation by centrifugation.

In more recent work (Mazia, 1957-8), it has been possible to isolate the mitotic apparatus by a considerably simpler method. The sea urchin eggs are shaken gently in an aqueous solution containing 1.0 M dextrose and 0.15 M dithiodiglycol at pH 6.2-6.4 to release the mitotic apparatus. It is then isolated and freed of cytoplasmic contaminants by centrifugation.

Isolation of chromosomes: The isolation of chromosomes was first reported by Claude and Potter (1943). This was accomplished by grinding the tissue with sand to break the nuclear membrane and thus release the nuclear contents. The chromosomes were then obtained by differential centrifugation. While working with Dr. Claude, the author learned that the sand used must be extremely fine to break the nuclear membrane and it appeared that the sand (or quartz) particles needed to be smaller than the nuclei.

Another method for the isolation of chromosomes was described by Mirsky and Ris (1947). This method differed from that of Claude and Potter in that the nuclear membranes were broken by the use of the Waring blendor.

Enzyme studies on the isolated chromosomes have not been reported. The question of whether the isolated structures are actually chromosomes has been the subject of considerable debate in the recent literature (summarized by Denues, 1953). Further work will undoubtedly be necessary before this problem is solved to the satisfaction of all. The crux of the problem rests upon the fact that it has not been possible to identify chromosomes as such within the resting nucleus. It seems to the author that the isolation of chromosomes would be placed upon a much firmer footing if the isolation was made from nuclei in the metaphase stage of mitosis. A large proportion of such nuclei can apparently be obtained in ascitic tumor cells after colchicine injection.

Isolation of chloroplasts: Chloroplasts were isolated from leaves by a method described by Granick (1938). The leaf cells were disrupted by grinding with sand (the Potter-Elvehjem homogenizer would seem to be more suitable), and the chloroplasts were isolated by differential centrifugation. The chloroplasts present in each fraction were quantitated by extracting the chlorophyll and measuring the color denisty in the Duboscq colorimeter. It is of interest to note that 0.5 M glucose or sucrose solutions were the best media for the preservation and isolation of chloroplasts. McClendon and Blinks (1952) have found, however, that in the isolation of the red plastids of algae, sucrose solutions could not be used because swelling and loss of pigment occurred. The latter effects did not occur if high molecular weight solutes, such as Carbowax 4000, were substituted for the sucrose. Stocking (1956) has found, however, that the use of Carbowax is not without its hazards, for it may precipitate enzymes.

Isolation of melanin granules: Melanin granules have been isolated from amphiuma liver (Claude, 1947-48), from the ciliary processes of beef eyes (Herrmann and Boss, 1945), from tumors (Claude, 1947-48), and from frog eggs (Recknagel, 1950) by centrifugal fractionation. These granules have also been isolated using chromatographic procedures (Riley et al., 1953). The work of Recknagel on the isolation of melanin granules is especially important, because he was able to obtain clear cut evidence for the separation of these granules from mitochondria.

Secretory granules: These granules are found in the cells of glandular tissues and are characterized by the fact that they stain vitally with neutral red. Some cytologists believe that these granules are the precursors of the Golgi substance seen in fixed preparations of these tissues. This view is not shared by all cytologists, however, and in the case of the epididymis, in which the Golgi substance can be seen directly, the neutral red granules are not associated with the Golgi substance. In liver, many of the neutral red staining granules disintegrate when homogenates are prepared (Hogeboom, Schneider and Palade, 1948) and consequently cannot be isolated from this tissue.

The secretory or zymogen granules of the pancreas have, however, recently been isolated in a high state of purity. Hokin (1955) first reported the separation of these granules from dog pancreas homogenates and subsequently Siekevitz and Palade (1958) made a thorough study of the isolation of zymogen granules from guinea pig pancreas using the electron microscope to characterize the isolated fractions. The latter workers reported that the zymogen granules could not be separated adequately from mitochondria by differential centrifugation. The use of a discontinuous density gradient permitted the resolution of mixtures of mitochondria and zymogen granules.

Zymogen granules have also recently been reported to have been separated from homogenates of the parotid gland in 0.25 M sucrose by Schramm and Danon (1961). Although these preparations were examined with the electron microscope, the failure to use ultra thin sections leaves unsettled the question of possible contamination by parotid mitochondria.

Another type of secretory granule was separated from homogenates of adrenal medulla by Blaschko and Welch (1953) and Hillarp et al., (1953). Although earlier studies claimed that these granules contained an enzyme system characteristic of mitochondria (succinoxidase) as well as high concentrations of catechol amine, more recent studies of Blaschko et al.(1957) showed that the catechol amine containing granules could be separated from the succinoxidase containing granules by using a discontinuous density gradient. It seems clear that the original granule preparations isolated from this tissue were mixtures of zymogen granules and mitochondria.

A somewhat different type of secretory granule has been isolated from milk by Morton (1954). The granules isolated were submicroscopic lipoproteins and contained a number of enzymatic activities including xanthine oxidase and alkaline phosphatase.

Lysosomes: The occurrence of these granules in the mitochondrial fraction of rat liver homogenates has already been noted above. Lysosomes have unique enzymatic properties, inasmuch as they are rich in hydrolytic enzymes, and apparently also have a distinct morphological appearance when examined with the electron microscope. Although these particles have not been purified completely, they can be obtained by modifying the centrifugal fractionation scheme outlined above to produce light and heavy mitochondrial fractions (de Duve et al., 1955). The light mitochondrial fraction can then be centrifuged in a density gradient.

Granules very similar in enzymatic properties to the lysosomes of liver have been isolated from rat kidney homogenates by Straus (1954, 1956, 1957). The kidney granules differed from the liver lysosomes by their great variation in size (0.1-5.0µ) and by their ability to engulf foreign proteins. The latter property was convincingly demonstrated by Straus (1957) who injected horse radish peroxidase into animals and showed that the granules contained high concentrations of the enzyme. Since other proteins also appear in these kidney granules when injected into animals, Straus has named them phagosomes. He has also been able to show that similar granules also occur in other tissues, including the liver.

Cell membranes: The recent isolation of cell membranes from liver tissue by Neville (1960) and Herzenberg and Herzenberg (1961) is a finding of considerable importance. Although fragments of material thought to be cell membranes were noted in preparations of nuclei by Hogeboom, Schneider and Striebich (1952), the present findings present the first clear evidence for such structures in the isolated form from mammalian tissues.

The method used by both groups of investigators in isolating the membranes was essentially the same. Liver homogenates were centrifuged at slow speed to sediment the nuclei and cell membranes. The latter were then separated by flotation in a sucrose solution whose density was 1.22.

Electron micrographs presented by Neville support his conclusion that the isolated membranes were cell membranes. The Herzenbergs, on the other hand, considered the material they isolated to have been derived from the nuclear membrane as well as the cell membrane.

Particulate glycogen: Glycogen exists in the liver cell as submicroscopic particles. These particles are, however, much denser than the protein containing submicroscopic particles and can be separated from the latter by differential centrifugation (Lazarow, 1942; Claude, 1946). These particles are so dense, in fact, that a small white translucent pellet of glycogen is frequently seen at the bottom of sedimented mitochondrial fractions prepared from the livers of unfasted animals.

Isolation of mitochondria from other tissues: Mitochondria have been isolated from tissues other than liver by procedures similar to those used above.   Sucrose solutions have found wide use for this purpose.   The tissues that have been used include kidney (Schneider, 1946a; Schneider and Potter, 1949), hepatomas (Schneider and Hogeboom, 1950b), heart (Plaut and Plaut, 1952; Harman and Feigelson, 1952; Cleland and Slater, 1953), brain (Abood and Gerard, 1952; Brody and Bain, 1952), skeletal muscle (Harman and Osborne, 1953), insect muscles (Watanabe and Williams, 1951; Sacktor, 1953) and plants (reviewed by Millerd and Bonner, 1953), and bacteria (Georgi et al., 1951).   Some of the methods mentioned include complete fractionation methods similar to those described above for liver.

Sarcosomes: Some confusion has arisen in the use of this term.   Cleland and Slater (1953) refer to the mitochondria of heart muscle as sarcosomes.   Harman and Osborne (1953), on the other hand, make a sharp distinction between mitochondria and smaller granules which they call sarcosomes in skeletal muscle.

W. C. SCHNEIDER

Chapter II

MANOMETRIC AND CHEMICAL ESTIMATION OF METABOLITES AND ENZYME SYSTEMS

INTRODUCTION

The popular usage of manometric equipment for measuring the overall metabolic gas exchange of biological systems has overshadowed to a considerable extent the great usefulness of this equipment for more specific chemical determinations. As has been previously pointed out, any reaction which results in either the production or utilization of a gas can be followed with great accuracy using a manometric apparatus. Further, reactions which give rise to end products having acidic groups can be accurately followed by allowing the reaction to take place in a bicarbonate medium.

In most manometric experiments involving biological transformations the quantity of metabolite involved is usually of the order of 0.5 to 5 mg. The manometric equipment is particularly suitable for semi-micro determinations in this range.

The development of micro-photometric methods and equipment has tended to replace older manometric methods. In many cases this represents a welcome improvement. However, there still remain a large number of metabolites which are peculiarly suited to manometric estimation. This is particularly true where specific enzyme systems can be utilized. Thus, the important metabolite succinic acid can be accurately determined in small quantities by means of a manometric method employing a succinoxidase preparation. In certain instances one may have a choice of an equally suitable colorimetric or manometric method. For example, urea can be readily determined colorimetrically (Archibald, 1945) or manometrically with urease at pH 5 (Krebs and Henseleit, 1932). The choice of one or the other method will be determined by the type of equipment available, the experimental setup, the experience of the investigator, the accuracy requirements of the experiment, etc.

Manometric methods still find their widest use in the study of tissue metabolism. However, tissue metabolism consists of many reactions not involving gaseous change, or reactions measurable by gas exchange are often associated with other reactions not so measurable. It is therefore very convenient to have available chemical methods to determine the disappearance of substrates, the appearance of products, or the change in one or more of the substances in the medium in which the tissue is suspended.

Since the manometric methods described are capable of measuring very small changes, chemical methods employed must be capable of measuring changes of the order of 5 to 10 micrograms. Their total range usually must be from 0 to 100 micrograms. The small quantities involved exclude all but the simplest fractionation procedures, so that any methods employed must be specific. In addition methods usually must be specific enough to measure small quantities of the compound involved without interference from other related materials which may be present in large quantities. Means of achieving specificity in micro-methods are described below.

It is not our purpose to describe a large number of methods. We are concerned only with basic methods which probably would be used frequently by one working with manometric techniques. Additional assistance may possibly be obtained by consulting the series of volumes on "Methods of Biochemical Analysis" (Vol. I, 1954, edited by Glick; see references).

MANOMETRIC ANALYSES

SUCCINIC ACID

Principle: This method was first worked out by Gozsy (1935) and simplified and improved by Krebs (1937). In principle the method depends upon the extraction of succinic acid by means of ethyl ether. The succinic acid is then oxidized by means of a succinoxidase preparation and the O_2 consumption measured. The following reaction takes place:

$$COOH\text{-}CH_2\text{-}CH_2\text{-}COOH + 1/2\ O_2 \longrightarrow COOH\text{-}CH = CH\text{-}COOH + H_2O$$

The specificity of the method is insured by (1) washing the succinoxidase preparation free of coenzymes, and (2) the insolubility in ethyl ether of coenzymes present in the biological system.

Preparation of the sample for extraction: It is desirable to add a deproteinizing agent to the sample before extraction in order to avoid emulsification at the ether-water interface. Sulfuric acid plus sodium tungstate usually has been employed. However, Krebs and Eggleston (1948a) have pointed out that in the presence of phosphate ions, excess tungstic acid is converted to phosphotungstic acid which is extractable with ether and which is a powerful inhibitor of succinic dehydrogenase. The formation of inhibitory quantities of phosphotungstate is readily prevented by avoiding an excess of tungstate. Krebs and Eggleston recommend a preliminary determination of the minimum amount of sodium tungstate required to give a protein free filtrate using an aliquot of the material being studied. Where the succinic content is low it is best to deliver the total sample into the extraction apparatus and then add the deproteinizing reagents and extract directly. To insure an adequate acidity, it is necessary to add an excess of H_2SO_4, usually 1-2 ml. of a 10% solution.

Extraction with ethyl ether: It is essential that the ethyl ether be freed of peroxides before using. This is best accomplished by storing a large quantity of ether over metallic sodium and freshly distilling portions as needed.[1] This involves little trouble if a condenser and a distillation and receiving flask are permanently fixed at the steam bath used for the extraction apparatus. Such a set-up allows for efficient recovery of the ether remaining after the completion of the extraction. The removal of peroxides is essential since the succinoxidase preparation has potent catalase activity, and the liberation of oxygen by this system will interfere in the manometric estimation of oxygen consumption.

A simple and efficient extraction apparatus is that of Kutscher and Steudel as illustrated in figure 52. The extractors may be made to contain different volumes of from 15 to 50 ml. The latter size has been found convenient and adaptible for extracting volumes of from 10-35 ml. Since the efficiency of extraction is determined in part by the height of the aqueous column, funnels of different diameters can be employed. Thus with small aqueous volumes, a funnel of wide diameter when filled with ether will heighten the aqueous column outside the funnel very considerably and so enhance the extraction efficiency. The efficiency of extraction is determined by such other factors as the rate of boiling, the temperature, the fineness and speed of the ether bubbles passing through the aqueous layer, etc. It is essential that the efficiency of extraction be determined for each extractor by estimating the recovery of known amounts of succinic acid. As an aid in estimating the rate of extraction, indicators with suitable partition coefficients may be

---

[1] The storage flask of ether plus sodium can be conveniently closed off by means of a "Bunsen valve". This is merely a short piece of rubber tubing sealed at one end with a tight fitting glass rod. The rubber tubing is slit with a razor blade, and then fitted over the glass tubing projecting from the cork stopper of the flask. When the pressure inside the flask increases it will permit escape of the gases (hydrogen or ether vapor) through the slit in the tubing.

employed (see Krebs, Smyth and Evans, 1940). The addition of a few drops of phenol red (0.01% aqueous) to the fluid to be extracted will serve not only as an extraction indicator (about 60 per cent of the succinic acid will have been extracted when the phenol red disappears from the aqueous phase) but in addition serves as a neutralization indicator in the extract. It should be pointed out that at a low pH phenol red has a pink color not unlike that seen in the region of pH 7.

When the extraction is completed, 1-2 ml. of 0.1 M phosphate buffer, pH 7.4 is added to the ether solution and the ether distilled off. The last traces of ether are removed by concentrating the aqueous residue on the steam bath to approximately 0.5 to 1 ml. The residue is then transferred to a small graduated cylinder (a graduated 15 ml. centrifuge tube is convenient) by means of a 1 ml. pipette. The flask is rinsed several times with small volumes (0.2-0.5 ml.) of 0.1 M phosphate buffer and the washings added to the contents of the graduated tube. Since the solution in the flask is colored due to the presence of the phenol red, the disappearance of the color in the successive washings can serve as a guide in determining the completion of transfer. The solution in the tube is now adjusted to the proper pH, i.e., 7.4, by the dropwise addition of dilute NaOH, if necessary. The final volume of the extract should be adjusted according to the succinic acid concentration. Since 1 ml. aliquots are usually employed, it is desirable that this amount should contain between 0.2 and 1 mg. of succinic acid. This would represent an uptake of 19 and 95 μl. of O_2 respectively, which is a convenient range.

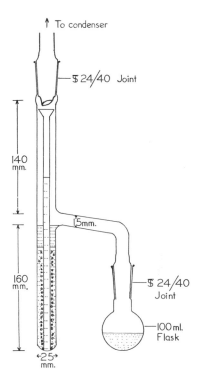

Figure 52
Kutscher-Steudel extraction apparatus

Preparation of succinoxidase: A simple and suitable succinoxidase preparation can be made as follows: Pigeon breast, pig or sheep heart muscle is freed of fat and connective tissue. It is then coarsely ground in a meat chopper and suspended in 10 volumes of ice-cold distilled water. The suspension is frequently stirred during the first 10 minutes and then allowed to settle in the cold room. The supernatant is decanted and the residue sucked through a double layer of cheesecloth on a Büchner funnel. The muscle pulp is then resuspended in cold distilled water and the procedure is twice repeated. After the third washing, the muscle pulp is dried as completely as possible by suction. For use, a portion of the pulp is suspended in four to five times its weight of 0.1 M phosphate buffer (pH 7.4.) This is best accomplished by grinding with a glass mortar and pestle. For storage, the muscle pulp is placed in a tightly covered container and allowed to freeze solid in the freezing compartment of a refrigerator. In this state the preparation remains active and with a low blank O_2 uptake for several weeks (Cohen, 1940). In this connection it should be pointed out that freshly dissected pigeon breast or freshly killed mammalian heart muscle can be stored for months if frozen solid in covered containers and still yield very active succinoxidase preparations. Where fresh tissue is not readily available at all times this procedure is recommended to insure a continuous supply of enzyme. The phosphate suspension of the muscle pulp develops an appreciable blank O_2 uptake after 24 hours. Since the suspension is rather pasty, it is necessary to pipette it with a wide mouthed pipette. This is best accomplished by breaking off the fine tip from a 3 ml. pipette, flaming it, and then recalibrating to deliver 3 ml.

A dry preparation of succinic dehydrogenase has been described by Weil-Malherbe (1937). Brilliant cresyl blue is used as a carrier.

Manometric estimation of succinic acid: Warburg flasks of about 20 ml. capacity with a center well and a sidearm of 1 ml. capacity are usually employed. To the center well is added 0.2 ml. of 10% KOH plus a square of filter paper. The succinic acid solution, usually 1 ml., is added to the sidearm. The succinoxidase suspension, usually 3 ml. is pipetted into the main compartment. The control vessel is made up in the same way except that 1 ml. of 0.1 M phosphate buffer, pH 7.4 with a drop of phenol red, is placed in the sidearm. The bath temperature is usually 40° C. After a 10 minute shaking period with the stopcocks open for equilibration, the manometer fluid is adjusted so as to provide a maximum scale for reading and the stopcocks are then closed. Readings are then taken every 5 minutes until the O_2 uptake is constant in the different manometers. This may require anywhere from 1 to 5 successive readings depending on the temperature of the solutions, the rate of shaking, the thickness of the succinoxidase suspensions, etc. After equilibration is attained, the content of the sidearm is delivered into the main compartment and the manometers swirled once or twice to insure mixing. The manometers are then tipped back and forth once or twice to insure mixing of the solution remaining in the sidearm with the enzyme suspension. A small amount of the suspension is left in the sidearm to insure oxidation of the last traces of the succinic acid. Readings are then taken every 10 minutes until the $\triangle$ values (uptake per unit time) of the control and the experimental manometers are equal on two successive readings. The reaction is usually complete in 40 minutes. However, in the presence of high salt concentrations, high concentrations of fumaric, α-ketoglutaric and oxalacetic acids, the reaction rate is slowed up so that periods as long as 90-120 minutes may be required to complete the reaction.

Determination of succinic acid in the presence of malonic acid: It is usually necessary to add malonic acid to aerobic biological systems in which succinic acid synthesis is to be determined. This substance inhibits the oxidation of succinic acid. It is therefore necessary to remove the malonic acid before the succinic acid determination can be carried out. This is most simply done by oxidation with acid permanganate using a procedure similar to that employed for α-keto-glutaric acid determination. Malonic acid is readily oxidized by acid permanganate while succinic acid is not. If α-ketoglutaric acid is present in this system, which will be likely, it will be converted to succinic acid by the permanganate treatment and therefore will be included in the succinic acid determination. Should it be desired to determine succinic acid only, it is possible to remove the succinic and malonic acids from the α-ketoglutaric acid by the addition of $NaHSO_3$ to a concentration of 0.3 M and enough H_3PO_4 to reduce the pH to about 3.0. Since the sulfite addition product of α-ketoglutaric acid is relatively insoluble in ether, the succinic and malonic acids can be extracted with ether (Weil-Malherbe, 1937). After removal of the ether the malonic acid can be destroyed by oxidation with acid permanganate, leaving succinic acid (Krebs and Eggleston, 1940).

Analytical range: The smallest quantity of succinic acid which can be determined by the manometric method is limited chiefly by the accuracy of the manometric equipment. Since 0.05 mg. of succinic acid is equivalent to 4.75 μl. of O_2 uptake, this amount can be considered the lower limit of the method.

Calculation:

μl. O_2 uptake is converted to mg. of succinic acid as follows

$$\frac{\mu l. \ O_2}{112} \ \times 1.18 = mg. \ succinic \ acid$$

MANOMETRIC ESTIMATION OF GLUTAMIC ACID WITH
GLUTAMIC ACID DECARBOXYLASE

Principle: The enzyme glutamic acid decarboxylase catalyzes the following reaction:

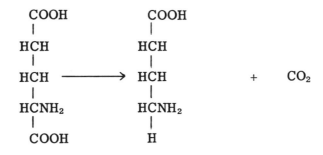

glutamic acid   γ-aminobutyric acid

Preparation of enzyme and reagents: The simplest and most useful preparation of glutamic acid decarboxylase is that prepared from E. coli, (American Type Culture, strain 4157; 2029 M Street, N.W., Washington, D.C.). The organism is transferred from a nutrient agar slant into 100 ml. of the medium listed below and incubated at 30° for 24 hours. Sixteen liters of medium are then inoculated with the 100 ml. of culture, held at 30° for 5 hours and then incubated at room temperature for 24 hours. Occasional shaking of the incubation mixture is desirable for maximum yields. The organisms are then harvested in a Sharples centrifuge at 20,000 r.p.m. The collected paste is washed twice with 10 vol. of 0.85% saline and then spread out in petri dishes and dried in vacuo over $CaCl_2$. The resulting dried powder is finely ground and stored in a desiccator. The yield from such a preparation is 3 to 4 g. of dry powder.

Najjar and Fisher (1954) have prepared a highly specific and stable glutamic acid decarboxylase from another strain of E. coli (American Type Culture Collection No. 11246). This preparation can be stored as an acetone powder for months and can also be fractionated with ammonium sulfate to yield a highly purified enzyme preparation.

Several biochemical supply houses now sell glutamic acid decarboxylase prepared from E. coli or Clostridium welchii.

Incubation Medium (Umbreit and Gunsalus, 1945):

NaCl	100 grams
Trypticase (Difco)	100 grams
Yeast extract (Difco)	10 grams
Cerelose	100 grams
K_2HPO_4	25 grams
Distilled H_2O	10 liters

Buffer:

3 M Acetate buffer, pH 5.

27.2 g. Sodium acetate ($NaC_2H_3O_2 \cdot 3H_2O$)
plus 6 g. glacial acetic acid are made up
to 100 ml. with distilled H_2O.

Manometric assay: The solution to be analyzed for glutamic acid is brought to pH 5 by the addition of 3 M acetate buffer. (0.2 ml. of buffer is usually sufficient for volumes of 2-3 ml. buffered with 0.01 M phosphate at pH 7.4.) A suitable aliquot (sufficient to yield a measurable gas production in the manometer) of the order of 1-2 ml. is added to the main compartment of a manometric flask. To the side arm is added 0.5 ml. of a suspension of dried E. coli preparation (20 mg. suspended in 1 ml. of 0.1 M acetate buffer, pH 5.0). A suitable blank should be employed. After equilibration, the flask contents are mixed and CO_2 evolution is measured until no more gas is evolved. This usually requires 20-30 minutes depending on the activity of the enzyme.

Calculations: 1 micromole of glutamic acid will yield 22.4 µl. of CO_2.

OXALACETIC AND ACETOACETIC ACIDS

Principle: This method is based on the fact that β-keto acids are catalytically decomposed by primary amines in an acid medium to yield CO_2:

$$RCOCH_2COOH \longrightarrow RCOCH_3 + CO_2$$

Ostern (1933) first applied this principle to the determination of oxalacetic acid using aniline as a catalyst. The reaction was carried out in acetic acid-acetate buffer, pH 5, and at 5° C. Quastel and Wheatly (1933) introduced the use of aniline hydrochloride for the determination of acetoacetic acid. Edson (1935) employed aniline citrate for the same reaction, to better advantage. The use of aniline citrate for oxalacetic acid determination was reported by Greville (1939). The advantage of aniline citrate over that of other aniline salts is the greater solubility of this compound which insures a high concentration of the catalyst.

While aniline decarboxylates both acetoacetic and oxalacetic acids, Al^{+++} salts decarboxylate oxalacetic acid only (Krebs, 1942a; Krebs and Eggleston, 1945). However, in the presence of pyruvate, CO_2 may be liberated from acetoacetic acid (or a condensation product) by aluminum ions (Krebs and Eggleston, 1948b).

Reagents:

0.75 M phthalate buffer - 15.3 gm. potassium hydrogen phthalate and
1.8 gm. NaOH in 100 ml.

Aluminum sulfate   - 33.3 gm. $Al_2(SO_4)_3 \cdot 18 H_2O$ per 100 gm. H_2O.

Aniline citrate   - 4.5 ml. freshly distilled aniline plus
5.5 ml. of 50 percent citric acid.

2 N HCl

Procedure: At the end of the incubation period, 0.25 volumes of 2 N HCl are added to the flasks which are then placed in an ice bath. Slices are removed at this time in the usual manner. In the case of tissue minces or homogenates, the cold, acidified solutions are centrifuged and suitable aliquots are taken for analysis. The rate of spontaneous decomposition of the β-keto acids is lowered by the use of mineral acids. Thus Krebs and Eggleston (1945) recommend the addition of 2 N HCl to the solution to be tested to bring the final concentration to about 0.2 N.

Determination of Acetoacetic Plus Oxalacetic Acids: The main compartment of the vessel is filled with 3 ml. of the unknown solution, 0.3 ml. of 2 N HCl and 0.5 ml. of 50 percent citric acid, the sidearm with 1 ml. of aniline citrate. The determination is best carried out at low temperatures; however, 20-25° C. is satisfactory. An initial equilibration period of 5 minutes with the taps open is necessary to insure removal of dissolved CO_2. After the taps are closed, readings are taken every 5 minutes until constancy is reached. The flask contents are then mixed. Readings are then taken as usual until no more CO_2 is produced, or until the pressure changes in the control and experimental flasks are constant. Immediately on mixing a reduction in pressure will usually result due to the difference in density of the aniline citrate solution and the solution in the main compartment. This is corrected for by the use of a control vessel, which contains water in place of β-keto acid.

Determination of Oxalacetic Acid: Warburg flasks with double sidearms each having a capacity of 1 ml. are used. The main compartment contains 2 ml. of the solution to be tested (previously acidified to approximately 0.2 N with 2 N HCl). One sidearm contains 1 ml. of 0.75 M phthalate buffer and the other 1 ml. of 33.3 per cent aluminum sulfate solution. A bath temperature of 20-25° C. may be used. After equilibration, the phthalate buffer is introduced from the sidearm followed by the aluminum sulphate solution. A control experiment using water in place of the unknown solution is necessary in order to correct for the pressure changes caused by mixing the different solutions. The CO_2 evolution is usually complete within 60 minutes. Recovery experiments give yields approximately 5 percent below theory due to spontaneous decomposition of oxalacetic acid during equilibration. Acetoacetic acid is determined by difference between the aniline citrate and the aluminum sulfate values.

Calculations: Microliters of CO_2 produced is converted to mg. of oxalacetic and acetoacetic acids as follows:

$$\frac{\mu l.\ CO_2}{224} \times 1.32 = \text{mg. of oxalacetic acid}$$

$$\frac{\mu l.\ CO_2}{224} \times 1.02 = \text{mg. of acetoacetic acid}$$

Specificity: Aniline salts will catalyze the decomposition of all β-keto acids. Aluminum ions (and other multivalent cations) on the other hand catalyze the decomposition chiefly of β-ketodicarboxylic acids and have no effect on α- or β-keto monocarboxylic or α-keto-dicarboxylic acids.

UREA

Principle: (Krebs and Henseleit, 1932). Urea is converted by urease to ammonium carbonate at pH 5. The ammonium carbonate in turn reacts to yield CO_2 according to the following equation:

$$\underset{NH_2}{\overset{NH_2}{\mid}}CO\underset{}{\mid} \xrightarrow[2H_2O]{urease} (NH_4)_2CO_3 \xrightarrow{2H^+} 2(NH_4)^+ \ H_2O \ + \ CO_2$$

The CO_2 formed is measured manometrically.

Reagents:

1. Urease: While urease itself is highly specific in its action, the ordinary sources of urease may contain enzyme systems which will yield CO_2 under similar conditions. In particular, carboxylase may yield CO_2 from pyruvic acid under the above conditions. Thus it has been shown that commercial jack bean meal contains a potent carboxylase system (Cohen, 1946). Soy bean meal extracts, on the other hand, are practically devoid of this enzyme. The carboxylase activity of the jack bean meal extract is readily lost on dialysis against dihydrogen sodium phosphate solution without influencing the urease activity. In practice, however, it has been found far more convenient to purchase a purified urease (Arlco urease, made by Arlington Chemical Co., Arlington, Mass.) which is free of carboxylase. Since this material is stable for a long time and requires no preparation other than solution before use, it is more economical from the standpoint of both time and money. It is best prepared in a concentration of 10 mgs. per ml. of solution, the latter being 9.5 parts distilled water plus 0.5 parts acetic acid-sodium acetate buffer, pH 5.

2. Acetic Acid-Sodium Acetate Buffer: 27.2 g. sodium acetate ($NaC_2H_3O_2 \cdot 3H_2O$) plus 6 g. glacial acetic acid are made up to 100 ml. with distilled water. This represents a 3 N acetic-ion concentration and has a pH of 5.

Procedure: If tissue slices are used, these are removed from the flasks and the remaining solution acidified with 0.3 ml. of acetic acid-sodium acetate buffer; 0.5 ml. of urease solution is added to the sidearm.

In the case of tissue minces or homogenates, acetic acid-sodium acetate buffer is added directly to the flask and the total volume noted. The preparation is then centrifuged and a suitable aliquot is placed in the main compartment of a clean flask with 0.5 ml. urease solution in the sidearm. The control vessel contains distilled water plus acetic acid-sodium acetate buffer in place of the experimental solution. After a suitable equilibration period, the solutions are mixed and the manometric changes observed. The reaction is usually run at 38° with air as a gas phase. The reaction should be completed in 20-30 minutes.

Calculation: The μl. CO_2 produced is converted to mg. urea as follows:

$$\frac{\mu l. \ CO_2}{224} \times 0.60 = mg. \ urea.$$

Specificity: As previously pointed out, in the presence of pyruvate and related substances, high "urea" values may be obtained because of carboxylase activity in the crude urease preparations. By the use of purified urease preparations this difficulty is eliminated. Krebs (1942b) has called attention to another source of CO_2 unrelated to urea, i.e., acetoacetic acid. This substance is found in considerable amounts when liver slices are incubated in the presence of ammonium salts (Edson, 1935). Since acetoacetic acid slowly decomposes to yield CO_2, it may interfere with the urea determination. In order to destroy the acetoacetic acid, Krebs recommends the addition of 0.1 ml. of aniline plus 1 ml. of acetic acid-sodium acetate buffer to the unknown solution. The aniline catalyzes the decomposition of the acetoacetic acid so that it is completely broken down within the usual equilibration period of 20 minutes. (See method for acetoacetic acid determination, page 198).

GLUTATHIONE

Principle: This method (Woodward, 1935) depends on the fact that the glyoxalase system requires reduced glutathione as a coenzyme. The rate of conversion of methylglyoxal to lactic acid is dependent on the concentration of glutathione within certain limits. The reaction is carried out in a bicarbonate-CO_2 system. The CO_2 formed as a result of the conversion of methyl glyoxal to lactic acid is measured manometrically:

$$CH_3COCHO \xrightarrow[GSH]{H_2O} CH_3CHOHCOOH$$

Reagents:

1. Acetone dried yeast: This is prepared according to Albert, et al. (1902). 500 grams of starch-free bakers' yeast is coarsely pulverized and passed through a sieve (10 mesh) into 3 liters of acetone in a flat dish. After stirring, the yeast is allowed to remain in the acetone for 10 minutes. The acetone is then decanted and the residue sucked dry on a hard filter paper. The resulting cake is again broken up and suspended in one liter of acetone for 2 minutes. After decanting the supernatant, the yeast residue is sucked dry. The resulting cake is then broken up and covered with 250 ml. of ethyl ether and mixed for 3 minutes after which the suspension is filtered by suction. The yeast cake is finely pulverized and spread out in a thin layer on filter paper for 1 hour. The resulting powder is then further dried by placing in a desiccator for 24 hours at 45°. Before use, the yeast must be freed of glutathione. This is most readily done by suspending 1 gram of dried yeast in 50 ml. of distilled water and centrifuging. The supernatant is decanted and the centrifugate suspended again with 50 ml. of distilled water. After centrifuging again and decanting, the yeast is made up as a 15-20 per cent suspension and stored in the ice box.

2. Methyl glyoxal: (Methyl glyoxal, pyruvic aldehyde, is obtainable from Commercial Solvents Corporation as a 30 per cent aqueous solution.) A solution of methyl glyoxal is readily prepared by distilling dihydroxyacetone from H_2SO_4 according to Neuberg et al. (1917). 0.5 grams of dihydroxyacetone is introduced into a 100 ml. distilling flask. A mixture of 5 grams H_2O plus 1 gram of H_2SO_4 is placed in a small separatory funnel which is tightly fixed in the flask neck with a rubber stopper. The distilling flask is connected with a small efficient water-jacketed condenser. The H_2SO_4 solution is added dropwise while the flask is being heated. After 5 ml. of distillate has come over (the distillate is best collected in a glass stoppered graduated cylinder) 5 ml. of distilled water should be added dropwise through the funnel. This procedure is repeated until a drop of the distillate no longer gives a precipitate when added to a dilute acetic acid solution of m-nitrobenzhydrazide. To determine the concentration of methylglyoxal, the method of Friedemann (1927) is both simple and sufficiently accurate. An aliquot is titrated with 0.1 N NaOH to a pink color with phenolphthalein. Neutral 5% H_2O_2 solution is then added followed by a known amount of 0.1 N NaOH. (The amount will be determined by the methylglyoxal concentration. As a guide, the solution should remain pink to phenolphthalein while standing for 10 minutes at room temperature.) The flask is stoppered and allowed to stand at room temperature for 10 minutes. The solution is then titrated with 0.1 N HCl until colorless.

3. 2% sulfosalicylic acid.

4. 95% N_2 - 5% CO_2 gas mixture.

5. 0.2 M Sodium bicarbonate.

<u>Procedure</u>: A standard curve is prepared by adding known amounts of reduced glutathione to the yeast-methyl glyoxal system. The levels of gluthathione suggested are 0.025, 0.05, 0.1 and 0.15 mg. A blank with no glutathione is run and subtracted from these values. The flasks are set up to contain the following in the main compartment: 0.15 ml. of a 15-20 percent yeast suspension. (The amount of yeast to be used is determined by its glyoxalase activity. This is estimated by measuring the amount of CO_2 found in 20 minutes in the presence of 0.1 mg. of glutathione and 10 mgs. of methyl glyoxal. An amount of yeast should be taken which will yield 200-250 µl. of CO_2 under these conditions); 10 mgs. of methyl glyoxal (usually about 0.5 ml.); 0.4 ml. of 0.2 M sodium bicarbonate; H_2O to make 2 ml. The sidearm holds the glutathione containing solution. If deproteinization is required, this is accomplished with 2% sulfosalicylic acid. The acid filtrate is neutralized before use with 0.2 M sodium bicarbonate to methyl orange. (This is best done with an aliquot.)

After gassing with 95% N_2-5% CO_2 mixture the flasks are placed in a bath (25° C) and the manometer fluid levels adjusted so that the level of the left hand column is between 0 and 5 mm. (This is accomplished by sucking gas out of the closed system after gassing and readjusting the level of the right column to 15. By this procedure the capacity of the manometer is almost doubled.) After an initial equilibration period with shaking (during which time the gas production in the control and experimental flasks should be equal) the contents of the side bulbs are tipped in. Readings are taken every 5 minutes without stopping the shaking apparatus. The first 5 minute reading is discarded since it will usually be too high due to mixing effects. Readings are taken for 20 minutes and the first 5 minute value calculated by extrapolation.

<u>Calculation</u>: The glutathione concentration is determined by reading the 20-minute CO_2 value from the standard curve.

<u>Accuracy</u> and <u>Specificity</u>: The accuracy of the method is determined chiefly by the pipetting accuracy of the different reagents. According to Woodward (1935) the limit of error does not exceed 6 percent.

This method is highly specific since no naturally occurring sulfhydryl compound other than glutathione will react in this system. Further, ascorbic acid is not active and thus the procedure can be used in the presence of this reducing substance. While the method does not lend itself to a routine use, it is most valuable where a quantitative estimation of glutathione in biological material is required.

D-AMINO ACIDS

The determination of D-amino acids ("non-natural") is of some interest since they have been shown to occur naturally in certain bacteria. While the more classical methods of determining optical rotation usually can be used for characterizing the D-amino acids, occasionally, due to the small quantity of material available, the use of a specific enzyme preparation may be necessary for establishing the presence or the amount of these substances (See Lipmann <u>et al</u>., 1940, and Lipmann <u>et al</u>., 1941). For this purpose the use of simple aqueous extracts of acetone dried kidney powder (Krebs, 1935b) is usually satisfactory. Should a pure reconstituted flavin-adenine-dinucleotide-protein system be required, the resolution and reconstitution technique of Warburg and Christian (1938) can be employed. The specificity of the two preparations is the same (Klein and Handler, 1941). For the details of preparation and procedure, the reader is referred to the original papers. See Greenstein <u>et al</u>. (1953).

L-AMINO ACIDS

The preparation of potent L-amino acid decarboxylases from bacteria has been reported by Gale (1946). These decarboxylases are particularly suitable for the manometric estimation of certain L-amino acids. Table 31 summarizes the information available on the specific amino acid decarboxylases and the conditions used for the estimation of the different amino acids. With some strains of S. faecalis, phenylalanine may be decarboxylated (McGilvery and Cohen, 1948). Krebs (1948) has reported that washed suspensions of Clostridium welchii, strain SR 12, not only specifically decarboxylate glutamic acid, but also contain a specific glutaminase. This preparation can therefore be used to determine both glutamic acid and glutamine by merely measuring the CO_2 produced in the case of the former and the NH_3 plus CO_2 produced in the case of the latter. Of interest is the statement by Krebs (1948) that stock suspensions of Clostridium welchii in 0.2 M acetate buffer (pH 4.9) are active for about one month. (Compare with Gale, 1947, Table 31.)

Enzyme preparations are sold by several biochemical supply houses for the decarboxylation of arginine, glutamic acid, histidine, lysine and tyrosine, and a few can supply aspartic acid decarboxylase. Apparently, most of these are preparations derived from bacteria as described by Gale (1946).

PEPTIDASE ACTIVITY

Zeller and Maritz (1945) have reported that peptidase activity can be readily measured by the use of ophio-L-amino acid oxidase (Zeller and Maritz, 1944). The latter is a potent enzyme present in snake venoms and tissues. By adding an ophio-L-amino acid oxidase preparation to a peptidase-peptide system the liberated amino acid is rapidly oxidized and the O_2-consumption can be measured manometrically. The ophio-L-amino acid oxidase does not attack peptides. The rates of amino acid oxidation for Vipera aspis venom are given in Table 30 and can be used as a guide in the choice of peptides suitable for this system.

Table 30

Amino Acid	QO_2	Amino Acid	QO_2
Phenylalanine	780	Diiodotyrosine	135
Leucine	612	Nitrotyrosine	129
Tryptophan	540	Histidine	78
Tyrosine	402	Valine	71
Methionine	390	Cystine	42
Dihydroxyphenylalanine	294	Alanine	30
Dibromtyrosine	216	Arginine	26
Isoleucine	162	Cysteine	22

Table 31

Specific Amino-Acid Decarboxylase Preparations for Estimation of Amino-Acids (Gale, 1947)

Enzyme	Organism (N.C.T.C. no.*)	Conditions of culture			Specific preparation	Activity Maintained	Manometric estimation	
		Medium	Temp.	Time (hr.)			Buffer	CO_2 evolution as % theory
L-Lysine decarboxylase	Bacterium cadaveris (6578)	3% casein digest 2% glucose (1 L. medium = 50 estimations)	25°	24	Acetone (5 vol.)-ether-dried powder, kept 3 days at 0° before use Use ca. 10 mg. per test	4-6 weeks in desiccator	M/5 phosphate, pH 6.0 +acid-tip	92 / 98
L-Arginine decarboxylase	Escherichia coli (7020)	3% casein digest 2% glucose (1 L. medium = 40 estimations)	25°	24	Acetone (5 vol.)-ether-dried powder Use ca. 10 mg. per test	4-6 weeks in desiccator	M/5 phosphate-citrate pH 5.2	95
L-Histidine decarboxylase	Clostridium welchii, B.W. 21 (6785)	3% casein digest 2% glucose Heart muscle (1 L. medium = 20 estimations)	37°	16	Acetone (3 vol.)-ether-dried powder Use ca. 30 mg. per test	2-3 months in desiccator	M/5 acetate, pH 4.5	96
L-Ornithine decarboxylase	Clostridium septicum, PIII (547)	3% casein digest 2% glucose Heart muscle (1 L. medium = 20 estimations)	37°	16	Washed suspension of organism 20-30 mg. dry weight cells/ml. Use 0.5 ml. per test	24 hours	M/5 phosphate-citrate, pH 5.5 +acid-tip	92 / 98
L-Tyrosine decarboxylase	Streptococcus faecalis (6783)	3% casein digest 1% glucose 0.1% marmite (1 L. medium = 50 estimations)	37°	16	Acetone (5 vol.)-ether-dried powder Use ca. 10 mg. per test	2-6 weeks in desiccator	M/5 phosphate-citrate, pH 5.5	96
L-Glutamic acid decarboxylase	Clostridium welchii, SR 12 (6784)	3% casein digest 2% glucose Heart muscle Hydrogen (1 L. medium = 30 estimations)	37°	12	Washed suspension of organism 20-30 mg. dry weight cells/ml. Use 0.5 ml. per test	48 hours in H_2	M/5 acetate, pH 4.5	98

*National Collection Type Cultures, England

MANOMETRIC ESTIMATION OF ENZYME ACTIVITY

Since many enzymes catalyze reactions which directly or indirectly involve the production or utilization of a gas, manometric methods have been extensively used in both assaying for enzyme activity, and in studying the kinetics of a given reaction. For obvious reasons, manometric methods have been most extensively employed in the study and assay of respiratory and other oxidation enzymes. The features of the manometric techniques used for enzyme study are:

1. The need for only small amounts of enzyme preparation,
2. The accuracy and speed of the estimation, and
3. The ease with which one can study the effects of inhibitors, substrate concentration, pH and other aspects of kinetics.

A detailed discussion of the preparation and manometric study of different enzyme systems is beyond the scope of this chapter. The reader is referred to Green (1940), Sumner and Somers (1947) and to Colowick and Kaplan (1955, 1956) for a compilation of methods and details.

The principles and practice of manometry have been discussed in this volume, and this technique should be applicable to any enzyme system which catalyzes a reaction which directly or indirectly involves the uptake or the production of a gas.

H. F. DeLUCA and P. P. COHEN

CHEMICAL ANALYSES

PREPARATION OF TISSUE FOR ANALYSIS

The usual procedure for the analysis of the contents of respirometer flasks involves stopping the reactions at the desired point. Usually this is done by adding, at the appropriate time, sufficient trichloracetic acid to yield 5-10% (by weight) final concentration of the acid. A solution of trichloracetic acid containing 100 g. of acid per 100 ml. is readily prepared and convenient for such additions. Addition of 0.33 ml. of the solution from the sidearm of a flask containing 3 ml. of solution will serve to stop the reactions, precipitate the proteins and frequently will extract materials from the cells. The contents of the flask are removed, centrifuged, and the clear supernatant fluid is used for analysis.

GENERAL PRINCIPLES

As indicated in the introduction to this chapter, specificity is one of the chief considerations in the choice of a colorimetric method. This requirement is satisfied either by (1) finding a reaction essentially specific for the material to be measured or (2) by separating the component to be measured from interfering materials. An example of an inherently specific method is the colorimetric method for phosphorus (conditions are chosen to minimize interference from arsenic and silica). As most methods are less specific than this, it often is necessary to resort to fractionation. In the following section methods designed to purify materials on a micro scale by distillation, precipitation, extraction and adsorption are described.

<u>Distillation</u>: If the material to be measured is volatile (ammonia, ethanol, diacetyl, <u>etc</u>.), if it can be converted into a volatile material (as an ester to the free acid and alcohol), or if substances which interfere with the color reaction (or other method of estimation) can be removed as volatile materials, a process of distillation is indicated. Small stills employing either direct distillation over a flame or employing steam (the usual micro Kjeldahl still) are capable of handling quantities of 10-100 μg. However, there are certain other ingenious devices which permit distillation from the frozen state or distillation <u>in vacuo</u> which are particularly convenient for manometric work. Some of these are mentioned below, and it is assumed that any specific method will require modification for the particular circumstances under which one is working. <u>In vacuo</u> distillation from the frozen state avoids heat decomposition and may be conducted essentially as follows in a device described by Grant (1946): The substance to be distilled is placed, by means of a curved pipette in compartment A, figure 53, which is then immersed in a dry ice-acetone bath until frozen solid. C is then attached to a rotary-seal oil pump and the system is thoroughly evacuated and closed off under vacuum by stopcock D. The B section of the tube is then immersed in the dry ice-acetone bath while portion A remains outside of it. In the course of 4 or 5 hours all the volatile material in A distills over (usually without melting) and condenses in B. It is important in this method that A be taken completely to dryness. Modifications of this procedure are obvious. Large size Thunberg tubes may be used with the stopper serving as A and the tube as B. The small size (15 ml.) tube has too small an opening to permit adequate distillation. A relatively volatile material which can be distilled into a substance to yield a non-volatile derivative (ammonia into acid, an aldehyde into hydrazine, <u>etc</u>.) may be distilled directly in a Warburg flask. The trapping agent is put in the sidearm. The flask contents are frozen and while frozen are evacuated by attaching to an inner standard taper joint equipped with a stopcock and connected to a rotary seal oil pump. After evacuation, the system is allowed to stand either at room temperature or in a warm water bath or incubator until distillation is complete (2-3 hours or overnight).

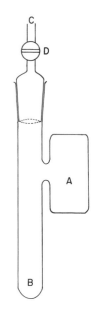

Figure 53
Tube for vacuum distillation from the frozen state

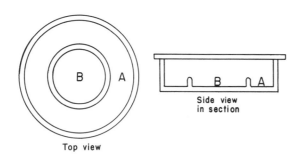

Top view

Side view
in section

Figure 54
Top and side views of
Conway diffusion dish

For similar determinations a Conway diffusion dish may be employed (fig. 54). In the determination of ammonia, for example, the sample is placed in A and standard H_2SO_4 is placed in B. The glass plate is put on, the sample mixed with alkali (placed at another spot in trough A), and incubated 6-8 hours at 37° C. The ammonia is trapped in the H_2SO_4 and is determined by titration or Nesslerization. Similar methods of distillation are employed for other volatile materials. Examples of the application of the method are given by Conway (1947), Borsook and Dubnoff (1939), Werch (1941), Winnick (1941, 1942), Warner (1942), and Malley, <u>et al</u>. (1943).

Precipitation: If the compound to be measured will form very insoluble precipitates that can be reacted to produce a color, the compound can be separated and estimated in this manner. The handling of such small precipitates is a difficult task, but is usually eased by adding an inert material such as barium sulfate or diatomaceous earth on which the smaller precipitate may be adsorbed. Such a procedure has been employed, for example, by Grant (1947) in the determination of formic acid.

Extraction: The material to be estimated may be extracted from the reaction mixture (e.g., ether extraction is used in the determination of succinic acid, page 194). When the proper solvents are chosen, an extraction, for example, from acid solution with an immiscible solvent followed by reextraction of this solvent with an alkaline solution may give good specificity to a relatively non-specific starting colorimetric reaction. Extraction does not have to be complete if the percentage extraction is reproducible under standardized conditions. Rather simple extraction procedures may be employed; for example, one may determine keto acids by reacting them under acid conditions with 2,4-dinitrophenylhydrazine, extracting the mixture by shaking with an equal volume of toluene, and then adding a specified portion of the toluene to alcoholic KOH. Toluene extracts primarily the derivative of pyruvic acid, ethyl acetate extracts more of the dicarboxylic acids; use of these and other solvents may provide a simple analytical separation of keto acids. It is apparent that extractions need not necessarily be elaborate and laborious affairs and that they have a much wider application than is usually considered.

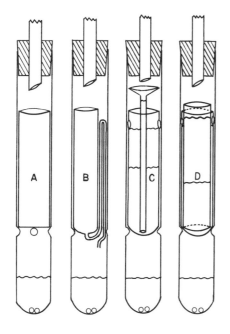

Figure 55

Various forms of extraction apparatus.
See text for description

The simple, economical and compact apparatus illustrated in figure 55 may be employed for a variety of extractions. The basic unit is a 25 x 200 mm. Pyrex tube connected to a reflux condenser; the tube is indented to hold the sample reservoir above the boiling chamber. By placing an alundum or paper extraction thimble containing a solid above the indents, a continuous drip extraction may be performed (fig. 55, A). A Soxhlet thimble also furnishes a device for the extraction of a solid sample (fig. 55, B). For extraction from a liquid by a non-miscible liquid of lower specific gravity the arrangement shown in figure 55, C is employed; this is much more compact than the usual Kutscher-Steudel extractor with a side tube. The arrangement shown in figure 55, D permits extraction from a liquid by another liquid of greater specific gravity (the lighter liquid is added last to the inner tube which is open at both ends). By inserting a set of stainless steel or block tin tubes in a common water bath to serve as condensers, a compact extraction unit may be built; 24 extractors should occupy only about 1 to 1.5 square feet of desk space. In using this apparatus concentrations normally are adjusted so that the entire extract in one tube is analyzed as one sample; this avoids the necessity for preparing aliquots after extraction.

In addition, there is another remarkably efficient method of separating and estimating volatile materials which has been described by Seligson (1959). As shown in figure 56, the stainless-steel stirring bar, the sample and the reagents to liberate the volatile material are placed in a penicillin bottle. The bottle is closed immediately with a rubber stopper carrying a glass rod whose extended and ground end is wet with an absorbing agent (e.g., for determination of NH_3 the glass rod is dipped in 10 N H_2SO_4 before inserting it into the bottle). The closed bottle is rotated in the device shown in figure 57, to accelerate diffusion. Ammonia is collected in 30 minutes. The rod then can be removed, dipped into Nessler's solution and the intensity of the color developed measured. Other volatile materials can be handled in a comparable manner.

W. W. UMBREIT

Figure 56
Microdiffusion Bottle

Figure 57
Rotator

METHOD FOR NITROGEN

<u>Total Nitrogen</u>: Johnson (1941) has described the following micro method for determining nitrogen. A sample containing 10 to 40 micrograms of nitrogen is pipetted into an 18 x 150 mm. Pyrex test tube (the tubes are matched for colorimetric analysis), 1 ml. of 2 N H_2SO_4 containing 0.2 g. per liter of $CuSeO_3$ (or an equivalent mixture of $CuSO_4$ and Na_2SeO_3) is added, and the tube is covered with a loose glass cap. The contents of the tube are then digested overnight in a digestion rack kept in an oven. The electrical elements serving as the heat source for the oven are located at the base of the tubes; they raise the temperature of the oven to 100-115° C. which insures rapid evaporation of water, but the temperature at the base of the tubes is much higher. The heating is such that after the water has evaporated, the H_2SO_4 condenses within 3 cm. of the bottom of the tube. To the tube, after digestion, are added in order 2 ml. of water, 2 ml. of color reagent, and 3 ml. of 2 N NaOH. (The color reagent contains per liter, 4 g. of KI, 4 g. of HgI_2, and 1.75 g. of gum ghatti. Dissolve the KI plus HgI_2 in 25 ml. water. Select light colored pieces of gum ghatti to reduce the blank, grind them in a mortar, drop the powder

into 750 ml. of boiling water and reflux until dissolved. Add the KI and HgI_2 solution to the gum ghatti solution, dilute to 1 liter and filter. Replace the filter paper periodically to speed filtration. Hydrolyzed polyvinyl alcohol can be used in the reagent instead of gum ghatti.) After standing for 15 minutes, the tube is placed in a photoelectric colorimeter, and a reading taken. A 490 or 420 mμ filter is used. Blanks and nitrogen standards are always run with each series of samples. The extinction coefficient is proportional to the quantity of nitrogen for samples containing less than 45 micrograms of nitrogen. Known samples can be recovered with an error of 3% or less. When this method is used with samples having a low percentage of nitrogen, 2 ml. of digestion reagent may be used. A drop of nitrogen-free 30% H_2O_2 may be added if digestion proves difficult. Hiller, Plazin and VanSlyke (1948) have described and evaluated in detail methods for total nitrogen adapted to the micro and macro ranges.

Ammonia: Place an aliquot containing less than 40 micrograms of ammonia nitrogen in an 18 x 150 mm. test tube and adjust the volume to 2 ml. Add 2 ml. of color reagent and then 3 ml. of 2 N NaOH, and proceed with the determination as described under total nitrogen.

Ammonia can be recovered from contaminating materials by microdiffusion as described above.

METHOD FOR GLUCOSE AND OTHER SUGARS

Details of detection and quantitative estimation of a number of sugars are given by Bates (1942) and by Gurin and Hood (1939, 1941).

Glucose may be determined by the method of Folin and Malmros (1929). The sample is made to 4 ml. in a colorimeter tube, 2 ml. of 0.40% $K_3Fe(CN)_6$ and 1 ml. of carbonate-cyanide mixture are added. The sample is mixed, heated 8 minutes in a boiling water bath, cooled 1-2 minutes, and 5 ml. ferric iron solution is added to produce the color. The volume is made to 25 ml. with distilled water, and the color is read using a 520 mμ filter.

Range: 10-100 micrograms glucose equivalents (this method actually measures "reducing value" rather than glucose as such. Precision: $\pm$ 0.4 microgram.

Reagents: Carbonate-cyanide: Dissolve 8 grams anhydrous Na_2CO_3 in 40-50 ml. water, and add 15 ml. freshly prepared 1% NaCN. Dilute to 500 ml. Stable for long periods. Ferric iron: Soak 20 grams gum ghatti in one liter of water for 24 hours. The gum is suspended in the water in a cheesecloth bag. Add a mixture of 5 grams anhydrous $Fe_2(SO_4)_3$, 75 ml. 85% H_3PO_4 and 100 ml. water. After mixing, add slowly about 15 ml. of 1% $KMnO_4$ to destroy reducing materials present in the gum ghatti and allow the solution to stand for a few days. Stable for long periods.

Micro modification: Park and Johnson (1949) have modified the method to make it suitable for the analysis of smaller amounts of glucose. The procedure follows: Dilute the sample to 1 ml., add 1 ml. carbonate-cyanide mixture and 1 ml. $K_3Fe(CN)_6$ solution. Mix. Heat 15 minutes in a boiling water bath. Cool. Add 5 ml. ferric iron solution. After 15 minutes, read in a colorimeter with a 690 mμ filter. Range: 1-9 micrograms. Precision: $\pm$ 0.2 micrograms.

Reagents for micro modification: Ferricyanide solution: 0.5 g. $K_3Fe(CN)_6$ per liter; store in a brown bottle. Carbonate-cyanide: 5.3 g. Na_2CO_3 plus 0.65 g. KCN per liter. Ferric iron: 1.5 g. $FeNH_4(SO_4)_2 \cdot 12H_2O$ plus 50 ml. 1 N H_2SO_4 plus 1 g. Duponol (ME dry); diluted to 1 liter.

General Method for Carbohydrates: Anthrone (9-oxyanthracene) reacts with all carbohydrates to give a characteristic blue color. It reacts with mono-, di- and polysaccharides, dextrins, dextrans, starches, gums and glucosides, but the color yield is not the same for different carbohydrates.

Reagent: 2.0 g. of anthrone is dissolved in 1 liter of 95% sulfuric acid (prepared by the cautious addition of 1 liter of concentrated sulfuric acid to 50 ml. of water with cooling). The reagent darkens with time, so standards always must be run. By storing the reagent in the refrigerator it is possible to extend its usable life to 1 or 2 weeks.

Procedure: Measure 3 ml. of the solution to be determined into an 18 x 150 mm. matched test tube and add 6 ml. of the reagent. Mix the solutions thoroughly at once by swirling. Place the tube in a boiling water bath for 3 minutes and then cool. Measure the color in a colorimeter with a 620 mμ filter and compare against a blank containing only water and reagent. Run duplicates and always include duplicate 60 microgram glucose standards (or other standards which give a comparable optical density). The color follows Beer's law. The practical range is 12 to 120 micrograms of glucose.

W. W. UMBREIT and R. H. BURRIS

METHOD FOR PYRUVIC ACID OR α-KETOGLUTARIC ACID

Pyruvic acid and α-ketoglutaric acid are readily determined in biological materials by the method of Lu (1939) as modified by Bueding and Wortis (1940), Elgart and Nelson (1941) and Koepsell and Sharpe (1952). When pyruvic acid is to be determined in blood, it is essential that it be stabilized immediately by the addition of iodoacetate to a final concentration of 0.2%. The iodoacetate prevents the loss of blood pyruvate, but care should be taken to deproteinize the blood as soon as possible in order to prevent an increase in pyruvate. Suspensions of cells or tissue homogenates which have been used in manometric experiments may be pipetted directly from the respirometer flask into trichloracetic acid.

Reagents: Solutions are given as grams of solute per 100 ml. final volume of solution. (1) 25% solution of iodoacetic acid in water adjusted to pH 7.8 with sodium hydroxide. (2) 10% trichloracetic acid. (3) 0.1% 2,4-dinitrophenylhydrazine in 2 N HCl. (4) Ethyl acetate. (5) 10% sodium carbonate. (6) 2 N NaOH.

Procedure: Three ml. whole blood (drawn into a tube containing sufficient iodoacetate to give a final concentration of 0.2%) are added slowly with continual shaking to 12 ml. 10% trichloracetic acid in an Erlenmeyer flask. Tissue suspensions from Warburg flasks are added to 4 volumes of trichloracetic acid. After standing for a few minutes the precipitate is filtered or centrifuged off.

Three ml. of the clear filtrate (or supernatant fluid) are added to 1 ml. of the 2,4-dinitrophenylhydrazine solution in a conical centrifuge tube. After standing at room temperature for 10 minutes, 4 ml. of ethyl acetate are added and the two layers are mixed (preferably by bubbling a stream of nitrogen through a capillary pipette whose tip rests lightly on the bottom of the tube). After mixing, the layers are allowed to separate and the lower one (water) is carefully drawn off (with the same pipette) and transferred to a second centri-fuge tube. The aqueous layer (in the second centrifuge tube) is extracted twice with 2 ml. portions of ethyl acetate and the extracts added to the 4 ml. of ethyl acetate in the original tube. The aqueous layer should now be colorless and may be discarded. The combined ethyl acetate extracts are treated with exactly 2 ml. of 10% sodium carbonate. The layers are mixed (preferably with nitrogen) for several minutes. After the layers have separated the sodium carbonate layer is quantitatively transferred to another tube and the extraction of the ethyl acetate repeated twice using exactly 2 ml. of sodium carbon-ate each time. The combined sodium carbonate extracts are then extracted once with 1 ml. of ethyl acetate, the latter removed, and the carbonate extract transferred to a colorimeter tube. Four ml. of 2 N NaOH are added and the contents mixed. The color is read in 10 min-utes in a photoelectric colorimeter with a filter having the maximum transmission at 520 mμ. Range: 5 to 35 micrograms of either acid. Precision: ± 2 micrograms.

A calibration curve is obtained by the use of freshly distilled pyruvic acid (see page 268) as a standard. Recrystallized α-ketoglutaric acid also is used as a standard. When both pyruvic and α-ketoglutaric acids are present in the same sample, the quantitative deter-mination of each can be achieved by procedures described by Koepsell and Sharpe (1952). This involves measurement of light absorption by the alkalinized solution at two different wavelengths (380 mμ and 520 mμ) and calculating the amount of each component by use of simultaneous equations. Where large numbers of samples are to be analyzed, a series of tubes fitted into an aeration train arranged so that nitrogen can be bubbled through them all simultaneously is convenient.

If acetoacetic acid is present in the material to be analyzed it may be eliminated by add-ing 1/10 of its volume of concentrated HCl to the protein-free filtrate and heating on a boiling water bath for 1 hour (Elgart and Nelson, 1941). Concentrated NaOH (equivalent to the HCl) is then added, the solution cooled, and analyzed as described.

Pyruvic acid also may be estimated colorimetrically by the salicylaldehyde method of Straub (1936) or manometrically using carboxylase (cf. Warburg et al., 1930; Westerkamp, 1933).

METHOD FOR CITRIC ACID

Citric acid may be determined colorimetrically with a rather high degree of accuracy. The citric acid is oxidized under controlled conditions with potassium permanganate in the presence of bromine, and is thus converted into pentabromoacetone; this may be measured by the color produced upon addition to sodium sulfide. Pucher, et al. (1934, 1936, 1941) and Purinton and Schuck (1943) have proposed specific quantitative methods based on this principle. All of these require the quantitative extraction of the penta-bromoacetone and employ other rather involved procedures. The following method is somewhat simpler and only a single extraction is made. A single extraction was found to remove a constant amount of the total pentabromoacetone in any series of samples of uniform volume. The method is described by Perlman, Lardy and Johnson (1944).

Reagents: (1) Sulfuric acid: equal volumes of 95% sulfuric acid and water. (2) 1 M KBr. (3) Saturated bromine water. (4) 3% H_2O_2. (5) Petroleum ether (acid washed "Skelly Solve B"). (6) Dioxane-water mixture (equal volumes of dioxane and water). (7) Sodium sulfide solution (4 gms. $Na_2S \cdot 9H_2O$ per 100 ml. solution). (8) 1.5 N potas-sium permanganate. (9) "Weak" permanganate (0.1 N).

Preparation of samples: If the samples are known to contain reducing materials, aliquots (preferably containing less than 25 mg. citric acid) are placed in 1" x 8" Pyrex test tubes, 2 ml. sulfuric acid is added and the total volume is adjusted to about 20 ml. After boiling for a few minutes, the solutions are cooled and 3-5 ml. of bromine water is added. After 10 minutes any precipitate which may form is removed by centrifugation. The supernatant liquid is decanted off and made to 25 ml. If the samples do not contain appreciable amounts of reducing materials, this treatment may be omitted.

Procedure: Aliquots of the sample (containing between 0.2 to 2.0 mg. citric acid in a volume of 3.5 ml. or less), are placed in test tubes (the 18 by 150 mm. size is convenient) graduated at 5 and 10 ml. Add 0.3 ml. sulfuric acid, 0.2 ml. KBr and 1 ml. of the 1.5 N permanganate and adjust the total volume to about 5 ml. The tubes are allowed to stand for 5 minutes at room temperature and then chilled in an ice bath. The excess permanganate is decolorized with hydrogen peroxide (care must be taken to keep the reaction mixture below 5° C. during this step). Any excess peroxide is removed with "weak" permanganate. The total volume is now adjusted to exactly 10 ml. and 13 ml. of petroleum ether is added. The tubes are stoppered, shaken vigorously and centrifuged (to break any emulsion that may form). Ten ml. portions of the petroleum ether extract are added to colorimeter tubes containing 5 ml. water-dioxane and 5 ml. sodium sulfide solution. The colorimeter tubes are stoppered, shaken vigorously and centrifuged. The color produced should be a light yellow and will be fully developed in 5 minutes. It is stable for several hours. The absorption (in the aqueous bottom layer) is measured at 400-450 mμ.; usually the 420 filter is used. A tube containing no citric acid, but which has gone through exactly the same procedure is used as a blank. The content of citric acid is calculated from at least two standards (at different levels) which are run with each set of samples. Range: 200-1800 micrograms citric acid. Precision: $\pm$ 10 micrograms.

Precautions: If too large a sample of citric acid has been used, a somewhat red (rather than yellow) color will be developed. In this case a smaller aliquot of the petroleum ether may be added to the dioxane-water-sulfide thus avoiding another complete analysis. When only small quantities of the material are available for analysis, the preliminary acid and bromine treatment may be carried out in a volume of less than 5 ml. in which case the whole sample may be treated with permanganate. The following are critical points in the procedure: (1) An excess of H_2O_2 or permanganate must not be present in the solution before the petroleum ether extraction. Excess H_2O_2 gives low recoveries, excess permanganate gives high recoveries. (2) The solutions must be thoroughly chilled before the excess permanganate is removed or erratic results will occur. (3) Some stabilizing agent must be present during the formation of the colored reaction product of the pentabromoacetone and the sodium sulfide. Both 50% dioxane-water and 50% pyridine-water have proven satisfactory (4) Sometimes the petroleum ether contains interfering materials. These can be removed by washing with acid. (5) The pentabromacetone should not be allowed to remain in the petroleum ether for more than 15 minutes. Isocitric acid, cis-aconitic acid, trans-aconitic acid, oxalacetic acid, and gluconic acid do not interfere with this method.

DETERMINATION OF PHOSPHOGLYCERIC ACID BY OPTICAL ROTATION IN THE PRESENCE OF MOLYBDATE

This method is so clearly described in the original publication (Meyerhof and Schulz, 1938) that the only reason for describing it here is to provide the details for those to whom the original journal may not be available. The method is far more specific than that of Rapoport (1937); the only interfering substances being other α-hydroxy acids and excessively large amounts of inorganic phosphorus. Inorganic phosphorus may be removed with magnesia mixture and the phosphoglyceric may be separated from most other acids by precipitation with lead acetate at a pH of about five.

The optical rotation of the acidified solution of phosphogylceric acid is determined before and after the addition of 1/3 volume of 25% ammonium molybdate. For $\underline{d}$ (-) 3-phosphoglyceric acid in N HCl Meyerhof gives $[\alpha]_D^{20} = -13.2°$; with molybdate $[\alpha]_D^{20} = -745°$. The $[\alpha]_D$ of the naturally occurring equilibrium mixture of $\underline{d}$(-) 3-phosphoglyceric and $\underline{d}$(+) 2-phosphoglyceric acids is according to Meyerhof -650° to -670° in the presence of molybdate.

Example: The specific rotation is defined as

$$[\alpha]_D^t = 100\,\alpha/(e\,c)$$

Where: α = observed angle of rotation.
         e = length of tube in decimeters.
         c = grams of material dissolved in 100 ml. solution.
         t = temperature of the experiments.
         D = wave length of light used (D line of sodium).

Solution of 0.907 mg. 3(-)phosphoglyceric per ml. used (pure ester).

(no molybdate) = O; after addition of 1/3 volume of 25% ammonium molybdate = -0.45°; length of tube = one decimeter. (21° C.).

$$c = 100 \; \alpha/e\,[\alpha]_D^t = 100 \times -0.45/1 \times -745 = 0.0604$$

Thus 0.0604 g. exist in 100 ml., or 0.604 mg. per ml. This had been diluted 1/3 by addition of molybdate, hence original concentration found was 0.604 x 3/2 = 0.906 mg./ml. found; taken: 0.907 mg./ml. Specificity permits its use in extracts without extensive purification.

                                                                    H. A. LARDY

ION EXCHANGE SEPARATION OF NUCLEOTIDES

The resin for this procedure was obtained from the Dow Chemical Company, Midland, Michigan. It is designated as Dowex 1, chloride form, 200-400 mesh, medium porosity, 10% cross-linked. Most of the resin is approximately 300 mesh with a small percentage of "fines". The "fines" must be removed to assure good flow rates. This is accomplished by suspending the resin in several volumes of distilled water and allowing it to settle. After the bulk of the resin has sedimented, the supernatant fluid is discarded. This process is repeated several times until no material remains which does not sediment readily. About 90% of the resin is recovered.

Cohn (1950) used the resin in the chloride form for nucleotide separations, and employed relatively dilute eluting solutions; the nucleotides are recovered as rather dilute solutions. To obtain more concentrated fractions, Hurlbert et al. (1954) have used the resin in the formate form and eluted with solutions of formic acid and ammonium formate (this procedure will be described here). The resin in the acetate form, eluted with acetic acid and sodium acetate solution, gives comparable results. To convert the resin to the formate form, put it in a large column and percolate 3 molar sodium formate solution through it until a negative test for chloride is obtained on the effluent (solution treated with nitric acid and silver nitrate to precipitate silver chloride). A 300 ml. batch of resin requires approximately 2500 ml. of solution for complete conversion. Wash the resin further with distilled water. Store it in a refrigerator as a heavy slurry with very little water above it. Columns are prepared in glass tubes constricted near the bottom. Place a plug of glass wool over the constriction, and pour the heavy slurry of resin into the column to the desired depth. Use of a heavy slurry facilitates estimation of the depth and obviates the necessity for care in packing, since a heavy slurry does not layer unevenly. Wash the column with 3-5 times its volume of concentrated formic acid (23 M, 88%), then with several similar portions of distilled water. This removes ultra-violet-absorbing material which otherwise contaminates eluates.

The sample can be a trichloracetic or perchloric acid extract of tissue, or any fraction therefrom. If trichloracetic acid has been used, the trichloracetic acid is extracted from the sample with ether. If perchloric acid has been used, the sample is neutralized to pH 6.8 with potassium hydroxide and the potassium perchlorate removed in the cold.

In the example of ion exchange separation to be described, a 10 x 200 mm. column was used. The neutralized sample was run onto the column at approximately 0.5 ml./min. and was followed by one resin bed volume of distilled water. If possible, the sample volume should be kept below 3 resin bed volumes. The column was developed by gradient elution. The eluting solution from a reservoir flask was forced by air pressure into a 500 ml. flask of distilled water stirred with a magnetic mixer, and the mixture in turn was forced onto the column. A gradual increase in the concentration of the eluting solution is effected in the intermediate mixing vessel. The mixing vessel volume can be varied to give different rates of increase in the concentration of the eluting solution. The column was run at 1 ml./min., and 5 ml. fractions were collected with an automatic fraction collector. The reservoir contained 1 M formic acid initially, and this was changed as indicated. Figure 58 shows the distribution of a number of the nucleotides

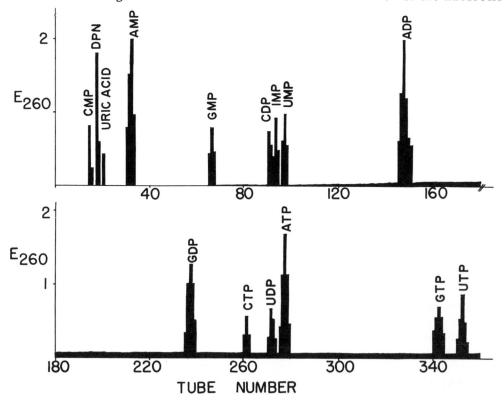

Figure 58

Dowex-1 Formate Chromatogram of Hypothetical Tissue
Extract showing position of various nucleotides

found in mammalian tissues. No significance should be ascribed to the magnitude of the peaks, since these change with physiological conditions and from one tissue to another. The light absorption of the fractions is measured in a Beckman DU spectrophotometer.

Compounds which are not resolved well on this chromatogram can be lyophilized and separated again on a column developed with ammonium formate solutions at pH 5.0; the distribution is modified on such a column. Removing the ammonium formate from some samples presents some difficulty. However, if identity only is required, one can heat the fractions with 1 M HCl for 1 hour at 100° C. to hydrolyze purine components to free bases and then run the hydrolysate through a Dowex 50 hydrogen form column (the 12% cross-linked resin is obtained from the Dow Chemical Co., and the fines are removed as with Dowex 1; the resin is washed with 6 M HCl to remove chromogens). This retains the purines, which can be eluated with 6 M HCl, dried down in vacuo and identified by paper chromatography. The pyrimidines come through this resin readily, and likewise can be dried and identified on paper chromatograms. The ammonium ions remain on the Dowex 50 and can be washed off with 2 M HCl before elution of the purines; xanthine and hypoxanthine will come off while salt still remains on the column. The buffered isoamyl alcohol solvent systems described by Carter (1950) are particularly suitable for identification of the purines and pyrimidines, and the solvents give suitable separations even when the samples contain some salts.

It should be noted that the hypothetical sample illustrated is simplified, and that many compounds not detected by ultraviolet absorption (e.g., sugar phosphates, amino acids) are present in the tissue extracts and will be eluted at various points from a column of Dowex 1. Preliminary fractionations, such as that obtainable with barium and alcohol may be helpful in simplifying the identification of compounds in complex samples.

G. A. LePAGE

Chapter 12
SPECTROPHOTOMETRY

Optical methods of chemical analysis are advantageous in many instances because of their speed, simplicity, precision, and a range extending downward beyond that of volumetric and gravimetric methods. The fact that a relatively smaller quantity of material, or a smaller volume of solution, often suffices for a determination favors their use simply as a means of reducing the cost of the reagents or the amount of the biological sample. One further advantage is that the solution tested often remains unchanged and, thus, it may be recovered, or when it comprises a reaction system in which the only change in absorbance is due to the change in concentration of a reactant or a product, or to the absorptivity of an indicator, the rate of the reaction may be followed without further ado.

Because the title of this chapter does not entirely indicate its contents, the attention of the reader is directed to a description of The Thunberg Method for estimation of Dehydrogenase Activity (page 230) and the Photometric Estimation of Methylene Blue Reduction (page 231).

Of the various optical methods of analysis, the spectrophotometric method is the one most widely used in biological laboratories. Although the spectrophotometers in use vary considerably as to their mechanical design, etc., this type of instrument essentially affords a comparison of the radiation absorbed in or transmitted by a solution containing an unknown quantity of some substance and a solution containing a known quantity of the same substance, the standard. The actual procedure employed in making such a comparison can differ markedly depending on the biological system under study and the type of information desired, as will be described below.

Long before spectrophotometers became generally available, the physical laws relating the intensity of the color of a solution to the concentration of the colored substance contained therein had been applied, first in visual colorimetry and, later on, in photoelectric colorimetry. When monochromatic light traverses an absorbing solution, successive layers of equal thickness absorb equal fractions of the incident light (Bouguer's law), which means that the fraction of light absorbed increases in direct proportion to the logarithm of increase in thickness of the solution layer. Since the light absorbed by a layer of solution is directly proportional to the concentration of the colored substance (Beer's law), it follows then, that the light absorbed is directly proportional to the thickness of the solution. These two laws, usually designated as the Lambert-Beer law, or simply as Beer's law, may be represented by the following equation:

$$I/I_o = e^{-kc\ell}$$

48

where I_o is the intensity of the incident light, and I the intensity of the light transmitted by ℓ centimeters of a solution of $\underline{c}$ concentration (e.g., milligrams per milliliter, or moles per liter) of solute having the characteristic absorption coefficient $\underline{k}$, a constant.

The above equation may be written in a more convenient form (where $\underline{k}$ is replaced by a new constant, $\underline{k}'$, which includes $\underline{k}$ and the factor converting logarithms of base e to those of base 10, and I/I_o is inverted to remove the minus sign):

$$\log I_o/I = k'c\ell$$

49

The constant $\underline{k}'$ is the specific extinction coefficient of the absorbing substance at the specified wavelength, λ . Very often $\underline{c}$ is in terms of moles per liter. In these instances $\underline{k}'$ is replaced by $\epsilon\lambda$, the molar extinction coefficient.

Suppose $\underline{c}$ and $\underline{\ell}$ both have the value of one, i.e., a 1.0 cm. layer of a 1.0 M solution, then

$$\log I_0/I = \epsilon\lambda$$

However, the absorbance (I_0/I) of the solution may be expected to vary with the wavelength of the light. If the light consists of a band of wavelengths it might be supposed that it would be necessary to integrate a series of values of $\underline{\epsilon}$, or $\underline{k}'$, if Beer's law is to hold. This is actually the case, but the integration is taken care of automatically because, as long as the absorptivity of the colored substance does not change, the ratio of the extinction coefficients for the different wavelengths remains the same. A real difficulty arises, however, if there is a change in the distribution of the energy in the wavelengths comprising the light, e.g., as a result of a change in the temperature of a tungsten filament used as a source of light. As would be expected, the broader the band of wavelengths the greater the deviation. The situation is considerably improved and in most cases completely rectified for all practical purposes by restricting the light to a narrow band of wavelengths complementary to the color of the substance being assayed.

While the above discussion was limited to the absorption of light (radiation of wavelengths within the visible spectrum) by colored substances (where the fact that they are colored indicates differential absorption within the visible spectrum), it should be apparent that the physical laws relating to the absorption of light by homogeneous media apply equally well to the absorption of ultraviolet and infra-red radiation. Regardless of whether a colorimeter or a spectrophotometer (whose wavelength range includes either the visible, ultraviolet, infra-red, or some combination of these regions of the electromagnetic spectrum) is employed, the usefulness of the instrument as a tool for quantitative analysis depends on the application of these laws.

It is evident from a consideration of Equation 49 that if $\underline{\ell}$ is held constant the absorbance of the layer of solution should be directly proportional to the concentration of the absorbing substance, $\underline{i.e.}$, a straight line should be obtained when $\log I_0/I$ is plotted against concentration. However, in actual practice this may not be the case; rather, the line may be curved, or it may be essentially straight over only a portion of the concentration range. These deviations may result from the use of radiation which is not sufficiently monochromatic, the presence of an extraneous absorbing substance, a change in the equilibrium of a reaction involving the absorbing substance, or changes in the absorptivity of the substance itself due to different degrees of ionization, aggregation, or combination with the solvent or reagents present as its concentration changes. The deviation is corrected for if one prepares a standard curve and uses this to interpolate the data obatined. It is particularly desirable to know whether or not this plot yields a straight line, $\underline{i.e.}$, whether or not Beer's law holds for the set of experimental conditions and over the range of concentration of the substance being determined. If the line is straight, any number of final results may be obtained more readily and perhaps more accurately by calculation using a suitable calibration factor than by interpolation from a standard curve.

In the practice of spectrophotometry, a number of symbols and terms are employed. For ease of reference those already used above and others, with their definitions, are included in the following list.

I_0 = transmission of the reference cell (solvent or reagents).

I   = transmission of the sample cell (absorbing substance in solution).

I/I_0 = transmittance

I_0/I = absorbance

ℓ = thickness of the absorbing layer of liquid (usually in cms.).

c = concentration (any designation, but used consistently).

k' = specific extinction coefficient of the absorbing substance at a specified wave-length.

ϵ = Σ = molar extinction coefficient of the absorbing substance at a specified wavelength (= k' when c is in moles per liter).

D = E = $\log_{10} I_0/I$ = optical density, density, or extinction.

SPECTROPHOTOMETERS

Spectrophotometers by definition are instruments for measuring the distribution of energy in the different wavelengths of spectra. As a tool in biological analyses, a spectrophotometer is employed principally to supply a discrete narrow wavelength band of radiation (spectral band) from any portion of the spectrum within its range (the ultraviolet, visible, or infra-red portion of the electromagnetic spectrum, or some combination of these). It is equipped with a suitable photocell, or photocells, coupled electrically with some type of indicator to measure the intensity of the beam of radiation emerging from the rear slit of the monochromator segment of the instrument. Provision is made for inserting a transparent absorption vessel between the slit and photocell, and for accurately aligning this vessel so that it is traversed by the entire beam of radiation.

From the above description, it is apparent that a spectrophotometer of this type may be used to determine the optical density (absorbancy) of a solution placed in the absorption vessel at some particular wavelength (in reality a band of wavelengths). In this case the instrument functions as a form of colorimeter. By adjusting the monochromator, the optical density of the solution may also be determined at each wavelength of the spectrum (as limited by the spectral range of the instrument). A plot of the optical density values as a function of wavelength yields a spectral optical density (absorbancy) curve, or, simply, an absorption spectrum of the solution.

Omitting any consideration of the special features which contribute to ease of operation and versatility, the characteristics of a spectrophotometer which determine its usefulness and performance are spectral (wavelength) range, resolution, spectral purity, reproducibility of nominal wavelength selection, and photometric sensitivity. Most of these instruments are capable of supplying wavelengths of radiation throughout the visible spectrum and extending into the ultraviolet and infra-red regions. Some have an effective wavelength range from about 200 to 2,500 mμ. This wide range, of course, increases the possibility of locating some wavelength that is strongly absorbed by a compound which does not absorb visible radiation (has no color), and it allows the extension of the absorption spectrum to include absorption at wavelengths that may assist in indentifying the substance. Resolution refers to the degree to which the instrument can separate out individual wavelengths. In practice this is dependent upon the extent to which the monochromator spreads the spectrum of the radiation source and the minimum width of the exit slit allowable for a photometric measurement at any particular wavelength (the wavelength corresponding to the midpoint of the emitted wavelength band). Even when the instrument is adjusted to deliver a particular band of wavelengths, some scattered light of random wavelengths from within the monochromator is included in the beam impinging on the absorption vessel. This extraneous radiation, which may vary in amount for the various wavelength bands selected, decreases the spectral purity of the beam and is a potential source of error in optical density determinations (cf. Mehler, 1954). Reproducibility of the nominal wavelength selection refers to the accuracy with which the same nominal wavelength is obtained each time the wavelength dial is set at the wavelength indicated. Photometric sensitivity refers to the ability of the photometric circuit to measure differences in the intensity of the radiation striking the photocell. The greater the sensitivity, the less need be the intensity of the radiation (which may allow a reduction in the width of the wavelength band with an increase in spectral purity) and, also, the greater the precision of the measurement of absorbance or transmittance of the sample.

This type of spectrometer is usually equipped with a graduated scale which allows the operator to read directly the transmittance (I/I_0) and the optical density ($\log{}^{I_0}/I$). Ordinarily the transmittance scale covers a range of 0 to 100, and the optical density scale a range of ∞ to 0.

Commercially available spectrophotometers vary greatly in design, details of construction, total spectral range, nominal band width, wavelength resolution, and sensitivity of the photocell radiation-intensity measuring system. The most common models provide a single beam of radiation which is intercepted alternately by the blank (solvent) and sample containing cuvettes. Others, employing a single monochromator, split the beam into two by means of a half-silvered mirror or employ a rotating in-phase sector mirror to alternate the beam over two paths. In either case, one beam traverses the blank cuvette and the other beam the sample cuvette. By properly compensating the output of the two photocells, the optical density or transmittance of the sample is obtained directly. Another type of spectrophotometer currently available, patterned after an original model developed by Britton Chance and his associates, alternates two preselected wavelengths of radiation through the absorption vessel containing the sample solution. The particular advantages of this system when coupled with high sensitivity in detecting changes in optical density and reduction of error due to scattering of radiation in the absorption vessel, in studies involving turbid media have been described by Chance (1954) and by Chance and Williams (1956).

Accessories, purchased separately or provided as integral parts of these instruments, include special types of cuvettes, radiation sources and their regulating devices, absorption vessel compartments for maintaining a constant temperature or for automatically positioning the sample and blank cuvettes, and devices that automatically record the change in optical density at one wavelength of a sample with time, or the optical density of a sample for a range of wavelengths over the whole or part of the spectral range of the instrument. This latter operation is referred to as "scanning". Some of these scanning devices can be programmed to repeat the operation at definite intervals of time. An idea of the elaborate instrumentation that can be had when purchasing a spectrophotometer, and the end is not in sight, is evidenced by a recent brochure of a well known company describing a double-beam dual monochromator type of instrument suited to the measurement of transmittance, absorbance, fluorescence, phosphorescence, emission and excitation spectra, polarized fluorescence, and radiation scattering!

The impetus to improve the quality and design of spectrophotometers has undoubtedly been due to the need of increased sensitivity and of overcoming as far as possible the difficulties inherent in working with suspensions, i.e., bacterial, yeast and algal cells, mitochondria and chloroplast preparations, and smaller particulate cell components. In developing instruments to meet this need, Britton Chance and his associates have played a stellar role (cf., Chance, 1954, for an account and references). As Keilin and Hartree (1958) have pointed out, four general methods had been developed for improving spectrophotometric measurements with the usual types of commercial instruments when dealing with suspensions, viz.: adjustment of the refractive index of the suspending medium to the same value as that of the suspended material by adding sucrose, glucose (cf., Chance, 1952), glycerol, dextrin, or protein; placing an opalescent screen in back of the absorption vessel (cf., Shibata et al., 1954), or using filter paper as a reference in approximating the scatter of the sample (cf., Lundegårdh, 1952); use of an integrating sphere to trap all of the radiation emerging from the absorption vessel (cf., Bateman and Monk, 1955); bringing the sample to liquid air temperature to sharpen and intensify the absorption bands (Keilin and Hartree, 1949, and see Baker and Lieberman, 1962). To these Keilin and Hartree (1958) added a fifth method, which involves an extrapolation procedure following determination of the variation in the transmission spectra measured with the photocell at different distances back of the absorption vessel (cf., Latimer and Eubanks, 1962). Apparently the difficulties in working with suspensions has been largely overcome by placing an end-window photomultiplier tube very close to the rear window of the absorption vessel in combination with a high sensitivity to changes in optical density and the use of dilute suspensions (cf., Chance, 1951a, 1951b, 1954, 1958, Chance and Legallis, 1951, and Chance and Redfearn, 1961).

Techniques for the examination of dense radiation scattering materials have been desribed by Lundegårdh (1952), Connelly and Chance (1954) and Butler and Norris (1960, and see Norris and Butler, 1961). Butler and Norris (1960) give an example of the use of artificial scattering media (which effects a lengthening of the path of radiation within the absorption vessel) to intensify absorption spectra. A combination of this technique and a sample temperature of -196° C. was used by Baker and Lieberman (1962) to obtain low temperature spectra of mitochondrial cytochromes.

ABSORPTION VESSELS

The absorption vessels, or cuvettes, supplied with a particular type of spectrophotometer may be constructed of soft glass, pyrex, corex, or quartz (silica). Quartz cuvettes are by far the most expensive of the lot; however, they are applicable over the whole range of wavelengths encompassed in the ultraviolet, visible, and infra-red ($< 3,800$ mμ) portions of the spectrum. Cuvettes of soft glass, pyrex, and corex because of their more limited spectral range of transmissivity to ultraviolet and infra-red radiation, are suitable ordinarily for use over the wavelength ranges 360-2,500, 340-2,500 and 320-2,500 mμ, respectively.

Besides the typical round or rectangular cuvettes, there are many examples of absorption vessels designed for special purposes, especially in studying the kinetics of systems responsive to spectroscopic analysis. Morell (1952) and Repaske (1962), respectively, mention the use of a Thunberg tube fused to the absorption vessel in studies involving the reduction of cytochrome c and DPN under anaerobic conditions (see p. 230 also). Riggs (1951) described a combination gas absorption chamber and absorption vessel which he used in determining the ratio of oxy- and reduced hemoglobin of blood in equilibrium with different concentrations of oxygen. Chance (1954) has described an absorption vessel fitted with a vibrating platinum electrode for measuring changes in oxygen concentration and a glass electrode for measuring pH changes associated with acid production which is suited to the simultaneous measurement of respiration and fermentation while yielding a direct spectrophotometric assay of the steady-state conditions of the catalysts involved in these two processes. Lundegårdh (1952) examined bundles of roots held in a quartz tube in determining the effects of bathing solutions of different substances on the state of the cytochromes within the cells.

For very rapid spectrophotometric measurements suited to studies of reaction kinetics and spectra of unstable compounds, Chance (1951a) has described a circular absorption vessel one millimeter in diameter which has joined to its top two delivery tubes connecting a reservoir of the reacting system (as a solution or suspension) and a reservoir of reagent solution. The system provides for the mixing of the two liquids just before the mixture flows past the window area. Pressure applied on the syringe reservoirs were capable of providing flow velocities in excess of 10 meters per second. With a distance between the points of mixing and observation of 7 mm., reaction times of the order of 1 msec. were attained. Modifications of the above system are to be found in articles by Chance (1951b), Chance and Legallais (1951) and Chance (1954). Wood (1960) described a system for simultaneously following the absorbance changes in 2-4 cuvettes over short intervals by sequentially recording the changes in each cuvette as it is positioned in turn by a precise clock-operated mechanism. In all of these cases the spectrophotometric equipment includes automatic recorders, and other electronic and mechanical gear; the complete lay-out is elaborate, therefore, in comparison with a manually operated spectrophotometer.

SPECTROPHOTOMETRIC TECHNIQUES

The following brief accounts of and references to different types of spectrophotometric techniques are given as guides to the successful use of spectrophotometers in the laboratory and as indicators of the versatility and efficiency of these instruments as tools for biological research.

Absorption Spectra: The absorption spectrum of a substance is particularly useful in selecting a suitable wavelength for spectrometric assay (see below). For a substance that absorbs radiation of some wavelengths within the spectral range of the spectrometer available, one determines the absorbance (optical density, or per cent transmission) of the substance dissolved in a transparent solvent, or as developed in a solution of reagents, at the different wavelengths comprising the portion of the spectrum under consideration. The concentration of the substance in the test solution should be about the same as its probable maximum concentration in the samples to be assayed, although it may be necessary to dilute this solution to avoid an optical density of infinity at some wavelength. Assuming that the optical density measurements have been obtained with a manually operated spectrophotometer, these values are used to plot a curve of absorbance against wavelength. The points through which this curve is drawn should be sufficiently close to each other so that the slope of the curve is accurately defined, especially in any regions where absorption changes rapidly with changes in wavelength of the radiation. Ordinarily, determination of the optical density at 2-10 mμ will suffice, and time may be saved by first making a cursory survey at 20 mμ intervals to locate the wavelengths where appreciable absorption occurs. This whole operation requires only a few minutes if the spectrophotometer is equipped with a scanning device. The curve should now be examined to locate, if possible, a region where absorption is high and does not change rapidly with changes in wavelength, i. e., no sharp peak of absorption. Radiation of a wavelength at or near the midpoint of this region will be satisfactory for the spectrophotometric assay (cf., figure 59). If one has to deal with a sharp absorption peak it should be borne in mind that large errors may be introduced in the assay due to inadequate wavelength resolution and reproducibility of the wavelength setting of the spectrophotometer.

No particular difficulties are attached to a determination of the absorption spectrum of a substance in solution; however, the situation is different when the substance is part of a particulate system and special techniques may be required (see above).

Absorption spectra are also used in identifying and estimating the purity of substances. Their application for such purposes is outlined in the following randomly chosen examples. Block and Johnson (1955) presented absorption spectra as supporting evidence for the presence of an enzyme in rat skin extracts which deaminates guanine to form xanthine. Cooper et al. (1955b) obtained the absorption curves of aminofumaric acid diamide at various pH values in order to identify and estimate the quantity of this compound in a study of some precursors of nucleic acid pyrimidines; somewhat the same procedure was used by

Bürgi and Schmid (1961) to determine the tryptophan and tyrosine content of a glycoprotein, and by Alivisatos et al. (1962) in connection with the biosynthesis of the pyrophosphates of 5'-inosinic and 5'-adenylic acids. Tagawa and Arnon (1962) made use of absorption spectra in comparing ferredoxin obtained from spinach leaves with ferredoxin isolated from Clostridium, as Nielands (1952a) did in comparing the properties of cytochrome c obtained from different sources. Absorption spectra were employed by Meyer et al. (1961) to obtain evidence of the double stranded form of DNA in preparations obtained from a bacteriophage.

Difference spectra: These are spectral curves formed by plotting the changes in the absorption spectrum (see above) of a substance in solution or of an absorbing system. The curve is formed by plotting the optical density differences at different wavelengths, both plus and minus, as abscissae versus wavelengths as ordinates. Such spectra are useful in detecting small changes in absorption, and especially in cases where the identity of the compound may be questionable, in overcoming interference by extraneous absorbing substances, and in identifying and measuring individual components of multi-component systems. Some of these desiderata are clearly illustrated in an article by Chance (1954, p. 768): The absorption spectra of reduced and oxidized cytochrome c are shown along with a graph of the reduced-oxidized difference spectrum obtained by subtracting the two; superimposed on the latter is the reduced-oxidized difference spectrum of cytochrome b. Inspection of this graph establishes that it is possible to select a pair of closely spaced wavelengths for each pigment which will be insensitive to the other pigment insofar as registering changes in optical density. Of the pair of wavelengths, one serves as a neutral reference wavelength (see above under the section on Instrumentation) and the other serves to indicate the optical density due to one pigment as it is insensitive in this respect to the other pigment. Thus it is possible to measure one pigment in the presence of the other, even when the absorbancy of both changes. Additional information on the role of difference spectra in studies of electron transfer, etc., involving respiratory pigments and enzymes responsive to spectrophotometric assay is given by Chance and Williams (1956). For other examples of a similar nature, see Chance (1958) and Baker and Lieberman (1962).

Other examples of the application of difference spectra are as follows: Kielley (1955) was able to show that purified xanthine oxidase from liver possessed the characteristic flavin absorption maxima at 370 and 450 mμ. (cf., Crane et al., 1956) by plotting the difference spectrum after obtaining the absorption spectra of the oxidized and reduced forms of the enzyme. A similar technique was used by Crescitelli (1955) to locate the wavelength of maximum absorption of the visual pigment from lamphrey eyes, and also as evidence that only one pigment was present. In this case, the difference spectra were obtained from a family of curves, of the pigment extract and of samples of the pigment extract following selective bleaching in long-red, red, and white light. Riggs (1951) made use of absorption spectra of hemoglobin in various states of oxygenation essentially as one would use difference spectra in developing a spectrophotometric method to determine the fractions of oxy- and reduced hemoglobin present in bullfrog blood in equilibrium with various partial pressures of oxygen. Chance and Hackett (1959) used difference spectra in studies on the electron transfer in skunk cabbage mitochondria as evidence that by a series of chemical treatments the cytochrome b component could be examined without interference from the cytochrome c-a-a$_3$ system. Absorption spectra and difference spectra were employed by Dempsey and Christensen (1962) in a study of the complexing of pyridoxal 5'-phosphate with bovine serum albumin.

Absorption Spectrophotometry: As stated above, a spectrophotometer equipped to measure the fraction of radiation absorbed by a liquid may be used as an instrument for quantitative analysis in exactly the same manner as a photoelectric colorimeter. This is the case when it is adjusted to deliver radiation of a particular wavelength and the optical density of a layer of solution containing an unknown concentration of a substance which absorbs this wavelength is compared with the optical density of a layer of the same thickness of a solution containing a known concentration of this same substance (the standard).

$$\text{Concentration of the unknown solution} = \left(\frac{\text{concentration of the standard}}{\text{optical density of the standard}}\right) \times \text{optical density of the unknown solution}$$

This equation applies only when the system meets the requirement expressed by Beer's law, i.e., when the numerical value of the term in parentheses is a constant. If it is a constant, a plot of the corresponding values of optical density and concentration over a range of known concentrations should yield a straight line with zero intercept. This test should always be made the first time this method is used for the quantitative determination of a substance. Even when a curve instead of a straight line is obtained, the method need not be abandoned, for having established this curve under the specified conditions (of wavelength, solvent, solution layer thickness and temperature) it may be used as a calibration curve.

Once the optical density of the unknown solution has been determined, the concentration of the substance in it may be obtained by calculation using the calibration factor or, in the absence of this constant, by interpolation from the calibration curve.

Analyses of this type have given commercially available spectrophotometers the position of essential instruments in almost every biological laboratory. In the general procedure for quantitative assays outlined above it was assumed that the operator knows which wavelength to use. If the proper wavelength is not known, the instrument can be used to obtain a spectral optical density (absorbancy) curve of a solution to aid in selecting a favorable wavelength (see p. 221), one which is strongly absorbed by the solute and, hence, one at which there is a maximum change in optical density per unit change in concentration of the absorbing molecules. Since the wavelength range of most laboratory spectrophotometers includes the ultraviolet and a portion of the infra-red as well as the visible part of the spectrum, the probability of locating a strong absorption band of the substance is considerably increased. Too, the spectral quality of the radiation entering the absorption vessel is limited to a rather narrow band of contiguous wavelengths. Of course, the width of the band will vary with the slit width and, for the same slit width, some variation is encountered over the wavelength range of the instrument.

It is a common practice to use as narrow a slit as possible with the idea in mind that the more nearly monochromatic the radiation, the more nearly the approach to the ideal situation in applying Beer's law. A further advantage of using a narrow slit opening is that there is less chance of including radiation of wavelengths that are absorbed by some solute present in the solution other than the one for which the method of assay was designed. However, a very narrow opening may lead to considerable error in a determination when the optical density is measured at the wavelength peak of a narrow absorption band because of the inability of the operator to reset the instrument to deliver the same band of wavelengths each time and because the narrow slit opening may reduce the intensity of the radiation falling on the photocell to a point below the sensitivity of the instrument.

These considerations are illustrated by the hypothetical absorption curves in figure 59. Although the absorption band of compound R is partially overlapped by that of compound S, by choosing a wavelength of 565 mμ and restricting the slit width to exclude wavelengths less than 555 mμ no error will be introduced in determining the optical density of R when

S is present at or below the concentration represented. The smoothly rounded peak of the absorption band of R actually minimizes the error in determining the concentration of R in different samples due to errors in reproducing the wavelength and band width each time the spectrophotometer is readjusted, because the absorption coefficient of R remains virtually the same over a band of wavelengths on either side of 565 mμ. Visualizing the same sources of errors in the photometric determination of S, it would be better to determine optical densities at 450 mμ rather than at 420 mμ.

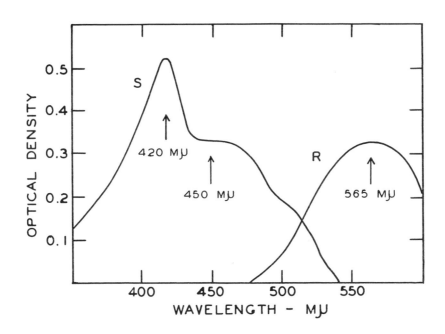

Figure 59

The absorption spectra of two substances, S and R. Each substance may be determined in the presence of the other by using an absorption spectrophotometer since the light entering the cuvette can be restricted to a narrow band of wavelengths that will be absorbed by only one of the substances. These curves also illustrate that the error introduced by an incorrect wavelength setting of the spectrophotometer for 565 mμ in determining R is less than for an incorrect setting at 420 mμ in a determination of S, and that in determinations of S this source of error would be minimized by determining the optical density at 450 mμ

Absorption spectrometry may be employed to determine the concentration of more than one absorbing component present in a solution when the absorption bands of the components do not coincide but do overlap. The technique used may be outlined by considering a case where the sample contains two absorbing substances m and n, having specific absorption coefficients of $k'm_1$ and $k'n_1$ at wavelength λ_1 and $k'm_2$ and $k'n_2$ at wavelength λ_2 respectively. Then, according to Beer's law,

$$D_{m\lambda_1} = k'_{m\lambda_1}c_m \quad \text{and} \quad D_{n\lambda_1} = k'_{n\lambda_1}c_n$$

$$D_{m\lambda_1} = k'_{m\lambda_2}c_m \quad \text{and} \quad D_{n\lambda_2} = k'_{n\lambda_2}c_n$$

Since both substances contribute to the optical density, D_x,

$$D_{x\lambda_1} = k'_{m\lambda_1}c_m + k'_{n\lambda_1}c_n$$

and

$$D_{x\lambda_2} = k'_{m\lambda_2} c_m + k'_{n\lambda_2} c_m$$

51

From Equation 50,

$$c_n = \frac{D_{x\lambda_1} - k'_{m\lambda_1} c_m}{k'_{n\lambda_1}}$$

and substituting this expression of c_n in Equation 51 and solving for c_m

$$c_m = \frac{k_{n\lambda_1} D_{x\lambda_2} - k'_{n\lambda_2} D_{x\lambda_1}}{k'_{n\lambda_1} k'_{m\lambda_2} - k'_{n\lambda_2} k'_{m\lambda_1}}$$

In a similar manner,

$$c_n = \frac{k'_{m\lambda_1} D_{x\lambda_2} - k'_{m\lambda_2} D_{x\lambda_1}}{k'_{m\lambda_1} k'_{n\lambda_2} - k'_{m\lambda_2} k'_{n\lambda_1}}$$

The quantitative determination of pyruvic acid and α-ketoglutaric acid when both are present in the same sample by means of this technique (Koepsell and Sharpe, 1952) is outlined in Chapter 11, p. 210. Another example of its application is the quantitative determination of chlorophyll a and chlorophyll b together (Arnon, 1949, and for a modification see Bruinsma, 1961). Koski (1950) has extended this general technique for the quantitative determination of protochlorophyll, chlorophyll a, and chlorophyll b in the presence of one another.

Returning to quantitative spectrometric analyses where only a single absorbing compound is dealt with, it is of interest to point to the use of the specific extinction (absorption) coefficient, k', in many standardized procedures. In the equation written out on page 223 the parenthesized term, which is a constant if there is a linear relationship of concentration and optical density, is equal to $^1/k'$, and when the concentration $\underline{c}$ is expressed in moles per liter, to $^1/\epsilon$. Then when the absorbing layer is 1.0 cm. in thickness

$$c = \frac{D}{k'} \qquad \text{or,} \qquad c = \frac{D}{\epsilon}$$

Because D ($= \log_{10} I_0/I$) is a dimensionless number, when $\underline{l}$ is in centimeters and $\underline{c}$ is in terms of weight per unit volume, $\underline{e.g.}$, moles per ml., then ϵ, which represents the area per unit of absorbing substance, has the dimensions of $cm^2/mole$ (or, $cm^2 \times mole^{-1}$).

An example of the use of the specific extinction coefficient is the spectrophotometric assay method of determining the two dehydrogenase coenzymes, DPN (diphosphopyridine nucleotide) and TPN (triphosphopyridine nucleotide). The origin of this method may be traced to the work of Warburg and Christian (1936). In the reduced state as DPNH and TPNH, both compounds have identical broad absorption bands in the ultraviolet with maximum, or peak, absorption at 340 mμ., but in the oxidized state their absorption at this wavelength is negligible. (Excellent reproductions of the ultraviolet absorption spectra of DPNH and TPNH, and of a number of other ribonucleotides, are to be found in circular OR-18 of Pabst Laboratories, 1037 W. McKinley Ave., Milwaukee 5, Wis., and see also Siegel et al., 1959). The specific extinction coefficient for the reduced compounds is 6.22 x 10^6 cm² per mole (Horecker and Kornberg, 1948).

Another example of the use of specific extinction coefficients in quantitative analysis, in this case to determine the concentration of cytochrome c, will be found on page 272. It should be noted that the nominal band width specified is 5 mμ at 550 mμ wavelength when using the extinction coefficient given.

The last example referred to above serves to emphasize the need for exact duplication of the parameters wavelength and band width when the specific extinction coefficient is used in quantitative spectrophotometric analyses. If there is any doubt that the wavelength scale of the spectrophotometer is correct, the instrument should be calibrated (the method of Ploeser and Loring, 1949, is recommended). A spectrophotometer calibrator suitable for use in the ultraviolet and visible wavelength regions is marketed by Arthur H. Thomas Co., Philadelphia 5, Pa. A table or graph showing nominal band widths corresponding to slit opening over the wavelength range is furnished by the manufacturer. This usually suffices for setting the slit opening to deliver a band of wavelengths of the desired width unless the edges of the slit jaws have been blunted by jamming, as indicated by the inability to obtain zero transmission at maximum sensitivity with the absorption cell out and the slit-opening scale set at zero. In this case the instrument should be returned to the manufacturer for repair.

There are many applications of absorption spectrophotometers in biological research besides their use in the usual, and rather simple, spectrometric methods of quantitative analysis. Some idea of the range of usefulness of these instruments may be had by referring to the examples given below.

It is possible to follow the changes in many reaction systems involving either the reduction or oxidation of DPNH or TPHN since there is little absorption at 340 mμ. by proteins and the other more common constituents of tissue extracts (absorption corrected for in the blank). The experiments of Horecker and Kornberg are model examples. These investigators obtained an extinction coefficient for DPNH and TPNH of 6.22 x 10^6 cm^2./mole (340 mμ.; 1.0 cm. corex-D cuvettes) from measurements of the change in optical density with concentration (the amount of DPNH oxidized or TPN reduced was determined stoichiometrically) when these substances served as substrates in reactions that were essentially complete. The reactions, catalyzed by the respective dehydrogenases, used were

$$\text{Pyruvic acid} + \text{DPNH} + \text{H}^+ \rightleftharpoons \text{Lactic acid} + \text{DPN}$$

$$\text{Acetaldehyde} + \text{DPNH} + \text{H}^+ \rightleftharpoons \text{Alcohol} + \text{DPN}$$

$$\text{D-Isocitric acid} + \text{TPN} \rightleftharpoons \alpha\text{-Ketoglutaric acid} + \text{CO}_2 + \text{TPNH} + \text{H}^+$$

with the entire system of each reaction confined in a 3 ml. absorption cuvette. In plotting optical density versus time in the reduction of DPN by acetaldehyde they obtained a curve, similar to that of curve A in figure 60, where a known amount of acetaldehyde was added as indicated by the arrow, to the cuvette which contained all of the other components of the system.

Consideration of the above experiments suggests that the absorptivity of the two coenzymes may be applied in a variety of analytical procedures, either qualitative or quantitative. This property has been used quite often in connection with methods of purifying and in determining the properties of various dehydrogenases normally containing DPN or TPN, e.g., D-glucose-6-phosphate dehydrogenase from Lebedev juice from brewers' yeast (Glaser and Brown, 1955), a glyceraldehyde-3-phosphate dehydrogenase from photosynthetic tissue (Rosenberg and Arnon, 1955), lactic dehydrogenase of heart (Neilands, 1952b), a DPN-linked isocitric dehydrogenase from animal tissues (Plaut and Sung, 1954; cf., Kornberg and Pricer, 1951), and a zinc-dependent lactic dehydrogenase from

Euglena gracilis (Price, 1962). The same is true for determining the effect of pH on the activity of some enzymes, e.g., a steroid-sensitive aldehyde dehydrogenase from rat liver (Maxwell and Topper, 1961), microsomal TPNH-cytochrome c reductase (Williams and Kamin, 1962), and xylulokinase (Anderson and Wood, 1962). Chakravorty et al., 1962, determined the equilibrium constants for several pairs of substrates by following the changes in the DPN-DPNH ratio.

Other types of determinations of interest to biologists to which absorption spectrometry has been applied with considerable success include, among others: the equilibrium constant of a reaction (which may be used in calculating the change in free energy); the Michaelis constant; the effect of pH on enzyme activity and on the equilibrium constant; reaction velocity; enzyme turnover number; the effect of inhibitors and activators on enzymes; co-factor requirements and substrate specificity of enzymes. The literature covering the above examples is already quite extensive, so much so that the methods used cannot be comprehensively presented here. However, information on the technique of each of these types of determinations may be obtained by examining one or another of the following references: Neilands, 1952b; Stern et al., 1952; Green et al., 1954; Glaser and Brown, 1955; Talalay and Marcus, 1956; Zelitch, 1955; Cowgill and Pizer, 1956; Hurwitz et al., 1956; Sanadi et al., 1956; Stern and Del Campillo, 1956; Smyrniotis and Horecker, 1956; Wolff and Kaplan, 1956. Additional examples where the spectrometric assay depended on the absorption of radiation by substances other than those already mentioned may be found by referring to: the enzymatic micro determinations of uric acid, hypoxanthine, xanthine, adenine, and xanthopterin described by Plesner and Kalckar (1955) (cf., Kalckar, 1947; Bergmann and Dikstein, 1956), and the determination of the activity of deoxyribonuclease (Rotherham et al., 1956) phosphorylglyceric acid mutase (Cowgill and Pizer, 1956), tryptophan and tyrosine content of a glycoprotein (Bürgi and Schmid, 1961), urea inhibition of several enzymes (Chakravorty et al., 1962) and proteolysis of some casein fractions by plasmin (Derechin, 1962).

Quite often in connection with the purification of enzymes or in comparing the enzyme activity in different preparations, the activity of the particular enzyme is expressed in terms of an enzyme 'unit'. The unit often referred to is the amount of enzyme present in a certain volume of the reaction system which brings about some unit of change in optical density in one minute under the conditions specified (e.g. see: Glaser and Brown, 1955; Zelitch, 1955; Wróblewski et al., 1956). The protein content of enzyme preparations is sometimes determined by measuring the absorption at 280 mμ, or at 260 and 280 mμ, according to the method of Warburg and Christian (1941), or by the method of Lowry et al. (1951).

The activity of many enzymes and the kinetics of many enzyme systems have been followed spectrometrically by coupling the reaction catalyzed by the enzyme with a reaction in which either DPN or TPN is reduced or oxidized. Some of the reaction systems are quite complex, never-the-less they are often accommodated in a liquid volume of 3 ml. or less. Stern et al. (1952) in a study of the synthesis of citric acid from acetyl-CoA and oxalacetate catalyzed by the condensing enzyme coupled this reaction with the L-malate dehydrogenase system, in which DPN is reduced. The course of some of their experiments are illustrated with curves of the type of A and B of figure 61. Utter and Kurahashi (1954), in connection with the purification of oxalacetic carboxylase from chicken livers, demonstrated that the reaction catalyzed by this enzyme could be coupled with the malic acid dehydrogenase—DPN system. Horecker et al. (1953) in a study of the formation of sedoheptulose phosphate from pentose phosphate used a spectrometric assay method for transketolase that was based on coupling the transketolase reaction with a reaction in which DPNH was oxidized. Zelitch (1955) used an assay based on the oxidation of DPNH in an investigation of the action of crystalline glyoxylic acid reductase obtained from tobacco leaves. Marmur and Hotchkiss (1955) in a study of the mannitol metabolism of <u>Pneumococcus</u> sp. identified fructose-6-phosphate formed in the oxidation of mannitol catalyzed by the DPN linked dehydrogenase (<u>cf</u>., Wolff and Kaplan, 1956) by coupling this reaction to the two-reaction sequence catalyzed by isomerase and glucose 6-phosphate dehydrogenase to form 6-phosphogluconate with the concomitant reduction of TPN. The optical measurement of TPN reduction could be made without interference by DPNH by oxidizing the latter as it was formed through coupling it with acetaldehyde and yeast alcohol dehydrogenase. A curve, illustrating the reversal of the mannitol oxidation reaction by added fructose-6-phosphate, similar to curve A of figure 61, is shown. A sequential reaction system of approximately the same complexity as that of Marmur and Hotchkiss was used by Pullman and Racker (1956) in a study of oxidative phosphorylation (<u>cf</u>., Sanadi <u>et al</u>., 1956).

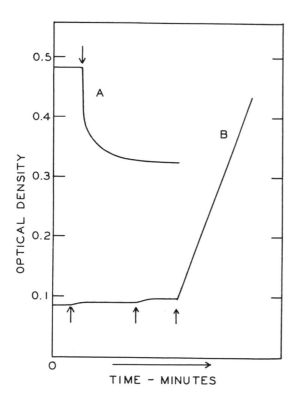

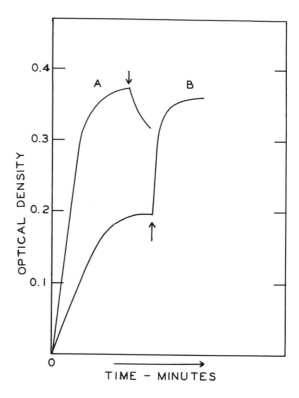

Figure 60

Examples of plots of optical density versus time which illustrate the types of curves which may be obtained when (Curve A) a quantity of a reactant added, as indicated by the arrow, to an otherwise complete reaction mixture results in a definite decrease in optical density as the reaction proceeds to completion (the change in optical density of the original contents of the cuvette on dilution is corrected for in a blank) and (Curve B) the reaction system is completed by introducing the third but not the first two substances indicated by the arrows (the slight changes in optical density following the first two additions are due to dulution

Figure 61

Examples of the types of curves which may be obtained by plotting optical density versus time which illustrate (Curve A) a reaction progressing toward equilibrium subsequent to the addition of an enzyme at zero time, and the reversal of the reaction by the introduction as indicated by the arrow, of an additional amount of one of the products, and (Curve B) a reaction having reached equilibrium following the introduction of an additional amount of a reactant at the time indicated by the arrow. Corrections for changes in optical density due to dilution of the contents of the cuvettes by the additions are obtained from suitable blanks

The investigation of the properties of enzymes and the kinetics of enzyme reactions employing the technique of absorption spectrometry is by no means limited to systems involving the oxidation or reduction of DPN and TPN. Green et al. (1954) in a study of butyryl coenzyme A dehydrogenase, linked the reaction catalyzed by this enzyme with the reduction of 2,6-dichloro-phenol-indophenol. The reduction of the latter was followed by the decrease in optical density at 600 mμ. They also used phycocyanin plus triphenyl-tetrazolium chloride and cytochrome c as electron acceptors, measuring the reduction by the change in optical density at 485 mμ. and 550.5 mμ. respectively. (See Table 32 for a listing of representative oxidation-reduction indicators which may be of use as electron acceptors or donars.) Kaufman and Alivisatos (1955) used the increase in optical density at 235 mμ. due to the succinyl CoA formed in studying the nuclotide specificity of the phosphorylating enzyme from spinach leaves. A plot of the data obtained on adding inosine triphosphate, ADP, and ATP in succession to the reaction system resulted in a curve resembling curve B of figure 60.

Table 32

Representative Oxidation Reduction Indicators

Indicator	E' at pH 7
Benzyl-viologen	- 0.359
2:6-Dichloro-phenol-indophenol	+ 0.217
Janus green	- 0.225
Lauth's violet (thionine)	+ 0.063
Methylene blue	+ 0.011
Methyl-viologen	+ 0.440
Neutral red	- 0.325
Phenol blue	+ 0.224
Phenol-indo-2:6-dichloro-phenol	+ 0.217
Toluylene blue	+ 0.115

These, and others as well, are available from companies specializing in biological chemicals for laboratory purposes.

An entirely different area of application of spectrophotometric assay in kinetic studies is that covering the participation of the pigments and enzymes in electron transport in respiration. More often than not, the information desired could be obtained only with the use of spectrophotometers of high wavelength resolution and stability equipped with accessories capable of recording optical density differences of the order of a few ten-thousands of a unit in following the changes occurring during a few milliseconds in the level of oxidation or reduction of the catalysts in the respiratory chain. Attendent difficulties also have had to be overcome because of the need to explore these changes in intact tissue, or single cells, or mitochondrial and chloroplast preparations. A brief digest of the special techniques for this purpose is given above under the sections on Spectrophotometers and Absorption Vessels. For more details and references to the contributions of numerous investigators, the reader is referred to Chance (1954), Chance and Williams (1956) and to Wood (1960), and to the more recent literature for the application of these techniques, e.g., Chance (1958), Chance and Hackett (1959), Chance and Redfearn (1961), Baker and Lieberman (1962), and Minakami et al. (1962).

J. F. STAUFFER

THUNBERG METHOD FOR ESTIMATION
OF DEHYDROGENASE ACTIVITY

Although uptake of O_2 serves as a suitable method for measuring the terminal reaction of aerobic respiration, it frequently is desirable to measure electron transport at a point before the terminal oxidation, or to measure the activity of systems which do not transport electrons to O_2. Thunberg emphasized the role of hydrogen activation in respiratory processes and measured anaerobic dye reduction by hydrogen (electrons) as an index of their activation by dehydrogenase enzymes.

The classical Thunberg technique employs tubes such as those shown in figure 62. The tubes are provided with a sidearm cap arranged to hold materials to be added to the main tube after evacuation. For evacuation the sidearm cap is turned so that a hole drilled in its standard taper inner joint coincides with the evacuation outlet. The tube can be closed after evacuation by rotating the sidearm cap.

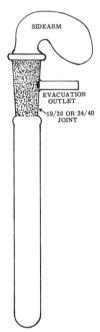

The position of the reacting components in the tube and their concentrations will vary with the application of the method, but the following directions constitute average conditions employed in measurements of methylene blue reduction.

Place 1 ml. 1/10,000 (0.000267 M) methylene blue, 2 ml. M/50 substrate and 2 ml. M/15 phosphate buffer (pH 7.0) in the tube and 1 ml. of bacterial suspension, tissue suspension or enzyme preparation in the sidearm cap. Put 2 lines of anhydrous lanolin or other grease on the ground joint of the cap 90° from the hole in the ground joint. Connect the cap and tube with the hole in the cap coinciding with the evacuation outlet on the tube joint. Press the cap firmly in place so the grease from the two lines flows over the entire joint; do not rotate the joint more than a few degrees. By setting the joint in this manner air is not trapped in the grease. Attach the evacuation outlet of the tube to a good water aspirator or a vacuum oil pump, and evacuate for 3 minutes, tapping the tube to release dissolved gas; keep the tube inclined at a low angle to minimize "bumping". A water aspirator is entirely satisfactory for evacuating Thunberg tubes. When evacuation is complete, rotate the cap slowly through an angle of 180°, and then oscillate it through a small arc to

Figure 62
Thunberg tube

set the cap. Put the tube in a constant temperature water bath, and after allowing 10 minutes to reach temperature equilibrium, invert the tube to mix the contents, and follow the methylene blue reduction visually or photometrically. For visual measurement a tube is included which contains all the components of the system being studied (the active tissue is poisoned or heat inactivated) but with the methylene blue at 1/10 normal concentration. This tube represents 90% reduction of the methylene blue, and when the other tubes match the color intensity of this tube the time is recorded as the end point.

The reliability of the results obtained by the Thunberg method depends in part upon the efficiency with which oxygen is removed. Obviously, since leuco-methylene blue is converted into the blue form by oxygen, it will be impossible to measure the real reduction time if some of the dye is being reoxidized by oxygen during the process. It has been found in practice that adequate removal of oxygen is obtained with evacuation by means

of an ordinary laboratory water-
pump provided the evacuation is continued for at least three minutes and
the tube is tapped vigorously during
the evacuation. As Thunberg tubes
must hold a vacuum against a full
atmosphere of pressure, it is essential that the joints be carefully ground
and that they be reasonably long. The
24/40 and the 19/38 standard taper
joints are satisfactory.

Methylene blue and other dyes sometimes exert a toxic effect on the
tissues; Quastel and Wheatley (1931),
Yudkin (1933), and Tam and Wilson
(1941) reported that free phosphates
protect against this effect, hence the
usual methods employ buffers high in
phosphate. Dyes with oxidation-
reduction potentials differing from
that of methylene blue often may be
used to advantage in the Thunberg
technique.

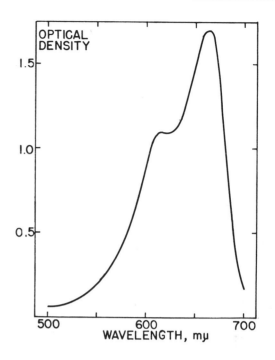

Figure 63
Absorption spectrum
of methylene blue

PHOTOMETRIC ESTIMATION OF METHYLENE BLUE REDUCTION

Methylene blue reduction is not a strictly linear function, and much more information on
the kinetics of the reaction can be obtained if the reduction is followed photometrically
rather than visually. Early applications of this technique were made by Ganapathy and
Sastri (1938) and by Jongbloed (1938). Thunberg tubes can be ordered to fit the colorimeter available to the investigator; the outside diameter of the tubes commonly will be
between 13 and 20 mm. Request that the glassblower make a set of tubes from matched
lengths of glass tubing to insure uniformity. Figure 63 shows the absorption spectrum of
methylene blue. Measure dye reduction near 660 mμ, as absorption is high and closely
approximates Beer's law at this wavelength.

To follow methylene blue reduction photometrically the tubes are brought to temperature
equilibrium, their contents mixed at 15 or 30 second intervals, the tubes wiped dry and
initial readings taken immediately after each tube is mixed. Tubes are returned to the
bath and read every 3 minutes, thus with 15 second intervals 12 tubes can be read every
3 minutes. Suspension concentrations are adjusted so time for reduction is 15 to 30
minutes giving 5 to 10 readings to plot. It is unnecessary to wait for complete reduction.
Upon finishing the experiment a few crystals of $Na_2S_2O_4$ are added to each tube to completely reduce the methylene blue, and the tubes are then read on the photoelectric colorimeter, (I_0). The concentration of methylene blue at any time is proportional to log
(I_0/I), where I is the galvanometer reading at any particular time and I_0 is the reading
after complete reduction. If reduction is linear with time a plot of log (I_0/I) against
time will yield a straight line. With the organisms they employed, Tam and Wilson (1941)
found that most substrates gave a reduction which was logarithmic rather than linear with
respect to time, hence it was necessary to plot log of methylene blue concentration, i.e.,

log log (I_0/I), against time. The slopes of the lines obtained were an index of the activities of the enzyme under various conditions.

A wide variety of studies can be made with a technique of this sort. For example, pH optima of substrates, the temperature relationships which permit the calculation of energy of activation, the comparative dehydrogenation of a wide variety of substrates, and the effect of a variety of inhibitors can be determined.

The Thunberg method for following methylene blue reduction has evolved in recent years into spectrophotometric methods with increased specificity. Now the reduction of methylene blue, or some other suitable oxidation-reduction dye, often may be used for general survey work only. Later, the investigator is likely to examine spectrophotometrically the reduction or oxidation of pyridine nucleotides, cytochromes, flavins or other naturally occurring electron carriers. The measurements are not unlike those encountered in the Thunberg technique, but spectrophotometers permit measurements with a narrow band pass over a wide range of wavelengths. For precise spectrophotometric measurements, a Thunberg tube with optically flat faces may be substituted for the conventional cylindrical tube. Pyrocell Manufacturing Co., 207 E. 84th St., New York, and Quaracell Products Inc., 401 Broadway, New York, fabricate such from silica.

At times methylene blue (or other dye system of proper potential) may be used to "by pass" a normal system in the cell; for example, its use in restoring the respiration of red blood cells poisoned with cyanide (Barron and Harrop, 1928) has become classic. In some reconstructed enzyme systems methylene blue may be used as an actual carrier of the hydrogen. By establishing anaerobic conditions with an atmosphere of hydrogen in Warburg vessels it is possible to follow hydrogen uptake by hydrogenase preparations when methylene blue is supplied as hydrogen acceptor. It is necessary to use high concentrations of methylene blue, as the reduction of 1 ml. of a M/1,000 solution requires only 22.4 μl. of hydrogen.

R. H. BURRIS

Chapter 13
DESIGN OF CHROMATOGRAPHIC
PROCEDURES

INTRODUCTION

The body of literature on chromatography is enormous, and is growing at an increasing rate. The books, papers, and reviews on the subject give a great deal of information on chromatographic procedures for specific separations, and very adequate information on chromatographic theory. Very seldom, however, is information on the design of practical chromatographic procedures given in a form useful to scientists inexperienced in chromatography. It is the purpose of this chapter to describe and discuss the theoretical and practical factors which are important in analytical or preparative chromatographic separations. Exact conditions for specific separations will be given only as examples. The reader will be assumed to have a working knowledge of chemistry, an understanding of simple algebra, a little common sense, and no knowledge of chromatography. Some mathematical derivations will be included, but these will be relegated to an appendix. Factors which influence the efficiency of separations will be stressed, and the treatment will be as practical as is feasible in a discussion of general methodology.

NATURE OF THE CHROMATOGRAPHIC PROCESS

Effective Distribution Coefficients. The term "distribution coefficient", as ordinarily used, refers to the distribution of a solute between two liquid phases. In chromatography, it is convenient to use the term to describe the distribution of a solute between any two phases. For example, the distribution coefficient of a substance between alcohol and alumina might be 0.1, meaning that the concentration in the alcohol (w/v) was one-tenth the concentration on the alumina (w/w). Thus, the distribution coefficient of ethyl alcohol between air (w/v) and water (w/v) at 30° may be said to be 3.05 x 10^{-4}, since 1 liter of air will contain 3.05 x 10^{-4} times as much alcohol as a liter of water with which it is in equilibrium. The distribution coefficient K will always be expressed, for chromatographic purposes, as concentration in the mobile phase divided by concentration in the stationary phase.

A term which is very conveniently applicable in chromatography is effective distribution coefficient, B. This may be defined as the total amount of substance present in one phase, divided by the total amount present in the other phase. For example, suppose that the distribution coefficient between benzene and water for a substance is 1.0. If we equilibrate some of the substance between 10 ml. of benzene and one ml. of water, the concentration in the benzene phase will be the same as the concentration in the water phase, but the total amount of solute in the benzene layer will be 10 times the total amount in the water layer, so B = 10, but K = 1.0. It is apparent that the effective distribution coefficient is the product of the distribution coefficient K multiplied by the ratio of the amounts of the two phases present in the system.

Structure of a chromatographic column. A chromatographic column may be constructed in any one of a number of ways, but it always consists, basically, of two phases. The stationary phase, which may be solid or liquid, or may consist of a mixture of a solid and a liquid, is finely divided, and is fixed in place. The mobile phase, which may be liquid or gaseous, fills the interstices of the stationary phase, and is able to flow through the stationary phase. The stationary and mobile phases are so selected that compounds which are to be separated by the chromatogram have a definite distribution coefficient between the two phases. Almost any mechanism of distribution may be employed. The distribution may be simple partition between two immiscible liquids. It may be an adsorption equilibrium between a solid absorbent stationary phase and a liquid mobile phase. It may be an ion exchange equilibrium between an ion exchange resin stationary phase and an electrolyte as mobile phase. In any case, one can speak of the effective distribution coefficient. This can now be defined as the ratio, at equilibrium, of the amount of solute dissolved in the mobile phase contained in unit length of column to the amount of solute held by the stationary phase contained in the same length of column. Consider, for example, a column consisting of a glass tube packed with moist powdered silica. The amount of moisture is such that 0.1 ml. of water is contained in 1 cm. of column length. Suppose that the mobile phase of the column is water-saturated ethyl ether. The ether surrounds the moist particles of silica, 1 cm. of column length contains 1 ml. of ether. Let us suppose that the solute is acetic acid. The distribution coefficient, K (ether/water), for acetic acid is approximately 0.5. But, since ten times as much ether as water is present per centimeter of column length, the effective distribution coefficient, B, will be 5.0, or, in other words, when acetic acid is present in the column, five times as much of it is held in the mobile phase as in the stationary phase. The effective distribution coefficient is the factor that determines the rate of migration of a solute on a chromatographic column.

A mechanism of distribution that deserves special mention is one that has been proved valuable in the purification of high molecular weight compounds. If a column, with an aqueous solution as the continuous phase, is packed with particles of a gel such as "Sephadex" (Porath and Flodin, 1959) or agar (Andrews, 1962), and if the gel is such that low molecular weight compounds can diffuse into it, but high molecular weight compounds cannot, the retention volume of the column depends on the molecular weight of the solute, and hence, by a "molecular sieve" mechanism, the effective distribution coefficient also depends on the molecular weight of the solute.

Mechanism of chromatographic separation. Let us imagine a chromatographic column consisting of a glass tube packed with a powdered stationary phase, which we will call the packing, surrounded by a liquid mobile phase, which we will call the solvent. Let the column be 7 cm. long, and let it contain 1 ml. of mobile phase per cm. Such a column is shown in figure 64. We will first add to the top of the column 1 ml. of solvent in which is dissolved 64 μg. of sample. When we do this, 1 ml. of solvent will flow out of the bottom of the column, still leaving a total of 7 ml. of solvent in the column.

Let us assume that B = 1, that is, that the sample will distribute itself equally between the solvent and packing. The sample will then occupy the top centimeter of the column, 32 μg. of it being dissolved in the solvent, and 32 μg. being held on the packing. The diagram at the extreme left of figure 64 represents this stage of the process. Let us now rapidly add one ml. of solvent to the top of the column, causing 1 ml. of solvent to flow out of the bottom of the column. The solvent which previously occupied the top centimeter of the column, and which contains

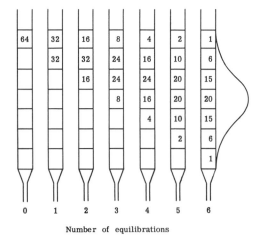

Figure 64
Distribution of solute in an idealized chromatographic column

32 μg. of sample, will be driven down to the second centimeter of the column, leaving 32 μg. in the top centimeter of the column. This is illustrated in the second diagram of figure 64. The sample present in each of the column sections will, of course, distribute itself equally between the solvent and packing, each of the two 1-cm. sections having 16 μg. of sample on the packing and 16 μg. of sample in the solvent. Now let us add a second 1-ml. portion of solvent to the top of the column. The 16 μg. present in the solvent in the top section will be washed down into the second section, leaving 16 μg. behind. The solvent originally in the second section will be forced into the third section, carrying 16 μg. with it, and leaving 16 μg. behind, held by the packing. The second section, therefore, now contains 32 μg., half of it newly received from the first section, and half of it "held over" from the previous equilibration. The column is now in the state indicated by the third diagram of figure 64. The changes taking place when the next milliliter of solvent is added are shown in the fourth diagram, and can readily be verified by the reader. The last diagram indicates the distribution of the sample on the column after 6 equilibrations. It will be noted that the sample is distributed through the entire column, with its highest concentration in the center of the column. If the effective distribution coefficient (B) had been less than 1, more than half of the sample would have been left on the packing after each equilibration, and the sample would have progressed down the column more slowly. A definite percentage of it would, of course, be in the bottom column section after 6 equilibrations, but the concentration peak would be above the center of the column. Similarly, if B were considerably greater than 1, most of the sample would be in the solvent phase, and its progress down the column would be more rapid. It is obvious that if B were zero (no sample in the solvent phase), the sample would remain at the top of the column, and that if B were infinite (no sample held by the packing) all of the sample would be at the bottom of the column after 6 equilibrations.

It may be noted from figure 64 that as the number of equilibrations increases, the sample spreads itself out over a greater column length, but does not spread itself over a greater <u>percentage</u> of the column length in use. On the contrary, the degree of spreading, when considered in this way, actually decreases as the number of equilibrations increases. Thus, after two equilibrations, the center third of the column contains 32/64ths of the sample, but after 5 equilibrations, the center third of the column contains 40/64ths of the sample. This figure continues to increase. For example, after 100 equilibrations, the center third of the column would contain about 99.3% of the total sample. Methods for determining distributions for large numbers of equilibrations will be considered later, but the points to be emphasized here are that the rate of progress of the solute through the column depends on its effective distribution coefficient, and that the sharpness of the solute band depends on the number of equilibrations that have taken place. Figure 72 shows graphically the effect on the shape of the solute band of increasing n, the number of equilibrations, in a column of given length. It will be seen that the band becomes very sharp in columns where the number of equilibrations is very large.

One difference between the ideal column of figure 64 and a real column is that in a real column, the solvent is added slowly and continuously, so that equilibration takes place continuously. The length of column required for the equivalent of one full equilibration varies from 0.1 mm. in very good columns to perhaps 3 mm. in very poor columns. Thus, even in moderately good columns, many hundreds of equilibrations take place. The number of equilibrations taking place in a column may be termed the number of theoretical plates in the column. The term "theoretical plate", used in this sense, is analogous to its use in describing distillation columns, where the number of theoretical plates in a column is equal to the number of effective equilibrations between phases that occur in the column. In the following pages, the letter "n" will be used to designate the number of theoretical plates (equilibrations) in a column. This term, and others which will be introduced, are defined on pages 254-255.

Separations in multiplate columns. When the number of equilibrations (theoretical plates) in a column is large, the behavior of a solute follows some rather simple rules. The derivation of these rules is given in the appendix; only the rules themselves will be considered here. The behavior of a so-called "complete column" will be described first. A complete column is the section of column extending from the point of application of the sample to the farthest point reached by that portion of the solvent added with the sample. Thus, in figure 64, after 3 equilibrations the complete column was 4 cm. long, and after 6 equilibrations it was 7 cm. long.

If in figure 64, the actual physical column length had been only 6 cm., after 6 equilibrations had been performed, the ml. of solvent added with the sample, would have appeared as effluent from the bottom of the column. At this point, the physical column would represent the upper 6 cm. of a hypothetical complete column 7 cm. long. Thus, the complete column may be longer than the actual physical column.

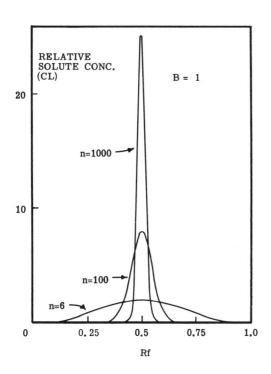

Figure 65
Effect of number of plates (n) on the
shape of the solute band

In a complete column, as has been mentioned, the position of the solute band depends on the effective distribution coefficient, B. The actual relationship between B and the position of the band is given by equation (52). The derivation of this equation, and of other equations to be given, will be found in an appendix to this chapter.

$$\frac{p}{L} = \frac{B}{B+1} = Rf \qquad \boxed{52}$$

where L is the length of the complete column, and p is the position of the peak of the solute band, measured (in the same units as L) from the point of application of the solute ("top" of the column). It will be noted that p/L is synonymous with Rf value, which is a term much used to describe rate of movement of solutes on columns.

It is obvious from the formula that when B is much larger than 1, p/L is almost 1, in other words, the solute band moves almost as fast as the solvent front, and is located close to the "bottom" of the complete column. Conversely, when B is much smaller than 1, p/L is also much smaller than 1, which means that the solute moves slowly compared to the solvent

front. When B = 1, p/L = 0.5, and the solute band will be at the center of the column, as in figures 64 and 65. It is important to note than p/L, or Rf, the relative position of the band on the column, is independent of the length of the complete column, and depends only on B.

In figure 66 are shown the positions and shapes of solute bands corresponding to various values of B for columns having 100 and 1000 theoretical plates. It will be noted that increasing the number of equilibrations in a complete column does not change the relative position of the bands, but increases their sharpness. The sharpness of the bands, as can be seen from the figure, depends on the value of n (the number of theoretical plates), and also on B, the effective distribution coefficient. In order to describe the relationship quantitatively, we must have a way of expressing sharpness. All of the bands in figure 66 have the same area, that is, they represent the same amount of solute. They differ in maximum height, that is, in maximum concentration. This maximum concentration can be conveniently expressed as C, the fraction of total solute present per unit length of column. (For example, if we express column length in millimeters, and if 1 millimeter column length contains 10% of the total solute, C = 0.1). The same length units must, of course, be used in expressing p, L, and C. C may be expressed in terms of B and n, or in terms of p, L, and n.

$$C = \frac{\sqrt{n}\,(B+1)}{L\,\sqrt{2\pi B}} \qquad C = \sqrt{\frac{n}{2\pi\,p(L-p)}}\ , \text{ or, } n = 2\pi C^2\,p(L-p) \qquad \boxed{53}$$

It will be noted that if L, p, and C can be measured, n may be calculated from the formula. This is one method that may be used to determine the number of theoretical plates in an actual column. Another method, which is usually more convenient, will be given later.

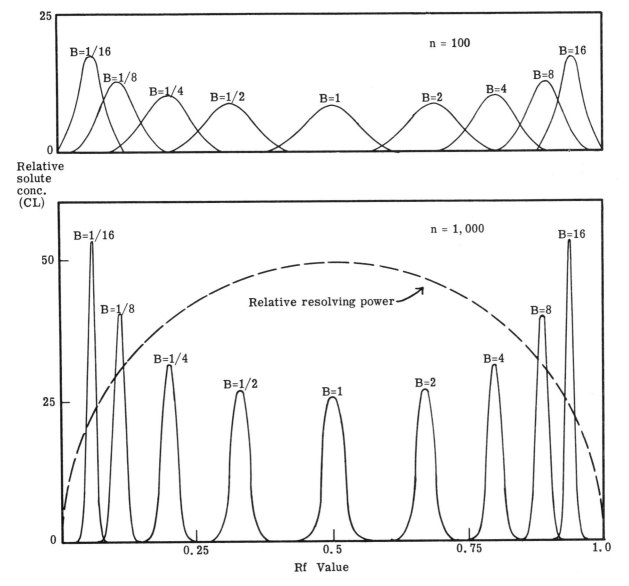

Figure 66
For a complete chromatogram, the effect of distribution coefficient (B), and number of plates (n) on band position and band shape

It will be seen from figure 66 that a complete column containing 100 theoretical plates will effect practically complete separation of two components whose B values differ by a factor of 2, provided that these B values are such that the solute bands are near the center of the column. A 1000-plate column will give good separation of such compounds even fairly close to the ends of the column, and, at the center of the column, will give separation of compounds whose B values are much closer together than the examples in the figure. The ability of a column to separate two compounds depends on the ratio of the B values of the compounds, on the number of plates in the column, and on the position of the bands on the column. In order to express the relative resolving power of a column, we must find a suitable definition of resolving power. Loosely, high resolving power is the ability to separate compounds differing only slightly in distribution coefficient. A better definition would be that high resolving power is the ability to separate compounds having only a small <u>percentage</u> difference in effective distribution coefficient. The percentage difference in effective distribution coefficient necessary for good separation may be used as a criterion of resolving power, but this has the disadvantage that a small percentage difference corresponds to a high resolving power, and <u>vice</u> <u>versa</u>. Hence, a better numerical definition of resolving power is the reciprocal of the percentage difference in effective distribution coefficient necessary for good separation. When relative resolving power is defined in this way, it can be shown (see Appendix) that

$$\text{Relative resolving power} = \frac{\sqrt{Bn}}{B+1} = \frac{\sqrt{np(L-p)}}{L} = \sqrt{nRf(1-Rf)} \qquad \boxed{54}$$

This expression means that, for a given B value, the resolving power of a column is proportional to the square root of the number of plates it contains. Thus, if other variables remain constant, increasing the length of a column 4-fold doubles its resolving power. The expression also means that, for a given column, the resolving power is zero at the top of the column, where $p = O$, and at the bottom of the column, where $p = L$, being maximal at the center of the column. The curve of relative resolving power for various positions on the column has the form of a semicircle, and is shown by the dotted line in figure 73. Some practical implications of the effect of number of plates and band position on resolving power will be discussed later.

<u>Flowing</u> <u>columns</u>. If, in the column of figure 64, addition of 1-ml. increments of solvent had been continued after the 6th equilibration, the solute would have begun to issue from the bottom of the column with the solvent effluent. In the same way, if solvent addition were continued in the columns of figure 66, the fastest moving component (B=16) would issue from the column first, followed in order by the compounds of lower B value. The compound having a B value of 1.0 would reach the end of the column after twice as much solvent had been added as was necessary to produce the stage of development shown in the figure. It is important to note that, in the 100-plate column, the first compound (B = 16) issues from the column after having undergone somewhat more than 100 equilibrations. The compound having a B value of 1.0 issues from the column after having undergone 200 equilibrations. Thus, while in a complete column, the number of equilibrations undergone by each compound is equal, in the "flowing column", this is not the case. The device of continuing solvent addition until the compounds to be separated issue from the column in the solvent effluent has many practical advantages when packed columns are used, since the column need not be extruded and extracted in sections to obtain the separated compounds. Because of the difference in procedure, however, there are differences in behavior.

In describing the behavior of flowing columns, two new terms must be introduced. The first of these is v, which is the volume of mobile phase present at any time in the column, generally termed the retention volume or holdup volume. This is also the volume of solvent which must be added to a column to give the picture shown in figure 64, where the first increment of mobile phase (added after the sample) has just reached the bottom of the column, but has not yet issued as effluent. The second term is V, the volume of mobile phase necessary to bring the peak of the solute band for a given compound into the effluent, or, in other words, the volume of effluent which must be collected before the peak of the solute band appears in the effluent. V varies with the B value of the compound in question, but v is constant for a given column. The expressions relating V, v, and B are

$$\frac{V}{v} = \frac{B+1}{B}, \text{ or } B = \frac{v}{V-v}$$

55

It is apparent from this relation that V/v, or the number of holdup volumes necessary to elute the peak of a given compound, depends only on the B value of the compound, and not on the length or diameter of the column being used. It will also be noted that

$$\frac{V}{v} = \frac{B+1}{B} = \frac{1}{Rf}$$

That is, the number of retention volumes necessary to elute a compound is equal to the reciprocal of its Rf value, measured while it is progressing down the column. The relation between band position in the effluent and effective distribution coefficient is illustrated, for a 100-plate and 1000-plate column in figure 67. By a 100-plate column is meant a column which would have 100 plates if operated as a complete column. It will be noted that the volume of effluent necessary for elution increases rapidly as B decreases. Comparison of figure 67 with figure 66 shows that a flowing column of a given length gives better separation than a corresponding complete column. This would be qualitatively expected from the fact that for compounds of low B value, the number of equilibrations is far in excess of the number of plates in the column. When a flowing column is referred to as a 100-plate column, the term "plate" is used in a somewhat different sense than in the case of a complete column. The symbol used for number of plates in a flowing column will be n'. The symbol for peak concentration of effluent, which is a measure of the steepness of the solute band, will be C', and will be expressed as fraction of total solute present in unit volume of effluent, the same volume units being used for v, V, and C'.

$$C' = \sqrt{\frac{n'}{2\pi V(V-v)}} \qquad n' = 2\pi V(V-v)(C')^2$$

56

The resolving power of a flowing column is, as might be expected, proportional to the square root of the number of plates. It also depends on the distribution coefficient of the compounds being separated. The formula is

$$\text{Relative resolving power} = \sqrt{\frac{n'}{B+1}} = \sqrt{\frac{n'(V-v)}{V}}$$

57

The relative resolving power is plotted as a dotted line in figure 67. It will be seen that it increases with increasing effluent volume, but rapidly approaches a maximum. This maximum resolving power, for a given column, is twice the maximum resolving power that can be attained if the column is operated as a complete column.

It should be emphasized that although compounds of low B value issue from the column as diffuse bands this does not indicate that separations are unsatisfactory. The separation between bands increases somewhat more rapidly than the width of the bands. The net resolving power is as indicated by the dotted line in figure 67. The disadvantage of low B values lies in the inordinately long times necessary for the bands to pass through the column.

Determination of number of plates in columns. It is often desirable to determine the number of theoretical plates a column contains. Formulas which are convenient in most practical cases are:

For complete columns $n = \frac{8p(L-p)}{w^2}$

58

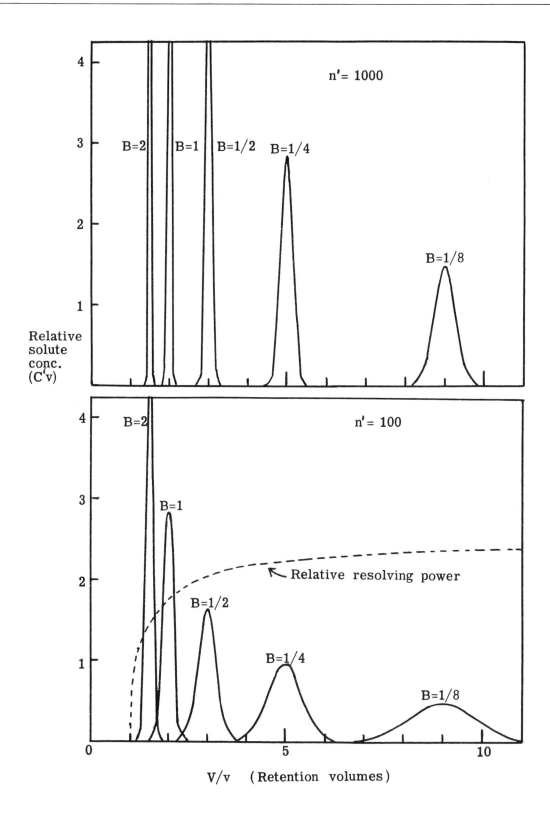

Figure 67
For a flowing chromatogram, the effect of distribution coefficient (B),
and number of plates (n') on band position and band shape

where n is the number of plates, and w the width of the solute band, in the same units as p and L, and measured at a point where the height is 36.8% (1/e) of the total height. See figure 68.

For flowing chromatograms $\quad n' = \dfrac{8V(V-v)}{(w')^2}$

$$\boxed{59}$$

where n' is the number of plates, v is the holdup volume, V the volume to elute the peak, and w' is the width of the solute band, measured as in figure 68. V, v, and w' are expressed in the same volume units.

When the number of plates in an actual column is determined by this method, it will generally be found that the apparent number of plates is larger when determined from the shape of a flattened band (a band near the center of the column in a complete column, or a slowly-moving band in a flowing column) than from a sharp band. This effect is a quantitative expression of the fact that the dispersion of the band due to finite sample volume, diffusion, or poor packing, is more important with sharp, closely-spaced bands.

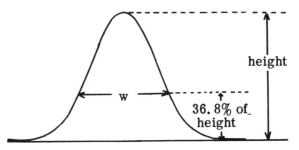

Figure 68
Method of measuring band width
for determination of n

FACTORS INFLUENCING RESOLUTION IN PACKED COLUMNS

There is no lack, in chromatographic literature, of specific directions for carrying out a large number of chromatographic procedures. The present purpose is not to review or supplement this literature, but to acquaint the reader unfamiliar with chromatographic techniques with the principles involved in the design of chromatographic procedures, with some of the more useful manipulative techniques, and with some of the difficulties that may be encountered. When the compounds being separated on a column move at widely different rates, effective separation is no problem, and even a poorly-designed procedure will give adequate separation. When, however, it is desired to separate compounds of closely similar properties, attention must be given to a number of factors that affect resolution. Some of these are considered below.

Preparation of columns. A packed column for chromatographic use ordinarily consists of a glass tube packed with a finely divided solid. This solid may itself constitute the stationary phase, being an adsorbent or an ion exchange resin. On the other hand, the finely divided solid may be an inert material which is moistened with a liquid stationary phase. In many cases, both the solid packing and the liquid stationary phase with which it is moistened are active. Packed columns are usually prepared by pouring a slurry of the stationary phase in the mobile phase into a glass tube closed at the bottom by a porous plate or perforated plate having openings too small to permit passage of the solid particles used. The column is then allowed to form by use of one or more of the following methods:

1. Simple gravity filtration.
2. Application of air pressure to the top of the column to hasten filtration and promote packing of the stationary phase.
3. Use of a ramrod, (which often consists of a cork at the end of a glass rod) of diameter slightly less than that of the glass tube, to aid even packing of the stationary phase.

Dry packing is sometimes preferable to slurry packing, but is generally not applicable when the stationary phase is a liquid on an inert solid carrier. When wet packing, as outlined above, is carried out, care is taken to avoid air bubbles within the column, and to produce as homogeneous a column as possible. After packing, the mobile phase is allowed to flow out of the column only until its upper level is at the level of the packing, in order to avoid air bubbles in the packing.

The sample, dissolved in the mobile phase, is then added to the top of the column, in the minimum possible volume. The effect of sample volume on column efficiency will be discussed later. It is important to avoid disturbing the column packing by addition of the sample. Addition should be made in such a way that the sample forms a thin layer at the top of the column, and penetrates the packing to an equal depth at all points. When the column packing is light colored, mixing a dye with the sample permits detection of gross mistakes. The dye used should have a very high B value, so that it passes through the column with the solvent "front", and will not interfere with analysis of effluent fractions. The sample is generally rinsed into the column with one or two small aliquots of mobile phase, allowing, each time, just enough effluent to issue from the column to bring the level of mobile phase just down to the surface of the packing. A large volume of mobile phase is now added to the section of the chromatographic tube above the packing. This must be done carefully to avoid disturbing the surface of the packing. Development of the column is now begun. Mobile phase is allowed to flow slowly into the column, and effluent fractions are collected. If the column is to be operated as a complete column, development is stopped when one holdup volume of mobile phase has been added, and the column is then extruded and analyzed by suitable methods. If, as is more commonly the case, the column is being operated as a flowing column, effluent fractions are collected and analyzed until the desired components have issued from the column. If a marker dye has been mixed with the sample, the uniformity of packing the column, and of adding the sample, can be checked by watching the dye band progress down the column. The band should remain narrow and horizontal. If the dye has an extremely high B value, that is, is not held by the stationary phase, it will issue from the column in one holdup volume. The holdup volume of a column may readily be determined by this method. Since the dye band should, theoretically, be infinitely narrow when it issues from the column, its actual width is a good indication of the resolution lost in the column by such factors as large sample volume, improper addition of sample, imperfect column packing, and apparent diffusion during development.

Distribution coefficient. If two components that are difficult to separate have a high distribution coefficient (B value), their Rf values will be close to 1.0. It may be seen from figures 66 and 67 that such components are difficult to separate unless the number of theoretical plates in the column is very large. If the components have a very low B value, they are difficult to separate if the column is being operated as a complete column. If the column is being operated as a flowing column, components having a low B value will issue from the column only after an inconveniently large volume of mobile phase has been passed through the column. In cases where the distribution coefficients of components are too high or too low, the coefficients can often be altered to give better resolution. As will be pointed out, chromatographic systems should be designed to permit such adjustment of distribution coefficients.

Sample volume. It has been mentioned that the volume in which the sample is added to the column should be kept small. As a first approximation, it may be stated that when the sample is added in a 10 ml. volume rather than in a 1 ml. volume, we are producing the equivalent of 10 solute bands on the column, which will begin to appear in the effluent at 1-ml. intervals. The width of the effluent band will therefore be increased by 10 ml. because of the volume of the sample. If the actual observed width of the band is 100 ml., it is obvious that no great improvement could be affected by reduction of sample volume. If, however, the observed width is of the order of 20 ml., much better resolution could be obtained by reduction of sample volume. It is thus easy to determine, in an actual case, whether sample volume is having an appreciable effect on resolution.

Alternative methods of sample introduction. Preferably, the sample is introduced in a minimum volume of mobile phase. In some cases, when the mobile phase is an organic solvent, it is difficult to prepare such a solution. A number of other methods have been used with varying degrees of success. When the stationary phase is an aqueous solution held on a solid packing such as diatomaceous earth, the sample may in some cases be mixed, as an aqueous solution, with a small amount of dry packing. The mixture is then added to the top of the column. The ratio of water to packing in the mixture should be approximately that used in packing the column itself. Zbinovsky and Burris (1954) describe techniques for adding aqueous samples and dry samples to columns in which the mobile phase is an organic solvent. Polar organic solvents have been used as solvents for sample addition. For example, in a column in which chloroform is the mobile phase and moist Celite the stationary phase, the sample might be added as a solution in butanol. In such a case, the butanol would extract water from the packing near the top of the column, dehydrating it. Farther down the column, when the butanol becomes diluted by chloroform, the water would be redeposited on the packing, thus resulting in a dry region and a water-logged region in the column.

Any unorthodox method of sample addition should be evaluated before adoption. Such evaluation is best done by comparing the resolution obtained by the new method with that obtained by the standard method, i.e., addition in a small volume of mobile phase. The difficulties most often experienced are slow extraction of the sample from the top of the column, giving broad, poorly separated bands, and interaction of the solvent used for addition with the solvents of the column, giving a non-uniform, poorly reproducible column.

Overloading. In the discussion of the mechanism of chromatographic separation, it was tacitly assumed that the distribution coefficient (B) was independent of solute concentration. When the coefficient, as often happens, is not independent of concentration, abnormal behavior of the column results. Let us consider the case in which, at high concentrations, the stationary phase approaches saturation with solute, but the solvent does not. B therefore is higher at high solute concentrations that at low concentrations. The leading and trailing edges of the solute band on the column contain solute at low concentrations, while at the center of the band, solute is present at high concentration. If B is greater at the center of the band, the center will move more rapidly than the leading edge, and will tend to overtake it. The band will thus acquire a very steep leading edge. The trailing edge will travel more slowly than the band as a whole, and will therefore form an elongated "tail". The band, as it issues in the effluent, will have a sharp leading edge and a long "tail". Bands of this shape are frequently observed, and are an indication of overloading, or, more accurately, of a distribution coefficient which changes markedly with concentration. Obviously, if B decreases at high solute concentrations, the center of the band will move more slowly than either edge, and the band will have a sharp trailing edge and an elongated leading edge. Moderate overloading of a column does no harm as long as the degree of spreading is not sufficient to prevent good separation of components. However, the amount of a component which can be successfully purified on a column is usually limited by the phenomenon of overloading. In the case of some compounds, the amount of solute necessary to overload the column may be very small. In other words, the distribution coefficient may vary with concentration even at low concentrations.

Flow rate. If the mobile phase is allowed to flow too rapidly, the resolving power of the column will be poor, since a given small volume of solvent will not remain in the vicinity of a particle of stationary phase long enough for the solute to equilibrate between the two phases. The maximum flow rates consistent with optimal resolving power vary greatly. Observed values vary from 1.0 to 100 ml. per hour per square cm. of column area. In general, columns capable of good efficiency (50 to 100 plates per cm.) require low flow rates for the realization of their high resolving power. Columns inherently capable of yielding 5 to 10 plates per cm. can usually be operated at higher flow rates without loss of efficiency. If the flow rate is too slow, diffusion of the solute in the column can cause loss of resolving power. Since the tendency is generally toward too high, rather than too low, flow rates, this difficulty is seldom a practical one. The best procedure is to determine experimentally the maximum flow rate consistent with good resolving power. One of the most useful features of automatic fraction collectors is their ability to counteract the natural tendency of the operator to run his column too rapidly.

DESIGN OF COLUMN PROCEDURES

Physical structure. In selecting or devising a column to be used for a given separation, the properties desirable for optimal operation should be considered. The physical structure of the packed column should be such that high plate efficiency is possible. The solid packing should be finely divided, and every part of it should be available to the flowing mobile phase. In general, the size of the particles should be as small as is consistent with proper flow rates.

When a solid packing is moistened with a liquid which forms part of the stationary phase, the ratio of liquid to solid is important. If too much liquid is used, many particles of solid will adhere to one another, all encased in one droplet of liquid. The result is a column of much coarser structure than is desirable. If too little liquid is used, the capacity of the column will be low. The maximum usable ratio of liquid to solid is a function not only of the capacity of the solid to absorb the liquid, but also of the interfacial tension between the liquid stationary phase and the mobile phase. For example, in columns containing water-moistened diatomaceous earth as packing, the packing may be more moist when butanol is used as the mobile phase than when benzene is used, because the interfacial tension between water and benzene is high.

Equilibration. The column should be operated in an equilibrium condition, so that the properties of the column do not change during development. For example, a column containing wet silica gel, with dry butanol as the mobile phase, will progressively dehydrate during operation. Any column in which the mobile phase is not in complete equilibrium with the stationary phase before development is started will change in characteristics during development. Such columns are difficult to reproduce, and it is difficult to predict their behavior.

Another factor influencing equilibration of phases in two-phase columns is temperature. Consider a column in which the stationary phase is water, in the form of moist silica gel, and in which the mobile phase is water-saturated butanol. If the butanol has been saturated with water at 25°, and if the column is then operated at 30°, the butanol will not be saturated, and each 100 ml. of butanol used in developing the column will extract about 0.3 ml. of water from the uppermost portion of the packing. Conversely, if the column is used at a lower temperature than that at which the original equilibration took place, water will be absorbed in the upper part of the column.

Capacity. If a column is to be used as a preparative tool as well as an analytical tool, it should have as large a capacity as practical. This means that the ratio of active packing to inert packing should be as large as possible, and the stationary phase should be such that it is not readily overloaded. Capacity can always be increased by increasing the diameter of the column. With large column diameters, however, it is very difficult to obtain uniformity of packing.

Adjustment of B values. A useful chromatographic procedure should be so designed that the distribution coefficients of the solutes to be used can be altered at will within wide limits. The composition of the mobile phase or the stationary phase, or both, should be continuously variable. An example is a column with phosphate buffer held on diatomaceous earth as the stationary phase and a mixture of butanol and chloroform as the mobile phase, used for separation of organic acids. The B values of the acids may be altered by changing the ratio of butanol to chloroform in the mobile phase, by changing the pH of the buffer in the stationary phase, or by both methods. If the B values cannot be adjusted, there is only a small probability that the properties of the column will be suitable for the desired separation.

Control of ionic form of solute. When a column is to be used for separation of acidic, basic, or amphoteric substances, it is essential that the chromatographic system be such that the ionic form of the substances is always controlled. Consider a column, operating by solvent partition, for separating organic bases from a crude biological source. The B value of a given base will depend on whether it is present as the free base or as the salt. The pH must therefore be controlled. If it is present as the salt, the calcium salt will have a different B value than the potassium salt. Therefore, the cation concentrations must be controlled. A practical column might have a phosphate buffer in the stationary phase. This would control the pH and would insure (by mass action) that any salt formed would be the phosphate salt. Alternatively, the mobile phase might contain a substantial concentration of hydrochloric acid, so that all bases would be present entirely as chlorides. The mobile phase might contain a strong base, so that all organic bases would be present as free bases. Any chromatographic system for use with ionizable substances must contain, in adequate concentration, an acid, base, or buffer, for control of the form in which the solute exists. It should be pointed out, however, that it is not necessary that the solute be present entirely in one form. Consider a column, for use with organic bases, in which the mobile phase is water containing a buffer of a pH such that half of a given base is present as free base, and the other half as salt. Let the stationary phase be a sulfonic acid type ion exchange resin, in the salt form. The free base cannot be held by the resin, while the base present in the salt form can be held by the resin. The resulting behavior will not be that half of the base passes rapidly through the column, while the other half is held. Free base is in equilibrium with ionized base, and, since the two are instantly interconvertible, all of the base can react with the resin. Raising the pH to a value such that much of the base is present in unionized form will affect the B value, but will not give two bands. If the sample is present in two forms which are not instantaneously interconvertible (for example, an acid and its lactone), the result will be two bands if the conversion is sufficiently slow, or a diffuse band if it is more rapid.

Change in developing solvent during development. When a relatively large number of compounds, having a large range of B values, are to be separated, it is advantageous to be able to change the characteristics of the column during operation. If the initial operating conditions are so chosen that those components having high B values are satisfactorily separated, components having low B values move so slowly that an inordinate time is required for them to traverse the column. By changing the composition of the mobile phase after the more rapidly moving components have been eluted, the B values of the more slowly moving components can be increased to a satisfactory value. In some types of columns, such as ion exchange columns, this can usually be readily done. In solvent partition columns, it is often difficult. Consider a column having water (plus an inert carrier) as the stationary phase, and chloroform as the mobile phase. If, during operation, water-saturated butanol is substituted for water-saturated chloroform as the mobile phase, the first butanol entering the column will become diluted with chloroform. This will make water less soluble in it, and water will separate out and waterlog the upper part of the column. It is apparent that careful thought must be given to column characteristics when solvent changes during column operation are planned.

If the solvent change is made gradually, many of the difficulties are minimized. Gradual change in solvent composition is known as gradient elution. Such a procedure is sometimes very advantageous. Bock and Ling (1954) describe convenient methods for achieving various types of gradients in composition of solvent. In general, gradient elution is advantageous when sudden changes in solvent composition give rise to difficulties. It is also of value when both very fast-moving and very slow-moving components are present on the same column. If the range of B values is such that a number of changes in solvent composition are necessary during development of the column, it often is more convenient to arrange equipment for gradient elution than to make several changes of solvents.

Describing a column. In too many chromatographic procedures described in the literature, the column used is inadequately described. The writer should give the reader enough information to duplicate the column or to assess results obtained with its use. The following is an inadequate description:

> "The column used contained diatomaceous earth, moistened with water, as the stationary phase, and 10% butanol in chloroform, shaken with water, as the mobile phase."

A much more informative description would be the following:

> "The solvent was prepared by shaking together 100 ml. water, 100 ml. chloroform, and 900 ml. n-butanol. Four g. Celite 545 (Johns-Manville) was shaken with 2 ml. lower phase and about 100 ml. upper phase and the resulting slurry poured into a glass tube 1 cm. in diameter, and packed to a length of 18 cm. The resulting column had a liquid holdup volume of 13 ml. All operations were carried out at 25°."

The phrase "10% butanol in chloroform, shaken with water" is not fully descriptive. The amount of butanol lost into the water phase will depend on the amount of water used. The amount of aqueous phase used will affect the distribution coefficient, the capacity of the column, and its resolving power, and therefore should be stated. The tightness of pack also affects the behavior, and should be specified. The liquid holdup volume should be determined and stated, for a number of reasons. Usually, the most convenient method of determining holdup volume is by measuring the volume necessary to elute some solute not held by the stationary phase. In the column just described, a fat-soluble dye, added with the sample would be a convenient solute. Knowledge of the holdup volume, is of course, almost essential in evaluating the performance of a column. Only if the holdup volume is known can it be predicted whether a change in solvent, say, in the direction of lower B values, is likely to improve performance. Only if the holdup volume is known can a rough calculation of the number of theoretical plates in the column be made. When a reader sees, in the literature, chromatographic data indicating that fraction X issued as a single sharp band from a column, and when he reads the author's conclusion that fraction X is one compound, he should not accept the conclusion before at least satisfying himself that the band did not issue from the column after addition of one holdup volume of solvent. If the holdup volume is not stated, this is sometimes difficult. Another useful relationship involving holdup volume, which is apparent from the theoretical relationships already considered, but which is sometimes not applied by users of chromatography, is the following: If, in the example just given, the worker had used 16 g. of Celite instead of 4 g., but had maintained the same ratio of aqueous phase to Celite and the same density of pack, the resulting column, regardless of its ratio of diameter to length, would show behavior identical to that of the original column provided eluate volumes were expressed as holdup volumes rather than as milliliters or fraction numbers. That is, if compound X issued from the small column after 5 holdup volumes of eluate had been collected, it would also issue from the large column after 5 holdup volumes. This rule also holds for columns in which the solvent is changed during development, provided the change is always made at the same point, measured in holdup volumes. In gradient elution columns, the rule holds if the gradient rate in the two columns, in terms of holdup volumes, is the same.

The liquid holdup volume (v) of a column may be determined in a number of ways. The most usual method is to add, with the sample, a readily-detected compound (such as a dye) that has an R_f value of 1.0. This marker compound will obviously issue from the column after one holdup volume of effluent has been collected. Often a readily-detected impurity present in the sample can serve to measure the holdup volume. It should be noted that ion exchange resin columns have different holdup volumes for ionic and nonionic markers. Thus, the holdup volume of a sulfonated polystyrene column is less when measured with sulfate ion than with glucose. The sulfate ion, being repelled by the negative charge on the resin, does not equilibrate with the water inside the resin particles as rapidly as does glucose.

PAPER CHROMATOGRAPHY

General. It will be assumed that the reader is already familiar, in a rough way, with the general procedures covered by the term "paper chromatography". In the terminology used in this discussion, a paper chromatogram is a complete column, since the compounds being separated are, at the end of the process, still on the column. The part of a paper chromatographic strip extending from the point of application of the sample to the "solvent front" constitutes a complete column. The solvent front is the farthest point reached by the developing solvent at the end of the developing process. This relationship is shown in figure 69A. Figure 69B shows methods of applying the sample. It may be applied as a spot (1), or as a band (2). The latter procedure has the advantage of increasing the capacity, thus minimizing overloading difficulties, but, in some systems, the solvent tends to flow faster in the center of the strip than at the edges, thus bending the band. Often, a wide strip is used (3), on which a number of samples are spotted. When increased capacity is desired, one sample may be streaked across the whole width of a wide strip (4). In two-dimensional paper chromatography, (fig. 69C) the sample is spotted on one corner of a sheet. The first developing solvent is used to separate the mixed sample into a number of components. In the figure, compounds a and b (open circles) are imperfectly separated, as are compounds c and d. The paper is dried, then solvent 2 is allowed to flow in a direction at right angles to the flow direction of solvent 1. All components are now separated (shaded circles). It should be noted that if solvent 2 had been used alone, a and c, which have very similar Rf values in this solvent, would have been imperfectly separated. The same can be said for b and d.

Paper chromatograms should always be developed in a tight vessel the air in which is in equilibrium with the vapor(s) of the developing solvent. The solvent flow may be either up or down. A typical arrangement for upflow, or ascending, development is diagrammed in figure 69D. The strip is placed in the chamber, and ample time for vapor equilibration allowed before the strip is lowered (by some means not involving opening the chamber) until its lower end dips into the solvent. Solvent rises along the paper strip by capillary action. The height to which it will rise is limited, usually to 50 cm. or less. The rate of rise decreases during development. A typical arrangement for descending, or downflow, development is shown in figure 69E. The upper end of the strip dips into a trough, in which it is held by a clamp or weight. After the strip is put in position, time is allowed for equilibration of the atmosphere inside the vessel with the solvent layer at the bottom. Solvent is then added to the trough through the normally stoppered hole in the cover, and development begins. With descending development, the length of strip is not limited, and the flow rate is relatively constant.

Many modifications of the above general procedures have been used. Heavy paper may be used for increased capacity. Samples may be spotted in a circle near the center of a circular piece of filter paper and solvent caused to flow from the center outward. Often, solvent is allowed, in descending development, to flow longer than necessary to reach the bottom of the paper. The result can be considered, theoretically, as a long complete

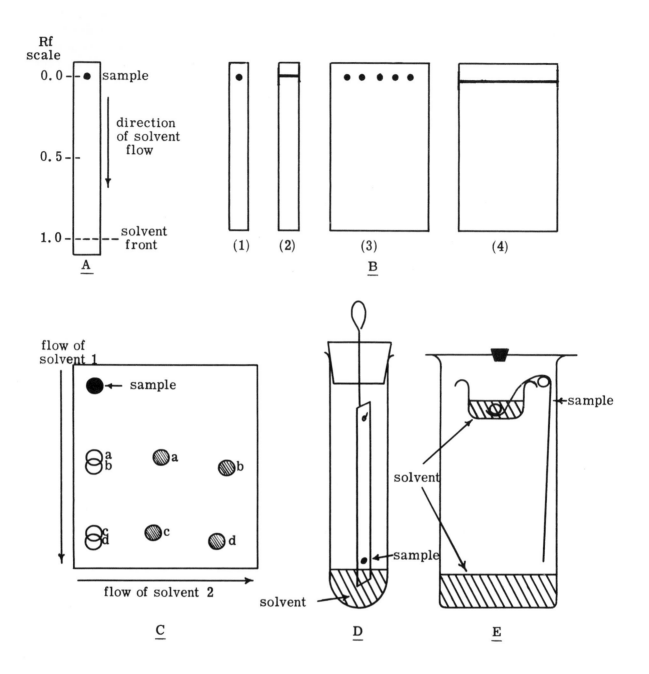

Figure 69
Paper chromatography

A - Rf scale

B - Methods of applying the sample

C - Two-dimensional chromatography

D - Upflow development

E - Downflow development

column, only the upper section of which is available for examination. Sometimes one-dimensional paper chromatography is combined with paper electrophoresis in the second dimension. It is not the purpose of this discussion to describe all modifications in technique, but to discuss general principles.

Factors affecting resolution on paper chromatograms. In a paper chromatogram, the mechanism of distribution of solute which takes place between the mobile phase (developing solvent) and the stationary phase may be distribution between the solvent and an immiscible liquid phase which moistens the paper, it may be adsorption of solute by the paper, it may be reaction of the solute with a salt or other compound present on the paper, or it may be a combination of two or more types of distribution. In any case, the behavior of a paper "column" is the same as that of a packed column, and the same factors influence resolution on both. As was shown in figure 66, resolution is best at the center of a paper chromatogram. Good paper chromatograms have resolving powers equivalent to 30 or more plates per centimeter.

The kind of paper selected may influence resolution. A coarse-grained paper will, in general, give poorer resolution than a fine-grained paper. Thin paper is, of course, more likely to become overloaded than thick paper. When chromatographic strips are cut from large sheets, they should always, for reproducible results, be cut in the same direction relative to the grain of the paper (the direction of movement in the paper-making machine). The direction of grain in a piece of filter paper may readily be ascertained by putting a drop of water on it. A ridge will form which is parallel with the direction of the grain. In a chromatogram, developing solvent will move more rapidly in the direction of the grain than at right angles to it. Filter paper strips, cut in various widths, are commercially available in the form of rolls. These, of course, are always cut parallel with the grain.

The rate of solvent flow can influence resolution. Since flow rate is not as readily controlled on paper chromatograms as in packed columns, there are few data available on the effect of flow rate. It is probable, however, that the flow rates usually obtained are not fast enough to decrease resolution appreciably. Flow rates can be decreased, when desired, by making the section of the filter paper strip which dips into the solvent narrower than the rest of the strip, the narrow portion extending for some distance above the solvent.

A very important factor influencing resolution, and one which is often given too little attention, is the control of the amount of liquid stationary phase on the paper. In a packed column in which the packing is moistened with an aqueous solution, a mobile phase is used which is saturated with this solution. Consider, for example, a column containing an inert packing which is moistened with water, and which is developed with water-saturated butanol. The amount of water in the packing is fixed at the outset, and does not change during the course of development of the chromatogram. Consider a corresponding paper chromatogram. A strip of paper is developed with water-saturated butanol, after being equilibrated in an atmosphere saturated with respect to both water vapor and butanol vapor. The paper may absorb water from the atmosphere or from the solvent during development. The amount of such absorption cannot readily be controlled. A strip of paper containing a very thin film of water around each fiber is in equilibrium with a water-saturated system, but a strip of paper which is dripping wet is also in exact equilibrium with a water-saturated system. It is very difficult to operate a paper chromatogram under such conditions, and the use of water-saturated systems should be avoided. In the literature, however, specifications for water-saturated systems are very common. Such systems never operate with good reproducibility, but can be made to function if saturation of the paper with water can be avoided. Such lack of equilibration can be achieved by a number of devices, such as use of an atmosphere not quite saturated with water vapor, use of a temperature somewhat higher than that at which the solvent was saturated with water, or limiting the development time so that there is not sufficient time for too much water absorption. Since such devices are likely to be poorly reproducible, it is advisable to use an unsaturated system from the outset. In our example, if the solvent had been, for example, a mixture of 9 parts water-saturated butanol and one part anhydrous butanol, the amount of water adsorbed by the paper at equilibrium would be definite and reproducible.

When buffer salts are present on the paper, the salts may determine the amount of water taken up by the paper. Suppose, for example, that the paper, prior to use, is dipped in a 10% solution of potassium phosphates. After dipping, a part of the solution is removed by blotting, and the paper dried. If this paper is then developed with butanol which has been shaken with a large volume of 10% buffer, the paper will continue to absorb water until the buffer concentration on the paper is 10%. If the developing solvent, on the other hand, is saturated with water, the paper will continue to absorb water from the developing solvent until the buffer on the paper is infinitely dilute. It is obvious that, when a paper chromatographic procedure is designed, consideration must be given to the amount of water which will be taken up by the paper under equilibrium conditions.

Another factor of great importance in paper chromatography is the means taken to insure complete equilibration of the atmosphere in the chromatographic vessel with the developing solvent. Suppose that a solvent used for chromatography of polar substances, such as amino acids or sugars, is a mixture of water, acetic acid, and acetone. Suppose that when this solvent was first tried, a rather large vessel was used, and only a small surface of solvent was exposed to the atmosphere of the vessel. Equilibrium therefore was not attained before the beginning of development. Acetone, the most volatile constituent of the mixture, was lost from the strip by evaporation during development. The composition of the solvent on the strip was therefore richer in water and acetic acid, and poorer in acetone, than the original solvent. This modified solvent caused polar compounds to migrate more rapidly. The Rf values thus obtained, let us say, were approximately optimal for the compounds of interest. However, because the Rf values obtained depended upon the degree of disequilibrium present, they were poorly reproducible, particularly when the type of vessel was changed. Needless to say, it would be much better to use an original solvent containing less acetone, and to take steps to insure equilibration. To insure equilibration, the chromatographic vessel should have in it a container of solvent which exposes a large surface of solvent, and which contains enough solvent to saturate the atmosphere without causing an appreciable change in solvent composition due to greater evaporation of the more volatile constituents. Sufficient time (several hours for larger vessels) should be allowed to elapse between the time the vessel, containing the strip, is closed and the time development is started.

The considerations governing overloading discussed for packed columns also hold for paper strips. The tailing caused by overloading is readily detected on paper chromatograms, and the cure, when one is necessary, is obvious. An effect which will be called physical overloading is often encountered in paper chromatography of crude substances. Suppose, for example, 10 microliters of a crude sample contains 10 µg. of amino acids, (which we wish to separate) and 100 µg. of protein. We spot the sample on the paper, and it dries, with the amino acids encased in a layer of protein which is insoluble in our solvent, and from which the amino acids are only very slowly extracted by the solvent. After development, some of the amino acids will still be at the origin, and the remainder will be well spread out over the whole strip, because they left the point of origin continuously throughout the development period. Such physical overloading occurs whenever too much material (organic or inorganic), insoluble in the developing solvent, is present as a contaminant in the sample. The cure, of course, is some rough preliminary purification step.

The control of ionic form of the sample is as important in paper chromatography as in column chromatography. When the substances to be separated have acidic or basic properties, it is essential that either the developer or the paper carries a constituent that controls the degree of ionization of the compound being separated. A solvent can be used which contains an acid or base, or the paper may be impregnated with a buffer. Sometimes buffering action is provided by the solvent. For example, if a solvent contains both an organic amine and an organic acid, it is possible, by varying their proportions, to vary the pH of an aqueous phase adsorbed on the paper. It is appropriate to mention that solvent mixtures containing an organic acid and an alcohol will undergo esterification on standing. Such mixtures should always be made immediately before use. A better solution to the difficulty is to avoid the use of such mixtures. Substitution of a ketone or an ether for the alcohol is one possibility.

In paper chromatograms, the same considerations govern adjustment of Rf values as hold for packed columns. It should be borne in mind (fig. 66) that the best resolution is obtained in the center of the chromatogram, and changes in solvent should be made with this in mind. Often, with solutes of low Rf values, development is continued much longer than is required for the solvent front to reach the bottom of the paper. This gives better resolution of compounds of low Rf, since the effective column is much longer than the actual strip.

THIN LAYER CHROMATOGRAPHY

A chromatographic technique that is proving itself to be a very useful tool is thin layer chromatography. Techniques, apparatus, and applications in this field have been reviewed by Wollish et al. (1961) and by Demole (1961). Thin layer chromatography is similar to paper chromatography, but has a number of advantages. A glass plate is coated with a layer (0.2 to 0.3 mm. thick) of finely divided (10 to 40 microns) solid. The solid is applied as a thick suspension in a liquid (water or other solvent) by means of a suitable applicator. Obviously almost any finely divided solid may be used. Silica gel, diatomaceous earth, alumina, and calcium phosphate are typical. A binding agent is usually added to the solid to produce a mechanically strong layer of solid. The binding agent may be anhydrous $CaSO_4$ (plaster of paris) or small amounts of an adhesive insoluble in the solvent system to be used. Various devices for applying uniform layers of slurry to glass plates have been described and may be constructed or purchased. The solid layer is dried and is then used in the same way as a paper sheet would be used for upflow one- or two-dimensional paper chromatography. A number of coated glass plates, on which samples have been spotted, are placed vertically in a closed container (usually a glass jar) containing the solvent mixture to be used. The plates are maintained out of contact with the solvent for equilibration. Then additional solvent is added to the jar, bringing the lower edge of the thin layer of coating into contact with the solvent. The solvent then rises through the thin layer by capillary action, just as in upflow paper chromatography.

Since the process is basically the same as paper chromatography, all of the considerations discussed for paper chromatography hold for thin-layer chromatography. The same precautions must be taken, and the same factors, in general, influence resolution. In thin-layer chromatography, of course, the size of the particles in the layer influence resolution in the same manner as the size of the paper fibers in paper chromatography.

The chief advantage of thin-layer chromatography over paper chromatography lies in its versatility. The solid phase in paper chromatography is usually filter paper. The investigator can only with great difficulty prepare papers of special properties. In thin-layer chromatography, he can readily prepare thin layers of almost any solid material. In devising a new procedure, therefore, he has at his command a large number of adsorbents, ion exchange materials, and inert supports. When the solid used is not reactive, he can use spray reagents such as sulfuric acid, potassium permanganate, or other reagents impossible with paper. He can use corrosive solvent systems. Another advantage is that, in general, thin-layer procedures can be modified into column chromatographic procedures more easily than can paper chromatographic procedures. Usually, thin-layer chromatograms develop much more rapidly than paper chromatograms, thus saving time. The resolution on thin-layer chromatograms is often better than that obtainable on paper. That is, thin-layer chromatograms often have more apparent plates per centimeter than paper chromatograms.

A disadvantage of thin-layer chromatography is that plates are more difficult to prepare and handle than are sheets of paper. It is usually easier to elute a compound from a piece of paper cut from a paper chromatogram than it is to scrape out an area of a thin-layer chromatogram for elution. Since thin-layer chromatograms cannot readily be run by the downflow technique, the practical length of a thin-layer chromatogram is severely limited. Obviously, both paper chromatography and thin-layer chromatography are useful techniques, and the choice of procedure in a given case will depend on a number of factors.

GAS CHROMATOGRAPHY

It is not the purpose of this section to survey the enormous literature that has accumulated in the past few years on the subject of gas chromatography. Keulemans (1959) and Bayer (1961) have written excellent books on the subject. The material below is intended only as an outline of general principles.

A gas chromatogram is a flowing column in which the mobile phase is a gas. As an example, let us consider a column containing an inert packing (in this instance, diatomaceous earth) coated with a thin layer of a non-volatile hydrocarbon (lubricating oil or petroleum jelly). Consider the mobile phase to be an inert gas (for example, helium), and the sample to be a mixture of volatile hydrocarbons. The hydrocarbons in the sample will dissolve in the stationary phase. Since they are volatile, however, a portion of them will be present as vapor, mixed with the mobile phase. There will be a definite distribution coefficient, for each of the hydrocarbons in the sample, between the stationary phase and the gaseous mobile phase. Because distribution coefficients exist, the conditions for chromatographic separation are satisfied, and each of the hydrocarbons in the sample will progress down the column at a rate determined by the distribution coefficient, exactly as in other forms of chromatography.

The most important difference between a chromatogram in which a gas is the mobile phase and one in which a liquid is the mobile phase is the difference between diffusion rates in a gas and in a liquid. The table below compares gaseous and liquid diffusion coefficients for a few compounds.

Table 33

Diffusion Coefficients

Compound	Diffusion coefficient, cm^2/sec.		Ratio, air/H_2O
	In air	In water	
Ethyl alcohol	0.119	1.0×10^{-5}	1.19×10^4
Butyl alcohol	0.090	0.77×10^{-5}	1.17×10^4
Acetic acid	0.133	0.88×10^{-5}	0.66×10^4
O_2	0.206	1.80×10^{-5}	0.875×10^4
CO_2	0.164	1.77×10^{-5}	0.97×10^4

It is apparent that diffusion is approximately 10,000 times as fast in air as in water. This means that since the rate at which a chromatogram can be developed is dependent on the rate at which diffusional equilibrium can be established between the mobile and the stationary phase, the rate at which gas chromatograms can be run is much greater than the rate at which liquid chromatograms can be run. The limiting factor in gas chromatograms is the rate at which equilibrium can be established between the gas and the liquid phase adsorbed on the inert carrier. This rate has been found, experimentally, to be much greater than the rate at which liquid chromatograms can be run. This means that gas chromatograms are much faster than liquid chromatograms. Development rates for liquid chromatograms vary from 0.01 to 1.0 ml. per min. per sq. cm. In gas chromatography, flow rates range from 50 to 1,000 ml. per min. per sq. cm. Because of these rapid flow rates, it is possible to obtain rapid elution of compounds having very low R_f values.

Because the mechanism of distribution of a compound between the mobile and stationary phases involves the vapor pressure of the compound, R_f values may conveniently be adjusted to desired values by changing the temperature of the column. Temperatures at which columns are operated range from temperatures in the liquid air range, for chromatography of "permanent gases", to temperatures of 300° C. or more. Obviously, gas chromatography is limited to compounds having an appreciable vapor pressure at a temperature lower than that at which the compound decomposes rapidly. This limitation prevents the use of gas chromatography for most compounds of great biological interest. In many cases where the compound itself has too low a vapor pressure, a derivative of sufficient volatility may be prepared.

Because the R_f values of compounds rise with temperature, the gas-chromatographic equivalent of gradient elution is temperature programming, that is, an arrangement where the column temperature is raised during development according to a predetermined pattern. By this device, mixtures containing both very volatile and very non-volatile compounds may be separated.

Since R_f values are temperature-dependent, a column for gas chromatography must be in an enclosure maintained at a controlled temperature. Very long columns may be used in a relatively small enclosure, because columns, (packed metal tubes) may readily be coiled. Although the usual gas chromatographic column does not give as many plates per centimeter as a good liquid-phase column, (5 plates per cm. is typical in gas chromatography) the ease with which very long columns can be made and used and the ease with which R_f values can be varied by changing temperature, make good separation of complex mixtures possible. Long (100 ft.) capillary columns, about 0.5 mm. in diameter, without packing but coated with a thin layer of liquid stationary phase, have been found very effective.

In gas chromatography, it is impractical to collect effluent fractions to be saved for later analysis. Detection of components in the effluent is almost invariably accomplished by a detector system connected to a strip chart recorder, so arranged that the electrical signal given to the recorder by the detector is proportional to the concentration of component in the effluent gas stream. The detector most often used is the thermal conductivity detector. This makes use of the fact that organic vapors have much lower thermal conductivities (roughly ten fold lower) than hydrogen or helium, which are used as carrier gases. In this detector, two resistors of high temperature coefficient of resistance (usually thermistors) form two arms of a Wheatstone bridge. The current flowing in the bridge is sufficient to heat them well above ambient temperature. One of the resistors is in a reference stream of carrier gas. The other is in the gas stream issuing from the column. If the bridge is in balance with no organic vapor issuing from the column, it will be thrown out of balance when a component of the mixture being analyzed issues from the column.

The electrical signal due to bridge unbalance is used to operate a millivolt recorder. The sensitivity of this type of detector can be pushed to 2×10^{-8} moles of vapor per mole of carrier gas (Kieselbach, 1960), but is generally much less than this.

When more sensitivity is desired, the hydrogen flame detector or the argon detector may be used. These detectors have been compared by Condon et al. (1960).

The general principles governing resolving power, overloading, flow rates, and general column operation, discussed in previous sections, hold for gas chromatography as well as for liquid chromatography.

M. J. JOHNSON

APPENDIX

In their original paper on partition chromatography, Martin and Synge (1941) presented the general theory of elution chromatography, but because of some simplifying assumptions that were made, arrived at only partially valid conclusions. Mayer and Tompkins (1947) gave a very adequate treatment of chromatographic theory, and Williamson and Craig (1947) have described the theoretical behavior of multiplate countercurrent distributions. Many other able discussions of chromatographic theory have appeared. It is the purpose of this appendix, not to supplement existing knowledge of chromatographic theory, but to develop, in as simple a manner as possible, the theory of the chromatographic process.

Assumptions: The relationships to be described hold for chromatograms when the column is uniform throughout its length, when longitudinal diffusion is negligible, and when the concentration of solutes is low enough so that distribution coefficient is independent of concentration. The relationships hold regardless of the mechanism of distribution. The mechanism may be adsorption, ion exchange, liquid:liquid or liquid:gas partition, or a resultant of the action of two or more mechanisms. It is also assumed that the number of effective equilibrations occurring is large, that is, that the column has a large number of theoretical plates.

Definitions of terms: A complete column is, in general, a column extending from the "top" of the column (the point of sample addition) to the "front" of the column (the farthest point to which mobile phase, added after the sample, has penetrated). Thus, a packed column is a complete column if the volume of mobile phase added after the sample is equal to the retention volume (holdup volume) of the column. If, say, twice this volume has been added, the complete column is an imaginary column twice as long as the actual column, only the top half of which is available for study.

L = Length of the complete column, expressed in any convenient units.
p = Distance from the beginning of the complete column to the peak of a given solute band within the column, expressed in the same units as L.
Rf = p/L.
C = Concentration of a given solute at the peak of the solute band, expressed as fraction of the total solute contained in unit column length (same length units as L).
n = Number of theoretical plates (effective equilibrations) in a complete column.

B = Effective distribution coefficient; ratio of the quantity of a solute in the mobile phase of the column to the quantity of the same solute in the stationary phase of the column. $B = K \cdot q_m/q_s$ where K is the distribution coefficient (concentration in the mobile phase over concentration in the stationary phase), and q_m and q_s are, respectively, the quantities of mobile and stationary phases present in the column.

w = Width of a solute band on a complete chromatogram, measured, in the same units as L and p, at a height which is 1/e (36.8%) of the maximum height of the band.

v = Volume of mobile phase present in the packed portion of a column from which effluent is being analyzed (flowing chromatogram). This volume is often called the holdback volume or retention volume.

V = The volume of mobile phase, added after the sample, which will just cause the peak of a given solute band to appear in the effluent from a flowing chromatogram.

C' = In a flowing chromatogram from which a solute is issuing in the effluent, the concentration of the solute at the peak of the band. It is expressed as fraction of total solute per unit volume of effluent (same volume units as v and V).

n' = Number of theoretical plates in a column operated as a flowing chromatogram. It is equal to the number of plates (n) the column would have if operated as a complete column.

w' = Width of a solute band in the effluent from a flowing column measured at a height which is 1/e (36.8%) of the maximum height of the band, expressed in same units as v and V.

Derivation of formulas for complete columns: It will be assumed that the number of plates (n) in the column is large, and that when plate r is considered, that n, r, and n-r are large enough so that the binomial expansion can be replaced by the equation for the normal curve of error.

It has been pointed out (Martin and Synge, 1941; Williamson and Craig, 1947) that the fraction of total solute in the rth plate of a column (or countercurrent distribution apparatus) having n plates is equal to the rth term of the binomial expansion.

$$\left(\frac{1}{B+1} + \frac{B}{B+1} \right)^n$$

This can be understood from consideration of a hypothetical column of the type of figure 64. In figure 64, it was assumed that B (the effective distribution coefficient) was unity.

Let us make no assumptions about the value of B, and consider figure 70, which is a more general version of figure 64. Before any distribution has taken place, the quantity in plate number zero is taken as (x+y) grams. Suppose that B = x/y. After one distribution, x g. will have moved into plate number one, leaving y g. behind. After 2 and 3 distributions respectively, the amounts in the various plates will be those indicated in figure 70. It will be noted that in each case, the amount in the rth place after n distributions is the rth term of the binomial expansion of $(y + x)^n$. Now if it be assumed that the total amount of solute is unity (x + y = 1) then, since B = x/y, $x = \frac{B}{B+1}$ and $y = \frac{1}{B+1}$. Therefore, in any complete chromatogram having n plates (the first plate being numbered zero), the fraction of the total solute in the rth plate is equal to the rth term of the expansion of

$$\left(\frac{1}{B+1} + \frac{B}{B+1} \right)^n$$

In any efficient chromatogram, the number of plates is large, and therefore the binominal distribution closely approximates the Gaussian distribution. For the binomal distribution

$$(g + h)^n, \text{ where } g + h = 1,$$

the equivalent Gaussian distribution gives, for any point on the curve (see any textbook of mathematical statistics),

$$y = \frac{1}{\sqrt{2\pi ngh}} \, e^{-\frac{(r-nh)^2}{2ngh}}$$

where $g = 1/(B+1)$, $h = B/(B+1)$, n the number of plates, and y the fraction (f_r) of solute in the rth plate.

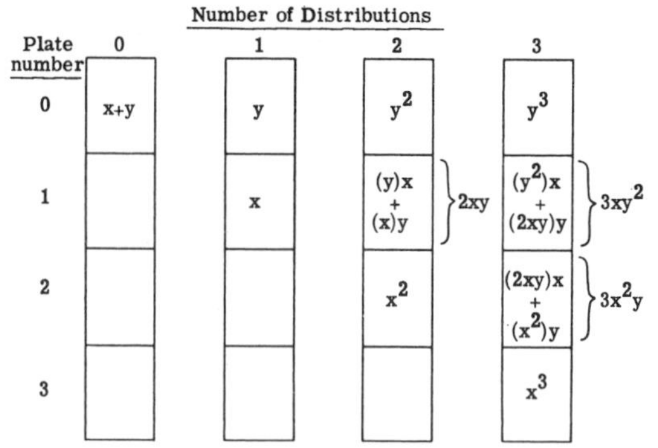

Figure 70

Position of a solute in a column as a function of number of distributions. Total solute = $1 = x + y$. $B = x/y$

The expression may thus be written

$$f_r = \frac{1}{\sqrt{2\pi n \dfrac{B}{(B+1)^2}}} \, e^{-\dfrac{\left(r - \dfrac{nB}{B+1}\right)^2}{\dfrac{2nB}{(B+1)^2}}}$$

f_r is maximal at the peak of the solute band. This occurs when $r = nB/(B+1)$.

Hence r_p (the peak plate) $= nB/(B+1)$, or

$$\frac{B}{B+1} = \frac{r_p}{n} = \frac{p}{L} = Rf \qquad \qquad \boxed{52}$$

Also, since the exponential term drops out when $R = nB/(B+1)$,

$$f_p = \frac{1}{\sqrt{\dfrac{2\pi n B}{(B+1)^2}}} = \frac{B+1}{\sqrt{2\pi n B}}$$

where f_p is the fraction of the solute in the peak plate. To convert this expression to a more useful form, specifying the fraction of solute in unit length of column rather than in a single plate, the right-hand side need only be multiplied by n/L, the number of plates per unit column length. Therefore,

$$C = \frac{\sqrt{n}\,(B+1)}{L\sqrt{2\pi B}}$$

Since, from eq. (52), $B = p/(L-p)$, $\qquad C = \sqrt{\dfrac{n}{2\pi p(L-p)}}$, and

$$n = 2\pi C^2\, p(L-p) \qquad\qquad \boxed{53}$$

Equation (53) may be used to calculate either C or n, when the other is known. Another method of calculating n, more generally useful, will be given later.

In figure 71, two partially separated solute bands are represented. Consider the plate r, at which the solute bands intersect. It is separated from the peak plate by a number of plates equal to Δr. In the expression for f_r given on the preceding page, the $r - \dfrac{nB}{B+1}$ is equivalent to Δr in figure 71. Therefore

$$f_r = f_p\; e^{-\dfrac{(\Delta r)^2\;(B+1)^2}{2nB}}$$

$$\ln \dfrac{f_p}{f_r} = \dfrac{(\Delta r)^2\;(B+1)^2}{2nB}$$

$$\Delta r = \pm \dfrac{\sqrt{\ln \dfrac{f_p}{f_r}}\;\sqrt{2nB}}{B+1}$$

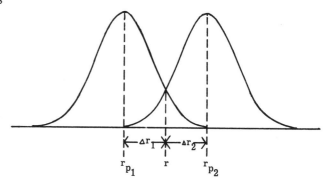

Figure 71

Two partially separated solute bands. r = plate at which intersection occurs. r_{p_1} and r_{p_2} are the plates at which peak concentration occurs.

The number of plates separating the two peaks of figure 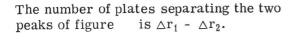 is $\Delta r_1 - \Delta r_2$.

$$\Delta r_1 - \Delta r_2 = \sqrt{\ln \sqrt{\dfrac{f_{p_1}}{f_r}}}\;\sqrt{\dfrac{2nB_1}{B_1+1}} + \sqrt{\ln \dfrac{f_{p_2}}{f_r}}\;\sqrt{\dfrac{2nB_2}{B_2+1}}$$

Since B_1 and B_2 are not identical, but are similar, we can make the following approximation:

$$\Delta r_1 - \Delta r_2 = 2\sqrt{\ln \dfrac{f_{p_m}}{f_r}}\;\sqrt{\dfrac{2nB_m}{B_m + 1}}$$

where B_m is the mean B value and f_{p_m} the corresponding f_p value.

The plates corresponding to the peaks of the solute bands of figure 71 are r_{p_1} and r_{p_2}. From eq. (52),

$$r_{p_2} - r_{p_1} = n\left(\dfrac{B_2}{B_2+1} - \dfrac{B_1}{B_1+1}\right)$$

As an approximation we may write

$$r_{p_2} - r_{p_1} = n\;\dfrac{B_2 - B_1}{(B_m + 1)^2}$$

This approximation is in error by not more than 1% when B_1 and B_2 differ by 20%. We can therefore write

$$\triangle r_1 - \triangle r_2 = r_{p_1} - r_{p_2} = n \; \frac{B_2 - B_1}{(Bm+1)^2} = 2 \sqrt{\ln \frac{f_{p_m}}{f_r}} \; \sqrt{\frac{2nBm}{Bm+1}}$$

$$2 \sqrt{2 \ln \frac{f_{p_m}}{f_r}} = \frac{B_2 - B_1}{Bm} \; \frac{\sqrt{n \, Bm}}{Bm+1}$$

In the above expression, the left-hand term represents a definite degree of resolution, since the ratio f_{p_m}/f_r specifies the ordinate at the intersection point of the two bands.

This degree of resolution may have any selected value. The term $(B_2 - B_1)/Bm$ is, for B values close together, the fractional difference in B values for the two components. The resolving power of a chromatogram may be defined roughly as its ability to separate components whose B values are close together. The resolving power of column No. 1 is twice as good as that of column No. 2 if column No. 1 will separate components whose B values are twice as close together as those separable on column No. 2. The fractional difference $(B_2 - B_1)/Bm$, rather than the absolute difference $B_2 - B_1$, is used because when the characteristics of a column are changed by, for example, altering the composition of the developing solvent, all B values tend to change by the same factor, not the same amount.

We may state

$$\text{Relative resolving power} = \frac{2 \sqrt{2 \ln \frac{f_{p_m}}{f_r}}}{\frac{B_2 - B_1}{Bm}} = \sqrt{n} \; \frac{\sqrt{Bm}}{Bm+1}$$

$$= \frac{\sqrt{np(L-p)}}{L} \qquad \qquad \boxed{54}$$

Derivation of formulas for flowing columns. A flowing chromatogram may be regarded as a complete chromatogram of which only the section from the top to a given point is under observation, and on which analyses are made by sampling the mobile phase at that point. This point is the actual end of the packed column, the imaginary lower section extending far enough to accommodate all of the mobile phase added during development. At the time when the peak concentration of a solute has just reached the bottom of the actual column, the following relations are seen to hold, from equation (52):

$$\frac{n'}{n} = \frac{p}{L} = \frac{v}{V} = \frac{B}{B+1} \quad \text{and} \quad B = \frac{v}{V-v} \qquad \qquad \boxed{55}$$

In order to derive, for flowing chromatograms, an expression corresponding to eq. (53), we must consider the relation between C (fraction of total solute per unit length of column, at the peak of the band, in a complete chromatogram), and C' (the fraction of solute per unit volume of effluent, at the peak of the band, in a flowing chromatogram). To convert C to C', we must take into account the fact that the concentration in the mobile phase is

B/(B+1) times the total concentration, and we must also convert from amount per unit length to amount per unit volume by dividing the number of volumes per unit length, which is V/L. Since B/(B+1) = v/V, we may write:

$$C' = C \cdot \frac{v}{V} \cdot \frac{L}{V} = \frac{CvL}{V^2}$$

If, in the following expression used in deriving eq. (53)

$$C = \frac{\sqrt{n} \ (B+1)}{L \sqrt{2\pi B}}$$

we substitute using the following relations:

$$C = \frac{C'V^2}{vL}, \quad n = \frac{n'V}{v}, \quad B+1 = \frac{V}{V-v}, \quad B = \frac{v}{V-v}$$

we obtain

$$C' = \sqrt{\frac{n'}{2\pi V(V-v)}} \quad \text{and} \quad n' = 2\pi V(V-v)(C')^2 \qquad \boxed{56}$$

The relative resolving power of a complete chromatogram, from equation (54), is

$$\sqrt{nB}/(B+1). \text{ Since } n/n' = (B+1)/B, \text{ for a flowing chromatogram,}$$

$$\text{Relative resolving power} = \sqrt{\frac{n'}{B+1}} = \sqrt{\frac{n'(V-v)}{V}} \qquad \boxed{57}$$

Determination of number of plates. A convenient method of estimating the number of plates in a complete column may be readily derived from the expression used above in discussing figure 71,

$$\ln \frac{f_p}{f_r} = \frac{(\Delta r)^2 \ (B+1)^2}{2nB}$$

When $f_p/f_r = e$, that is, at the point in the solute band where its height is 1/e of maximum,

$$\frac{(\Delta r)^2 \ (B+1)^2}{2nB} = 1$$

Since $\Delta r = \Delta pn/L$; $B = p/(L - p)$; and $B + 1 = L/(L-p)$; we may substitute these values in the above expression and solve for n, giving

$$n = \frac{2p \ (L-p)}{(\Delta p)^2}$$

Since w, the width of the solute band at 1/e (0.368) of its height, is $2\Delta p$,

$$n = \frac{8p(L-p)}{w^2} \qquad \boxed{58}$$

A convenient expression for the number of plates (n') in a flowing column can be derived from eq. (58). The relation between w (width of the band in a complete column, expressed in length units), and w' (width of the band in the effluent from a flowing column, expressed in volume units) must first be considered. To convert w from length to volume units, we must multiply it by the number of volumes per unit length, V/L. We must also take into account the fact that when the band issues from the column in the mobile phase, its concentration in that phase is B/(B+1) times its concentration on the column. Therefore the band, being only B/(B+1) times as high, is (B+1)/B times as long, since its area is constant. Since (B+1)/B = V/v,

$$w' = w \frac{V}{L} \cdot \frac{V}{v} = \frac{wV^2}{vL}$$

If, in equation (53), we substitute using the following relations:

$$w = \frac{w'vL}{V^2}, \quad p = \frac{Lv}{V}, \quad L-p = \frac{L(V-v)}{V} \text{ and } n = \frac{n'V}{v}$$

we obtain

$$n' = \frac{8V(V-v)}{(w')^2}$$

59

M. J. JOHNSON

Chapter 14

PREPARATION OF PHYSIOLOGICALLY IMPORTANT
INTERMEDIATES AND METABOLITES

In the study of tissue metabolism, certain materials are required which are not readily available to all laboratories, and the preparation of some of these is described here. Whenever possible, synthetic methods are given, on the condition that we ourselves have successfully employed these syntheses. Certain materials are obtainable only by isolation, and starting materials have been chosen as high as possible in the component to be isolated. Only isolations which we have successfully done are described. In recent years many materials described in the earlier editions of this book have become readily available, so descriptions of their preparation have been omitted in the present edition. Biochemical Preparations constitutes a particularly valuable series, because all of the methods described have been carefully rechecked. The following list of preparations described in Biochemical Preparations includes compounds of particular interest in intermediary metabolism.

INTERMEDIATES OF THE
EMBDEN-MEYERHOF SYSTEM AND RELATED COMPOUNDS

These phosphorylated materials play a key role in tissue metabolism. Discussion of their role will be found throughout the literature but especially in the papers and reviews of Burk (1939), Cori (1942), Barron (1943), Lipmann (1941), Kalckar (1941), Meyerhof (1941, 1942), Potter (1944, 1945b), Sumner and Somers (1947), and in any modern comprehensive textbook of biochemistry.

As stated in the introduction to this chapter, many of the intermediates of the Embden-Meyerhof System and related compounds are readily available. These are simply listed below, and methods of preparation given only for those which fall outside of this category for one or more of the following reasons: less readily procurable, or not at all, from commercial sources; it may be desirable or necessary to purify the commercial product; preparation in the laboratory is preferred.

The following compounds and/or their salts may be obtained from several biochemical companies located within the continental U.S.A.

Glucose-1-phosphate	Phospho(enol)pyruvic acid
Fructose-1-phosphate	Pyruvic acid
Glucose-6-phosphate	Adenine
Fructose-6-phosphate	Adenosine
Fructose-1,6-diphosphate	Adenylic acid
Glyceraldehyde-3-phosphate	Adenosine-di-phosphate
3-Phosphoglyceric acid	Adenosine-tri-phosphate
2-Phosphoglyceric acid	Phosphogluconic acid
	Acetyl phosphate

Preparative procedures, etc., for some of the above intermediates of the Embden-Meyerhof System and related compounds follow.

GLUCOSE-6-PHOSPHATE (ROBISON ESTER)

CHEMICAL SYNTHESIS:

Previous methods of preparing glucose-6-phosphate for use in biological experiments have been based on the isolation of this ester from a crude mixture of hexose monophosphates obtained by yeast fermentation. It has also been prepared by allowing phosphoglucomutase to act on glucose-1-phosphate (Colowick and Sutherland, 1942). A chemical synthesis of the ester as devised by Lardy and Fischer (1946) is given below.

1,2,3,4-Tetraacetyl-β-D-glucopyranose is prepared from 6-trityltetraacetyl-β-D-glucose according to the procedure of Helferich and Klein (1926) (see Reynolds and Evans, 1942) except that the crystallization is made from a concentrated chloroform solution (not syrup) by the slow addition of dibutyl ether. The first crop of crystalline tetraacetyl-β-D-glucopyranose corresponds to a yield of about 67% with a melting point of 124-127° C. This material can be phosphorylated directly or after recrystallizing from chloroform by the addition of dibutyl ether to give the pure substance, m.p. 128-129° C.

1,2,3,4-Tetraacetyl-6-diphenylphosphono-β-D-glucopyranose is prepared by adding 6.0 gm. of diphenylchlorophosphonate (Brigl and Müller, 1939) dropwise to a cooled solution of 7.1 gm. of 1,2,3,4-tetraacetyl-β-D-glucopyranose in 20 ml. of anhydrous pyridine with continuous shaking and cooling in an ice bath. The reaction begins at once, and within a few minutes a copious crystalline precipitate of pyridine hydrochloride appears. The mixture is kept in the ice bath for 15 minutes and then placed in a refrigerator at 10° C. overnight. A few drops of ice water are added to hydrolyze the excess of acid chloride and after one-half hour the product is separated by pouring slowly into 600 ml. of ice water under continuous stirring. When the precipitate becomes granular, it is filtered off and again stirred up in fresh ice water. The product is filtered off, washed with cold water, and dissolved in 100 ml. of chloroform. The chloroform solution is washed once with dilute HCl and two times with distilled water, dried with anhydrous sodium sulfate, and evaporated under reduced pressure to a syrup. The product is crystallized by careful addition of petroleum ether (b.p. 60-80° C.), swirling, and allowing to stand for several hours; the process may be hastened by seeding or scratching. The product is filtered with suction, washed with petroleum ether, and dried. The yield is about 10.9 gm. (92% of the theoretical). It melts at 64-66° C. and is of sufficient purity for subsequent use. The pure substance may be obtained by recrystallizing from isopropyl ether, or from acetone by the addition of water. Its m.p. is 68° C. It is soluble in chloroform, acetone, benzene and ethyl alcohol. It has an optical rotation of $[\alpha]_D^{22} = + 16.5°$ (c = 1.37 in anhydrous pyridine).

$C_{26}H_{29}O_{13}P$ (580.5). Calculated C 53.8, H 5.04, P 5.34

1,2,3,4-Tetraacetyl-β-D-glucose-6-phosphoric acid is prepared by shaking a solution of 7.0 gm. of tetraacetyl-6-diphenylphosphono-β-D-glucopyranose in 70 ml. of anhydrous methanol (prepared according to Lund and Bjerrum, 1931) with 0.7 gm. of platinum oxide (Adams' catalyst) in an atmosphere of pure dry hydrogen at a pressure slightly greater than 1 atmosphere. When the reduction nears completion, the free acid begins to crystallize in fine needles. The absorption of hydrogen stops abruptly when the theoretical quantity (8 moles) has been consumed (this required from 2.5 to 4.5 hours in several runs). After warming to dissolve the product, the catalyst is removed by filtering or centrifuging. An equal volume of petroleum ether is added in portions to the filtrate and crystallization allowed to proceed during slow cooling. The crystals are filtered with suction, washed with petroleum ether, and dried in vacuo at room temperature. The yield obtained is about 3.6 gm. (65% of the theoretical). The product melts at 126-128° C., and contains the theoretical amount of organic phosphorus. When recrystallized from anhydrous methanol by slow addition of petroleum ether, the substance melts at 127-128° C. A second crop of crystals of the original purity may be obtained by evaporating the mother liquors to dryness under reduced pressure at a bath temperature of 25° C. and recrystallizing the product from methanol-petroleum ether. Analyses have indicated that the substance crystallized with 1 mole of methanol which could not be removed by heating in vacuo without causing further decomposition. The optical rotation is $[\alpha]_D^{25} = + 17.4$

(c = 1 (of methyl alcoholate) in anhydrous pyridine); calculated for solvent-free compound:

$C_{14}H_{21}O_{13}P$ (428.3)   Calculated: C 39.3, H 4.94, P 7.23

$C_{14}H_{21}O_{13}P \cdot CH_3OH$ (460.3)   C 39.1, H 5.47, P 6.73

The potassium salt of glucose-6-phosphate is prepared as follows: To 3.3 gm. of tetraacetylglucose-6-phosphoric acid (from methanol, see above) partially dissolved in 75 ml. of cold anhydrous methanol, a sufficient quantity of potassium methoxide in anhydrous methanol (prepared by the cautious addition of clean potassium metal to anhydrous methanol; solutions 1-2 N have been used) to neutralize the free acid groups is added dropwise with shaking. Complete solution is attained after the first few drops are added. Cleavage of the acetyl groups is initiated by the addition of a catalytic excess of 1.5 milliequivalents of potassium methoxide. The potassium salt of glucose-6-phosphate begins to separate at once. The cleavage is allowed to proceed at refrigeration temperature in a tightly stoppered flask overnight. The product is separated by centrifuging, washing four times with anhydrous methanol, once with each of the following methanol-ether mixtures: 80:20,

50:50, 20:80, and twice with anhydrous ethyl ether. After drying in vacuo at room temperature the yield obtained by following this procedure was 1.65 gm. (68.5 % of theoretical). It is essential to use only anhydrous solvents and thoroughly dried equipment in order to obtain good yields. The potassium salt must be stored under anhydrous conditions. The optical rotation of the potassium salt was $[\alpha]_D^{24} = +21.2°$ ($\dot{c}$ = 1.3 in water).

$C_6H_{11}O_9PK_2$ (336.3)   Calculated: C 21.4, H 3.29, P 9.21

From the combined mother liquor and methanol washings an additional quantity of glucose-6-phosphate can be obtained as the barium salt. The slightly turbid alcohol solutions are treated with an excess of $BaBr_2$ in anhydrous methanol. When the barium salt has settled, it is separated by centrifuging, washed with absolute alcohol, and finally with ether. This procedure has resulted in a yield of 0.6 gm. of the barium salt (21% of theoretical of the original starting material) after purification as described below; thus the combined yield of the potassium and barium salts was 89.5% of theoretical. To obtain all of the product as the barium salt, $BaBr_2$ may be added after the deacetylation by potassium methoxide is completed, and the barium salt again purified as described in the following paragraph.

The tetraacetylglucose-6-phosphoric acid may be deacetylated as follows: 0.5 gm. of tetraacetylglucose-6-phosphoric acid is dissolved in 35 ml. of 0.66 N HBr and the solution heated on the steam bath for 3 hours. After cooling, pulverized barium hydroxide is added to neutrality. The solution is filtered and 4 volumes of ethanol added. When the precipitate has settled, the supernatant liquor is decanted. The precipitate is washed in succession with 90% ethanol, absolute ethanol, 75% ethanol-25% ether, 25% ethanol-75% ether, and finally with dry ether. After drying in air, the barium glucose-6-phosphate is dissolved by extracting successively with 20, 10, and 5 ml. portions of distilled water. To the clear filtrate 4 volumes of ethanol are added and the product separated and dried as above. The barium salt (0.33 gm.) prepared by this procedure was free of inorganic phosphate and on the basis of its organic phosphorus content was 93% pure (yield 72% of theoretical). Its rotation (purity based on phosphorus analysis) was $[\alpha]_D^{24} = +17.9°$.

ENZYMATIC SYNTHESIS:

In recent years a crystalline, highly insoluble barium salt of glucose-6-phosphate heptahydrate has been obtained which permits the virtually quantitative conversion of fructose-6-phosphate to glucose-6-phosphate. Seed crystals can be obtained from a variety of commercial companies who sell this crystalline salt.

The procedure described here is that of Wood and Horecker (Snell, 1953). From 1 to 5 grams of commercial barium fructose-6-phosphate is dissolved in 10 ml. water per gram. The insoluble residue is removed by centrifugation and if the solution is strongly colored it is heated with activated carbon and filtered while hot. The solution is cooled to room temperature and 2.0 ml. of a crude phosphohexoisomerase preparation is added. The enzyme is prepared by grinding fresh rat skeletal muscle with an equal volume of distilled water, centrifuging or filtering to separate the solid material and dialyzing against cold distilled water until free of inorganic phosphate.

When the enzyme has been added to the fructose-6-phosphate solution, seed crystals of barium glucose-6-phosphate are added. After standing at room temperature for 12 to 24 hours, the mixture is cooled in ice and filtered. The crystals are washed with small portions of water and dried at room temperature. About 0.5 gm. of crystalline product is obtained per gram of barium fructose-6-phosphate used. The product may be recrystallized from acid solution by neutralization.

When using this crystalline salt for enzymatic studies, it is dissolved in water with the aid of dilute HCl, the barium ion is precipitated by addition of the requisite amount of Na_2SO_4, and after removing the precipitate, the solution is neutralized.

FRUCTOSE-6-PHOSPHATE (NEUBERG ESTER)

This compound may be obtained commercially or by hydrolysis of hexosediphosphate (Neuberg et al., 1943). If the commercial grade is not sufficiently pure, it may be purified by the method of Neuberg et al. (1943).

FRUCTOSE-1,6-DIPHOSPHATE
(HEXOSEDIPHOSPHATE, HARDEN-YOUNG ESTER)

Fructose diphosphate may be obtained commercially. The products currently available are far from pure and, when necessary, may be purified through the barium and strychnine salts (Peanasky and Lardy, 1959).

H. A. LARDY

LACTIC ACIDS AND THEIR SALTS

L-lactic acid (the form occurring in animal tissues) has plus optical rotation, and is, of course, called d-lactic acid in the older literature. Its salts have minus optical rotation. Commercial lactic acid is not optically pure, and is very seldom entirely racemic. The preponderant form depends upon the organism used in its production. It is not chemically pure, being contaminated with other organic and inorganic materials. Commercial lactic acid is partially polymerized, the carboxyl group of one molecule esterifying with the hydroxyl group of another. It may be depolymerized by dilution to 10 per cent and autoclaving at 120° C. for two hours. It may be rapidly depolymerized by neutralizing with base, then heating to boiling under alkaline conditions.

Lactic acids are usually purified as the zinc salts. To prepare zinc lactate from lactic acid, boil dilute lactic acid with an excess of zinc carbonate, filter, decolorize with charcoal if necessary, and evaporate at 50-60° until crystallization begins. Cool, add alcohol to 50%, let stand overnight, filter, wash with alcohol, air dry, then dry to constant weight in a desiccator over $CaCl_2$. This desiccant will not remove the water of crystallization. Racemic zinc lactate forms a trihydrate (18.18% H_2O), while the D- or L-zinc lactate is a dihydrate (12.89% H_2O). Hence determination of water of crystallization is one check for chemical or optical purity. The specific rotation $(\alpha)_D$ of the anhydrous zinc salt is 8.25 when in 4 per cent solution. Specific rotation changes with concentration. The zinc salt of L-lactic acid has a negative rotation. The solubilities of the racemic and active forms of zinc lactate, expressed as grams anhydrous salt in 100 grams water, are (Pederson et al., 1926):

Deg. C.	Racemic salt	D- or L- salt
0	1.1	4.6
20	1.6	5.1
35	2.0	9.0

Since the racemic salt is less soluble, active salt will not crystallize preferentially from a mixture when large amounts of racemic salt are present. However, small amounts of unwanted enantiomorph can readily be removed by recrystallization.

To prepare lactic acid from the zinc salt, dissolve the zinc salt in water, add somewhat more than the calculated amount of sulfuric acid, and extract the solution with ether in a continuous liquid-liquid extractor. Since the distribution coefficient of lactic acid between ether and water is about 0.1 (ether/water), allow ample extraction time. The lactic acid in the extract may be converted to the sodium salt by titration with NaOH.

The optical purity of D- or L-lactic acids available commercially should not be assumed without checking. If the acid is to be purified via the zinc salt, rotation and water of crystallization of the salt are suitable. The best quantitative method for determination of optical composition of mixed isomers is the benzimidazole method of Moore et al. (1941). D- and L-lactic acids may be prepared by fermentation of glucose with suitable cultures of the lactobacilli as described by Brin (Snell, 1953).

M. J. JOHNSON

ENOL-PHOSPHOPYRUVIC ACID

The synthesis of enol-phosphopyruvic acid as the silver-barium salt dihydrate has been described in detail by Baer (Ball, 1952). The description includes the synthesis of beta-chlorolactic as the starting material. The silver-barium salt of phosphopyruvic acid is available from several commercial sources.

CRYSTALLINE SODIUM PHOSPHOCREATINE

The method described here is that of Ennor and Stocken (1948) as modified by Peanasky, Kuby and Lardy (Shemin, 1957). All aqueous reagents are prepared from distilled water freed of carbon dioxide by boiling.

Twenty grams of creatine hydrate is triturated with 60 ml. of 10 N sodium hydroxide and then diluted with 540 ml. of distilled water (at room temperature). If a little creatine comes out of solution, the suspension is stirred at room temperature for ten to fifteen minutes until it again dissolves. The clear solution is transferred to a 3-necked 2-liter round bottom flask equipped with a teflon stirrer and immersed in a bath at -10°. Sixty ml. of redistilled phosphorus oxychloride and 400 ml. of 10 N sodium hydroxide are added over a period of 2 hours in portions of 4.0 ml. of phosphorus oxychloride, followed immediately by 27 ml. of sodium hydroxide, to the vigorously stirred solution of sodium creatine. The pH of the reaction mixture is noted after each addition and is maintained at 13.5-14 (pH paper). Large amounts of precipitate are formed during the reaction, and stirring of the suspension must be adequate to allow efficient heat transfer from the vessel. The temperature of the reaction mixture is maintained between -3°C and +3°C at all times.

The product is stirred for 15 minutes after the last addition and then filtered at 2°C through a large sintered glass funnel (9 cm.) with suction. The residue of sodium phosphate is rapidly washed free of sodium phosphocreatine by stirring with successive amounts of ice cold water (200 ml. and 100 ml.). The residue is discarded and the combined washings and filtrate are then adjusted (mechanical stirring) to pH 7.6 with hydrochloric acid (about 120 ml. of 5 N). To this solution (about 1200 ml.) 3 volumes (about 3600 ml.) of ice cold absolute ethanol are now added with efficient stirring. The temperature is maintained at 3-5°C for 20 minutes. The walls of the vessel are scratched and the suspension is occasionally stirred to facilitate the precipitation of salt. The precipitated salts are collected by centrifugation or filtration and discarded. To the supernatant solution (about 4400 ml.), 1 liter of a 1.4 per cent (w/v) solution of barium bromide dihydrate in an 80 per cent (v/v) ethanol-water solution and one more volume (about 1200 ml.) of ice cold absolute ethanol are added with stirring. The mixture is stirred for an additional 10 minutes and is allowed to stand at 0°C for 2 hours in a glass cylinder. The greater part of the supernatant solution is siphoned off and the remainder is centrifuged. The supernatant solution is discarded and the precipitate is washed twice with ice cold absolute ethanol (about 1000 ml. and 500 ml.). The second washing may not be entirely clear even after centrifuging for 1 hour, but is discarded. The precipitate is then washed with cold anhydrous ether (about 500 ml.) and dried overnight in vacuo over calcium chloride. The procedure should not be interrupted to this point and requires about 11 hours.

The barium salts are extracted 3 times with 35 ml., 30 ml., and 25 ml. respectively of ice cold water adjusted to pH 9.5 by addition of a few drops of 0.1 N sodium hydroxide. The residue after the third extraction is suspended in 25 ml. of cold water, and sufficient hydrochloric acid (1 N) is added at 0°C either to effect solution or drop the pH to 3.0 whichever occurs first (about 15 ml. of acid are required). Sodium hydroxide (1 N) is added immediately to bring the pH to 9.5 (the total time of exposure to low pH should not exceed a minute). The precipitated barium phosphate is removed by centrifugation and discarded. The supernatant solution is combined with the original extract, the pH is brought to 7.4 and barium is precipitated by the addition of just sufficient 10 per cent (w/v) solution of sodium sulfate (about 20-22 ml. are required). Maintain pH at 7.4. An excess of sodium sulfate must be rigorously avoided and the endpoint approached by successive centrifugations and testing for barium in the supernatant solution. Two cold aqueous washings (about 30 ml. each) of the barium sulfate are sufficient to remove most of the adsorbed phosphocreatine. On combining the washings with the mother liquor a turbidity may occur and a few drops of 10 per cent (w/v) sodium sulfate should be added to ensure removal of the traces of barium soluble in the wash waters. The suspension is centrifuged and the residue discarded. The clear supernatant solution now amounts to about 220 ml. Four volumes of absolute ethanol are then added while mixing thoroughly, and the mixture is allowed to stand in a two liter Erlenmeyer flask immersed in a 20°C bath for 12 hours. Initially the sodium phosphocreatine appears as oily droplets which slowly settle and crystallize. After about 12 hours the supernatant is usually clear. Stirring and scratching the side of the flask brings out additional crystalline sodium phosphocreatine if the flask is kept at 20°C for 12 more hours. After complete crystallization, the supernatant liquid is perfectly clear.

The crystals are filtered with suction through a small sintered glass funnel (about 4 cm. diameter) at room temperature. The preparation is washed with three 5 ml. portions of ice cold 90 per cent ethanol and one 5 ml. portion of ice cold absolute ethanol. The supernatant solution and washings are combined and retained (see below). The crystals are dried in an evacuated desiccator over Drierite and calcium chloride. Periodic weighings are made to determine when constant weight is reached (16-30 hours required).

The yield of the crystalline sodium phosphocreatine tetrahydrate is about 3-4 grams.

The phosphocreatine remaining in the mother liquor and washings may be recovered as the barium salt by cooling to 0°C and adding 200 ml. of a 1.4 per cent (w/v) solution of barium bromide dihydrate in 80 per cent (v/v) ethanol-water solution. The barium salt is washed twice with cold absolute ethanol and absolute ether as described above. The yield is 0.3-1.0 grams.

                                                              H. A. LARDY

PRINCIPAL INTERMEDIATES IN THE KREBS' TRICARBOXYLIC ACID CYCLE

The tricarboxylic acid cycle has been established as a main pathway for the combustion of fat, carbohydrate and amino acid fragments in animals and many microorganisms. In some anaerobic microorganisms and in green plants the enzymes of the cycle are present and appear to participate in the formation of suitable carbon chains which are used in the biosynthesis of important cell constituents. Reviews of the subject have been written by Martius and Lynen (1950) and by Ochoa (1954), and all modern textbooks of biochemistry discuss the subject in some detail. Most of the intermediates of the cycle may be purchased from commercial sources. The preparation of some, which are not readily available or which may require purification, is described below. Brief remarks on the use of these are contained in Chapter 9. Analytical methods for these compounds are described in Chapter 11.

PYRUVIC ACID

Pyruvic acid may be synthesized from tartaric acid (Howard and Fraser, 1941) but more commonly it is purchased from commercial sources. In the latter case it is usually necessary to redistill the compound to separate it from polymer impurities. The pyruvic acid is distilled under reduced pressure in an all glass apparatus. Heating is accomplished with an oil bath. The fraction distilling between 75° and 80° at 25 mm pressure is retained. It is weighed and diluted at once to make an approximately 1 M solution. The exact molarity is determined by titration.

A 1 Molar solution of pyruvic acid is stable for many months if stored in the cold.

CRYSTALLINE SODIUM PYRUVATE

Pyruvate solutions for use in tissue respiration experiments are usually prepared by suitable dilution and neutralization (with $NaHCO_3$) of pyruvic acid redistilled at reduced pressure and stored in a cold place. Another convenient means of preparing pyruvate solutions for use as a substrate is by weighing out crystalline sodium pyruvate. This salt may be purchased or may be prepared analytically pure from commercial pyruvic acid by the procedure of Price and Levintow (Ball, 1952) or by the method of Robertson (1942) on which the method described here is based.

Commercial pyruvic acid is dissolved in ten volumes of ethyl alcohol. This solution, while being rapidly stirred with a power stirrer, is slowly neutralized with a solution of 1 volume saturated NaOH in 10 volumes of ethyl alcohol at room temperature. Sodium pyruvate crystallizes out immediately. The crystalline material is filtered off, washed with alcohol and ether on the filter and dried in a vacuum desiccator. The yield is about 85% of theory. This material is sufficiently pure for most purposes. Analytically pure salt may be obtained by dissolving in a minimum amount of water and adding cold ethyl alcohol to 80% by volume.

The potassium salt may be prepared in the same manner with somewhat better yields, although recrystallization is sometimes difficult. The lithium salt is preferred by some workers. Others suggest neutralization with $NaHCO_3$ rather than NaOH.

ISOCITRIC ACID

In many metabolic experiments isocitric acid may be replaced by cis-aconitic acid, for the two are in equilibrium in many tissues. The synthesis of isocitric acid has been described by Kato and Dickman (Snell, 1953).

CIS-ACONITIC ACID

Trans-aconitic acid is readily synthesized by the method of Bruce (1937). Cis-aconitic acid may be prepared from it by the method of Malachowski and Maslowski (1928) as follows:

Recrystallize trans-aconitic acid from ether and concentrated HCl until the melting point is at least 182° C. Pulverize finely and mix with an equal weight of acetic anhydride and keep at room temperature for three days. The residue is filtered off, washed twice with a 1:3 mixture of acetylchloride and chloroform and once with a small quantity of chloroform. The solid material is trans-aconitic anhydride. The filtrate and washings are combined and evaporated at room temperature under reduced pressure until the acetic acid has been removed. When dry, extract with boiling benzene and filter hot. Crystals of cis-aconitic anhydride with 0.5 mole of benzene form on cooling. The benzene is lost when the product is dried, and the anhydride melts at about 74° C. Further purification can be accomplished by recrystallization from benzene. The anhydride has been found to be stable for two years, and it immediately forms cis-aconitic acid in water.

H. A. LARDY

OXALACETIC ACID

Several companies sell oxalacetic acid. Immediately before use dissolve the acid in water and neutralize it by adding, with stirring, the theoretical amount of sodium bicarbonate in solution. Although oxalacetic acid in unstable in solution, the dry acid may be stored for long periods in the refrigerator.

R. H. BURRIS

IMPORTANT ELECTRON TRANSPORTING SYSTEMS

The materials used most often are coenzyme I (NAD, NAD^+, DPN, diphosphopyridine nucleotide, cozymase), coenzyme II (NADP, $NADP^+$, TPN, triphosphopyridine nucleotide) and cytochrome c. All three of these substances are available commercially; however, it is believed that a description of the preparation and standardization of cytochrome c may be helpful.

PREPARATION AND STANDARDIZATION OF CYTOCHROME C

The method employed is essentially that of Keilin and Hartree (1937, 1945, Ball, 1952).

"One ox heart is carefully freed from fat and ligaments and minced very finely with a Latapie mincer. After pressing out the blood as far as possible in a handpress, the pulp, 1100 gm., is mixed with 1100 cc. 0.15 N (2 1/2%) trichloroacetic acid and allowed to stand at room temperature for 2 hours with occasional stirring. The pH of this mixture is approximately 4. The fluid is pressed out, neutralized to about pH 7 with caustic soda, about 20 cc. 10% NaOH, and ...(step omitted)... treated with ammonium sulphate (50 gm. per 100 cc.), filtered, and the filtrate, 1700 cc., now free of haemoglobin, is treated again with ammonium sulphate (5 gm. per 100 cc.) and left overnight in an ice chest. The pH of the mixture is about 4.9. The next day the liquid is ... (step omitted)... treated with one-fortieth of its volume of 20% trichloroacetic acid, bringing the pH of the mixture to 3.7. Within 10 minutes the spectrum of reduced cytochrome disappears and the cytochrome is completely precipitated in the oxidized form." The precipitate is filtered on a fluted filter, drained thoroughly and then redissolved and washed through the filter with distilled water to give a volume of less than one liter. A dark brown insoluble residue may be filtered off at this point. The solution is brought to pH 7.4, treated with ammonium sulfate (55 gm. per 100 cc.) and filtered. The filtrate is treated with trichloroacetic acid as before to precipitate the cytochrome c. "The suspension is centrifuged for 10 minutes, the bright red deposit shaken with 500 cc. saturated ammonium sulphate solution and centrifuged again. The red solid is transferred to a cellophane sac by means of about 20 cc. distilled water and the mixture dialysed for 2 days at 4° C. against 1% sodium chloride solution. The content of the sac is shaken with a few drops of chloroform and filtered to yield about 30 cc. of a clear dark red solution containing 0.182 gm. pure cytochrome, the iron content of which is 0.34%."

In using this method we have dialysed against distilled water instead of 1% NaCl, in order to avoid having a compulsory addition of sodium chloride to our reaction mixtures. Since our cytochrome solutions keep very well in the cold, we have avoided the use of chloroform in the preparation. Keilin and Hartree also carried out large scale operations using about 6 beef hearts at a time, and pointed out that horse hearts are superior to beef hearts. For large-scale preparations it is advisable to use a power-driven meat grinder with a fine mince attachment. We were able to secure the cooperation of a local butcher shop for the grinding operation when no grinder was available in the laboratory.

The following table summarizes the results obtained in this laboratory in six consecutive preparations without particular attention to improvements in Keilin and Hartree's method (Table 34).

In terms of dry weight, the average yield is about 90 mg. per kg. of fresh beef heart. However, the preparation is not dried, but is kept in the frozen state in small vials of solutions that are ready for use when thawed. Cytochrome c preparations are available from the Sigma Chemical Co., St. Louis. Keilin and Hartree in 1938 mentioned that cytochrome c can be precipitated by the addition of 4 volumes of cold acetone and dried to a powder which is completely soluble in water. This seems to be true only when the solutions are kept very cold and the drying is very rapid, and we have avoided the procedure. The preparation has an equivalent weight of 16,500 and apparently contains an additional protein which can be removed to yield cytochrome with an apparent molecular weight of 11,700 (Theorell and Akesson, 1941) and an iron content of 0.43%.

It is convenient to dilute the stock solution to a strength of 1.0×10^{-7} moles per ml., that is, 10^{-4} molar. In the succinoxidase system for example, one adds 4×10^{-8} moles of

Table 34

The Preparation of Cytochrome C

No. of beef hearts	Kg. of mince	ml. Stock Cytochrome Solution	Concentration per ml. Moles x 10^{-7}	Total Yield Moles x 10^{-7}	Yield per Kg. Moles x 10^{-7}
5	6.69	160	2.19	350	52.4
6	6.43	151	2.28	344	53.6
6	6.99	143	3.03	433	62.0
6	7.29	186	2.60	485	66.5
10	14.30	180	3.06	552	38.6
10	10.87	122	4.88	596	54.8

cytochrome c per Warburg flask, which is therefore 0.4 ml. of the working solution. The average preparation from six beef hearts thus gives enough cytochrome for about 1000 Warburg flasks when the succinoxidase system is being studied. In the cytochrome oxidase system, much higher concentrations are needed, and concentrated stock solutions are used directly. In this case it is convenient to recover the cytochrome. The flask contents are pooled, frozen, and stored until needed. The solution is then brought to pH 3.5 - 4.0 with trichloracetic acid, and carried through the regular procedure. Recoveries of around 95 per cent have been obtained.

In the final dialysis step of the purification, it is desirable to put the preparation through several changes of glass-redistilled water, to cut down the concentration of metal contaminants. This is especially important in the study of the cytochrome oxidase system. As the dialysis proceeds a dark brown precipitate forms, which may be denatured cytochrome c. This is removed by centrifugation and filtration and is discarded; the prevention of its formation has not been studied. Although Keilin and Hartree state that cellophane strongly adsorbs cytochrome c during dialysis in the absence of salts and Theorell used adsorption on cellophane at one stage of purification, we have not felt that the losses outweighed the advantages of having a pure aqueous solution.

There seems to be a certain amount of loss of cytochrome through the walls of the membrane, especially in the final stages of dialysis. This can amount to as much as 20 per cent of the yield and can be observed when the dialysis is carried out against relatively small volumes of distilled water. The cellophane is seamless tubing and is doubly knotted at each end, and tied between the knots.

Preparation by Ion Exchange Chromatography: More recently Paleus and Neilands (1950) have used the polycarboxylic cation-exchange resin, Amberlite IRC-50 to obtain cytochrome c with a higher iron content, and Margoliash (1954) has developed this type of procedure for the preparation of both reduced and oxidized forms of cytochrome c with the highest purity so far obtainable. For this work, the Keilin and Hartree preparation, given above, provided the starting material. It was reported that in the succinic oxidase and cytochrome oxidase systems the activity per μmole of cytochrome c iron was the same in the new preparation as in the old, the non-cytochrome protein impurity being inert under the conditions employed. Nevertheless, the new preparation is free from a modified cytochrome c that is formed by the action of trichloroacetic acid. Since the modified substance catalyses the rate of ascorbic acid oxidation more effectively than the pure cytochrome c, the rate of this reaction obtained in the absence of cytochrome oxidase with various cytochrome c preparations varies inversely with their degree of purity.

Standardization of cytochrome c: For the most accurate work it is necessary to know the concentration of cytochrome c in the stock solution so that the proper amounts can be added in standardized experiments. Many experiments have been reported with no statement of the cytochrome c concentration; this is inexcusable. Even when the concentration of the cytochrome is unknown, it is possible to determine the amount which is necessary to saturate the system and to prove that additional amounts do not increase the reaction rate. Such data can then be included in the report.

Spectrophotometric Standardization: For more precise work, the spectrophotometric standardization seems the most satisfactory. Cytochrome c has a characteristic absorption spectrum in the oxidized state and an equally definite absorption in the reduced state (Theorell, 1936; Potter, 1941a). The reduced form has a pronounced maximum at 550 millimicrons, which is absent in the oxidized spectrum. The cytochrome c stock solution is a mixture of oxidized and reduced cytochrome c and must be converted to one form or the other before making any measurements for spectrophotometric standardization. The cytochrome can be oxidized with potassium ferricyanide and reduced with sodium hydrosulfite ($Na_2S_2O_4$). The hydrosulfite can be added after the ferricyanide to convert the oxidized form to the reduced form. Since the specific absorption coefficients are known for each form, one can measure the absorption at 550 mμ in both oxidized and reduced states, and the concentration can be calculated for each. If the cytochrome solution is free from other pigments the same concentration will be found in each calculation. If other pigments are present they will be unlikely to show the same shift in absorption when converted from the oxidized to the reduced state. Neither the ferricyanide nor the hydrosulfite absorb light at 550 millimicrons. The constants are as follows:

$\alpha_R = 2.81$ (cm^2/mole) x 10^7 (Reduced Cytochrome c at 550 mμ)

$\alpha_O = 0.90$ (cm^2/mole) x 10^7 (Oxidized Cytochrome c at 550 mμ)

An example of a cytochrome c standardization is given herewith (Table 35)

Table 35

An Example of Spectrometric Standardization of Cytochrome C at 550 mμ.

Reaction Mixture		Io	I	Log I_0/I = E	Moles/ml. (cell)	Moles/ml. (Stock Solution)
Water	1.7 ml.					
0.1 M phosphate pH 7.4	1.0 ml.					
Stock Solution Cytochrome	0.2 ml.	= oxidized state				
0.01 M $K_3Fe(CN)_6$	0.1 ml.					
final volume	3.0 ml.	94.2	62.0	0.181	0.201x10^{-7}	3.02x10^{-7}
Same solution plus						
0.1 to 1.0 mg. solid $Na_2S_2O_4$		= reduced state				
		93.5	25.8	0.559	0.199x10^{-7}	2.98x10^{-7}

Calculation for oxidized cytochrome c:

The fundamental relation is $C = E/\alpha$; the cells are 1 cm. long.

$$C = E/\alpha = \frac{0.181}{0.90 \times 10^7} = 0.201 \times 10^{-7} \text{ moles per ml.}$$

There are 3.0 ml. in the reaction mixture, of which 0.2 ml. were stock solution.

Therefore, the stock solution contains

$$0.201 \times 3 \times 5 \times 10^{-7} = 3.02 \times 10^{-7} \text{ moles per ml.}$$

The calculations for the reduced cytochrome are the same, except α_R is used. The two values gave the same result within the limit of error and the average value was taken. The fact that the ratio E_R/E_O is the same as α_R/α_O indicates that the cytochrome c solution is spectrophotometrically pure. For other criteria see Margoliash (1954).

V. R. POTTER

REFERENCES

Abood, L. G. and Gerard, R. W. (1952) Am. J. Physiol., 168:739, 728.

Aisenberg, A. C. and Potter, V. R. (1955) J. Biol. Chem., 215:737.

Aisenberg, A. C. and Potter, V. R. (1956) J. Biol. Chem., 220:831.

Aisenberg, A. C., Reinafarje, B. and Potter, V. R. (1956) Proc. Am. Assoc. Cancer Res., 2:89.

Albaum, H. G. and Cohen. P. P. (1943) J. Biol. Chem., 149:19.

Albaum, H. G. and Eichel, B. (1943) Am. J. Botany, 30:18.

Albaum, H. G. and Umbreit, W. W. (1943) Am. J. Botany, 30:553.

Albertson, P. A. (1960) Partition of Cell Particles and Macromolecules, Almquist and Wiksells, Uppsala; Wiley and Sons, New York.

Alberty, R. A. (1956) Advan. Enzymol., 17:1.

Alivisatos, S. G. A., LaMantia, L., Ungar, F. and Matijevitch, B. L. (1962) J. Biol. Chem., 237:1212.

Allen, M. B., Piette, L. R. and Murchio, J. C. (1962) Biochim. Biophys. Acta, 60:539.

Allen, S. C. (1948) Science, 107:604.

Allfrey, V., Stern, H., Mirsky, A. E. and Saetren, H. (1952) J. Gen. Physiol., 35:529.

Allison, F. E., Hoover, S. R. and Minor, F. W. (1942) Botan. Gaz., 104:63.

Anderson, R. L. and Wood, W. A. (1962) J. Biol. Chem., 237:1029.

Andrews, P. (1962) Nature, 196:36.

Anfinsen, C. B. and Claff, C. L. (1947) J. Biol. Chem., 167:27.

Appelmans, F., Wattiaux, R. and de Duve, C. (1955) Biochem. J., 59:438.

ApRees, T. and Beevers, H. (1960) Plant Physiol., 35:839.

Archibald, R. M. (1945) J. Biol. Chem., 157:507.

Arnon, D. I. (1949) Plant Physiol., 24:1.

Arnon, D. I., Allen, M. B. and Whatley, F. R. (1956) Biochim. Biophys. Acta, 20:449.

Aronoff, S. (1956) Techniques in Radiobiochemistry, Iowa State College Press, Ames.

Askonas, B. A. (1951) Biochem. J., 48:42.

Avery, O. T. and Neill, J. M. (1924) J. Exptl. Med., 39:357.

Avron, M. and Jagendorf, A. T. (1957) Nature, 179:428.

Avron, M., Jagendorf, A. T. and Evans, M. (1957) Biochim. Biophys. Acta, 26:262.

Axelrod, A. E., Swingle, K. F. and Elvehjem, C. A. (1941) J. Biol. Chem., 140:931.

Bain, J. A. and Rusch, A. P. (1944) J. Biol. Chem., 153:659.

Baker, J. E. and Lieberman, M. (1962) Plant Physiol., 37:90.

Ball, E. G. (1952), ed., Biochemical Preparations, Vol. 2; John Wiley and Sons, New York.

Barcroft, J. (1908) J. Physiol., 37:12.

Barcroft, J. and Haldane, J. S. (1902) J. Physiol., 28:232.

Barker, S. B. and Summerson, W. H. (1941) J. Biol. Chem., 138:535.

Barnum, C. P. and Huseby, R. A. (1948) Arch. Biochem., 19:17.

Barron, E. S. G. (1943) Advan. Enzymol., 3:149.

Barron, E. S. G. and Harrop, G. A. (1928) J. Biol. Chem., 79:65.

Bassham, J. A. and Calvin, M. (1957) The Path of Carbon in Photosynthesis, Prentice-Hall Inc., Englewood Cliffs, N. J.

Bassham, J. A., Shibata, K. and Calvin, M. (1955) Biochim. Biophys. Acta, 17:332.

Bateman, J. B. and Monk, G. W. (1955) Science, 121:441.

Bates, F. J. (1942) National Bureau of Standards, Circular C 440, Government Printing Office, Washington, D.C.

Bayer, E. (1961) Gas Chromatography, Van Nostrand and Co., New York.

Beams, J. W., Weed, A. J. and Pickels, E. G. (1933) Science, 78:338.

Beevers, H. (1954) Plant Physiol., 29:265.

Beevers, H. (1956) Plant Physiol., 31:339.

Beevers, H. and Gibbs, M. (1954) Plant Physiol., 29:318.

Behrens, M. (1932) Z. Physiol. Chem., 209:59.

Berenblum, I., Chain, E. and Heatley, N. B. (1939) Biochem. J., 33:68.

Berenbom, M., Yokoyama, H. O. and Stowell, R. E. (1952) Proc. Soc. Exptl. Biol. Med., 81:125.

Berger, J. and Avery, G. S., Jr. (1943) Am. J. Botany, 30:290.

Bergmann, F. and Dikstein, S. (1956) J. Biol. Chem., 223:765.

Berry, W. E. and Steward, F. C. (1934) Ann. Botany (London), 48:395.

Beyer, R. E., Ernster, L., Low, H. and Beyer, T. (1955) Exptl. Cell Res., 8:586.

Bier, M. (1962) In Methods in Enzymology, Colowick, S. P. and Kaplan, N. O., eds., Academic Press, New York, Vol. 5, p. 33.

Black, C. C. and Humphreys, T. E. (1962) Plant Physiol., 37:66.

Blaschko, H., Hagen, J. M. and Hagen, P. (1957) J. Physiol., 139:316.

Blaschko, H. and Welch, A. (1953) Naunyn-Schmiedebergs Arch. Exptl. Pathol. Pharmakol., 219:17.

Block, W. D. and Johnson, D. V. (1955) J. Biol. Chem., 217:43.

Bock, R. M. and Ling, N.-S. (1954) Anal. Chem., 26:1543.

Booth, V. H. and Green, D. E. (1938) Biochem. J., 32:855.

Borsook, H. and Dubnoff, J. W. (1939) J. Biol. Chem., 131:163.

Brackett, F. S., Olson, R. A. and Crickard, R. G. (1953) J. Gen. Physiol., 36:529.

Brekke, B. and Dixon, M. (1937) Biochem. J., 31:2000.

Brenner, S. (1947) S. African J. Med. Sci., 12:53.

Brenner-Holzach, O. and Raaflaub, J. (1954) Helv. Physiol. Pharmacol. Acta, 12:242.

Brigl, P. and Müller, H. (1939) Ber., 72B:2121.

Brock, N., Druckery, H. and Richter, R. (1939) Biochem. Z., 303:286.

Brodie, T. G. (1910) J. Physiol., 39:391.

Brody, T. M. and Bain, J. A. (1952) J. Biol. Chem., 195:685.

Brown, R. (1951) Nature, 168:941.

Bruce, W. F. (1937) Org. Syn., 17:1.

Bruinsma, J. (1961) Biochim. Biophys. Acta, 52:576.

Bryan, W. H. and Newcomb. E. H. (1954) Physiol. Plantarum, 7:290.

Buchanan, J. M., Hastings, A. B. and Nesbett, F. B. (1942) J. Biol. Chem., 145:715.

Bueding, E. and Wortis, H. (1940) J. Biol. Chem., 133:585.

Bunting, A. H. and James, W. O. (1941) New Phytologist, 40:262.

Burg, M. B. and Orloff, J. (1962) Am. J. Physiol., 203:327.

Bürgi, W. and Schmid, K. (1961) J. Biol. Chem., 236:1066.

Burk, D. (1934) Ergeb. Enzymforsch., 3:23.

Burk, D. (1939) Cold Spring Harbor Symp. Quant. Biol., 7:420.

Burk, D. (1953) Federation Proc., 12:611.

Burk, D., Hendricks, S. B., Korzenovsky, M., Schocken, V. and Warburg, O. (1949) Science, 110:225.

Burk, D. and Hobby, G. (1954) Science, 120:640.

Burk, D. and Milner, R. T. (1932) Ind. Eng. Chem., Anal. Ed., 4:3.

Burk, D. and Warburg, O., (1951) Z. Naturforsch., 6b:12.

Burris, R. H. and Wilson, P. W. (1940) Proc. Soc. Exptl. Biol. Med., 45:721.

Butler, W. L. and Norris, K. H. (1960) Arch. Biochem. Biophys., 87:31.

Calvin, M., Heidelberger, C., Reid, J. C., Tolbert, B. M. and Yankwich, P. E. (1949) Isotopic Carbon, John Wiley and Sons, New York.

Canzanelli, A. and Rapport, D. (1939) Am. J. Physiol., 127:296.

Carter, C. E. (1950) J. Am. Chem. Soc., 72:1466.

Carter, H. E. (1949), ed., Biochemical Preparations, Vol. 1; John Wiley and Sons, New York.

Casselton, P. J. and Syrett, P. J. (1962) Ann. Bot. (London), 26:71.

Chakravorty, M., Veiga, L. A., Bacila, M. and Horecker, B. L. (1962) J. Biol. Chem., 237:1014.

Chance, B. (1951a) Rev. Sci. Instr., 22:619.
Chance, B. (1951b) Rev. Sci. Instr., 22:619.
Chance, B. (1952) Nature, 169:215.
Chance, B. (1954) Science, 120:767.
Chance, B. (1958) J. Biol. Chem., 233:1223.
Chance, B. and Hackett, D. P. (1959) Plant Physiol., 34:33.
Chance, B. and Hagihara, B. (1960) Biochem. Biophys. Res. Commun., 3:1.
Chance, B. and Legallais, V. (1951) Rev. Sci. Instr., 22:627.
Chance, B. and Redfearn, E. R. (1961) Biochem. J., 80:632.
Chance, B. and Williams, R. G. (1956) Advan. Enzymol., 17:65.
Chase, G. D. (1959) Principles of Radioisotope Methodology, Burgess Publishing Co.,
    Minneapolis, Minn.
Chauveau, J., Moule, Y. and Rouiller, C. (1956) Exptl. Cell Res., 11:317.
Cheng, Ping-Yao (1952) Arch. Biochem. Biophys., 36:489.
Clark, W. M. (1920) The Determination of Hydrogen Ions, Williams and Wilkens, Balti-
    more, Maryland.
Claude, A. (1946) J. Exptl. Med., 84:51.
Claude, A. (1947-8) Harvey Lectures, 43:121.
Claude, A. and Potter, J. S. (1943) J. Exptl. Med., 77:345.
Cleland, K. W. and Slater, E. C. (1953) Biochem. J., 53:547.
Cleland, W. W. (1963a) Biochim. Biophys. Acta, 67:104.
Cleland, W. W. (1963b) Biochim. Biophys. Acta, 67:193.
Cleland, W. W. (1963c) Biochim. Biophys. Acta, 67:188.
Cleland, W. W. (1963d) Nature, 198:463.
Cohen, P. P. (1940) J. Biol. Chem., 136:585.
Cohen, P. P. (1946) J. Biol. Chem., 164:685.
Cohen, P. P. and Hayano, M. (1946) J. Biol. Chem., 166:239.
Cohn, W. E. (1950) J. Am. Chem. Soc., 72:1471.
Colowick, S. P. (1955) In Methods in Enzymology, Colowick, S. P. and Kaplan, N. O.,
    eds., Academic Press, New York, Vol. 1, p. 90.
Colowick, S. P. and Kaplan, N. O. (1955), eds., Methods in Enzymology, Vol. 1, 2;
    Academic Press, New York.
Colowick, S. P. and Kaplan, N. O. (1956), eds., Methods in Enzymology, Vol. 3; Aca-
    demic Press, New York.
Colowick, S. P. and Sutherland, E. W. (1942) J. Biol. Chem., 144:423.
Comar, C. L. (1955) Radioisotopes in Biology and Agriculture, McGraw-Hill Book Co.,
    New York.
Condon, R. D., Scholly, P. R. and Averill, W. (1960) In Gas Chromatography, Scott,
    R. P. W., ed., Butterworths, Washington, D. C., p. 30.
Connelly, C. M. and Chance, B. (1954) Federation Proc., 13:94.
Conway, E. J. (1947) Microdiffusion Analysis and Volumetric Errow, Crosby, Lockwood
    and Son, London.
Cooper, C., Devlin, T. M. and Lehninger, A. L. (1955a) Biochim. Biophys. Acta,
    18:159.
Cooper, C., Wu, R. and Wilson, D. W. (1955b) J. Biol. Chem., 216:37.
Copenhaver, J. H., Jr. and Lardy, H. A. (1952) J. Biol. Chem., 195:225.
Cori, C. F. (1942) In Symposium on Respiratory Enzymes, University of Wisconsin
    Press, Madison, p. 175.
Cowgill, R. W. and Pizer, L. I. (1956) J. Biol. Chem., 223:885.
Crane, F. L., Mii, S., Hauge, J. G., Green, D. E. and Beinert, H. (1956) J. Biol.
    Chem., 218:701.
Crane, R. K. and Mendlestam, P. (1960) Biochim. Biophys. Acta, 45:460.
Crescitelli, F. (1955-56) J. Gen. Physiol., 39:423.
Cruickshank, C. N. O. (1954) Exptl. Cell Res., 7:374.
Cutter, V. M., Wilson, K. S. and Dubé, G. R. (1952) Science, 115:58.

Czok, R. and Bücher, T. (1960) In Advances in Protein Chemistry, Anfinsen, C. B.,
    Anson, M. L., Bailey, K. and Edsall, J. T., eds., Academic Press, New York,
    p. 315.

Dalton, A. J. and Felix, M. (1953) Am. J. Anat., 92:277.
Dalton, A. J. and Felix, M. (1954) Am. J. Anat., 94:171.
Dalton, A. J., Kahler, H., Striebich, M. J. and Lloyd, B. (1950) J. Natl. Cancer Inst.,
    11:439.
Dalziel, K. (1962a) Biochem. J., 84:244.
Dalziel, K. (1962b) Nature, 196:1203.
Dannenberg, H. and Kiese, M. (1952) Biochem. Z., 322:395.
Davis, L. and Metzler, D. E. (1962) J. Biol. Chem., 237:1883.
Dawson, C. R. and Magee, R. J. (1957) In Ion Exchangers in Organic and Biochemistry,
    Calmon, C. and Kressman, T. R. E., eds., Interscience Publishers, New York,
    p. 377.
deDuve, C. and Berthet, J. (1954) Intern. Rev. Cytol., 3:225.
deDuve, C., Berthet, J. and Beaufay, H. (1959) Progr. Biophys. Chem., 9:325.
deDuve, C., Pressman, B. C., Gianetto, R., Wattiaux, R. and Appelmans, F. (1955)
    Biochem. J., 60:604.
deLey, J. (1949) Experientia, 5:299.
Demole, E. (1961) J. Chromatog., 6:2.
Dempsey, W. B. and Christensen, H. N. (1962) J. Biol. Chem., 237:1113.
Denues, A. R. T. (1953) Exptl. Cell Res., 3:540.
Derechin, M. (1962) Biochem. J., 82:42.
Deutsch, W. (1936) J. Physiol. (Paris), 87:56.
Devlin, T. M. and Lehninger, A. L. (1958) J. Biol. Chem., 233:1586.
Dickens, F. (1951) Biochem. J., 48:385.
Dickens, F. and Greville, G. D. (1933a) Biochem. J., 27:213.
Dickens, F. and Greville, G. D. (1933b) Biochem. J., 27:1479.
Dickens, F. and Greville, G. D. (1935) Biochem. J., 29:1468.
Dickens, F. and Simer, F. (1931) Biochem. J., 25:973.
Dickens, F. and Simer, F. (1933) In Abderhalden's Handbuch, Springer, Berlin, Abt.
    IV, Teil 13, p. 435 ff.
Dixon, M. (1937) Biochem. J., 31:924.
Dixon, M. (1943) Manometric Methods, Second Ed., University Press, Cambridge,
    England.
Dixon, M. (1945) Biochem. J., 39:427.
Dixon, M. (1951) Manometric Methods, Third Edition, University Press, Cambridge,
    England.
Dixon, M. (1951a) Biochem. J., 48:575.
Dixon, M. (1953) Biochem. J., 55:170.
Dixon, M. and Elliott, K. A. C. (1930) Biochem. J., 24:820.
Dixon, M. and Tunnicliffe, H. E. (1923) Proc. Roy. Soc. (London), 94B:266.
Dixon, M. and Webb, E. C. (1958) Enzymes, Academic Press, New York.
Dockstader, W. B. and Halvorson, H. O. (1950) Science, 112:618.
Dounce, A. L. (1943) J. Biol. Chem., 147:685.
Dounce, A. L. (1955) In The Nucleic Acids, Chargaff, E. and Davidson, J. N., eds.,
    Academic Press, New York, Vol. II, p. 93.
Dounce, A. L., Tishkoff, G. H., Barnett, S. R. and Freer, R. M. (1949) J. Gen.
    Physiol., 33:629.
Dounce, A. L., Witter, R. F., Monty, K. J., Pate, S. and Cottone, M. A. (1955) J.
    Biophys. Biochem. Cytol., 1:139.
Duane, W. C. and Krogman, D. W. (1963) Biochim. Biophys. Acta, 71:195.
DuBois, K. P. and Potter, V. R. (1943) J. Biol. Chem., 150:185.

Ebersole, E. R., Guttentag, C. and Wilson, P. W. (1944) Arch. Biochem., 3:399.

Edson, N. L. (1935) Biochem. J., 29:2082.

Eichel, B., Wainia, W. W., Person, P. and Cooperstein, S. J. (1950) J. Biol. Chem., 183:89.

Elgart, S. and Nelson, N. (1941) J. Biol. Chem., 138:443.

Eliasson, L. (1955) Physiol. Plantarum, 8:374.

Elliott, K. A. C. and Schroeder, E. F. (1934) Biochem. J., 28:1920.

Ellman, G. (1962) Anal. Biochem., 3:40.

Emerson, R. and Chalmers, R. (1955) Plant Physiol., 30:504.

Emerson, R. and Lewis, C. M. (1941) Am. J. Botany, 28:789.

Emerson, R. and Lewis, C. M. (1943) Am. J. Botany, 30:165.

Emerson, R. L., Stauffer, J. F. and Umbreit, W. W. (1944) Am. J. Botany, 31:107.

Ennor, A. H. and Stocken, L. A. (1948) Biochem. J., 43:190.

Ernster, L., Lindberg, O. and Löw, H. (1955a) Nature, 175:168.

Ernster, L. and Löw, H. (1955b) Exptl. Cell Res. Suppl., 3:133.

Fan, C. S., Stauffer, J. F. and Umbreit, W. W. (1943) J. Gen. Physiol., 27:15.

Feinstein, R. N. and Stare, F. S. (1940) J. Biol. Chem., 135:393.

Fenn, W. O. (1928) Am. J. Physiol., 84:110.

Field, J. (1948) Methods Med. Res., 1:289.

Fleming, A. and Allison, V. D. (1924) Lancet, 206:1303.

Flodin, P. and Porath, J. (1954) Biochim. Biophys. Acta, 13:175.

Folin, O. and Malmros, H. (1929) J. Biol. Chem., 83:115.

Foster, J. W. (1949) Chemical Activities of Fungi, Academic Press, New York.

Foster, J. W., Cowen, R. M. and Maag, T. A. (1962) J. Bacteriol., 83:330.

Fraser, D. (1951) Nature, 167:33.

Friedemann, T. E. (1927) J. Biol. Chem., 73:331.

Friedlander, G. and Kennedy, J. W. (1955) Nuclear and Radiochemistry, John Wiley and Sons, New York.

Gale, E. F. (1946) Advan. Enzymol., 6:1.

Gale, E. F. (1947) Biochem. J., 41:viii.

Ganapathy, C. V. and Sastri, B. N. (1938) Current Sci., 6:331.

Garver, J. C. and Epstein, R. L. (1959) Appl. Microbiol., 7:318.

Gautheret, R. J. (1959) La Culture des Tissus Vegetaux, Masson & Cie, Paris.

Geffken, G. (1904) Z. Physik. Chem. (Leipzig), 49:257.

Georgi, C. E., Militzer, W., Burns, L. and Heotis, J. (1951) Proc. Soc. Exptl. Biol. Med., 76:598.

Gilson, W. E. (1963) Science, 141:531.

Glaser, L. and Brown, D. H. (1955) J. Biol. Chem., 216:67.

Glick, D. (1961) Quantitative Chemical Techniques of Histo- and Cytochemistry. John Wiley & Sons, New York.

Goldstein, A. (1949) Science, 110:400.

Good, N. E. and Brown, A. H. (1961) Biochim. Biophys. Acta, 50:544.

Gornall, A. G., Bardawill, C. J. and David, M. M. (1949) J. Biol. Chem., 177:751.

Gozsy, B. (1935) Z. Physiol. Chem., 236:54.

Graca, J. G. and Makaroff, W. N. (1952) Science, 115:374.

Granick, S. (1938) Am. J. Botany, 25:558, 561.

Grant, W. M. (1946) Ind. Eng. Chem., Anal. Ed., 18:729.

Grant, W. M. (1947) Ind. Eng. Chem., Anal. Ed., 19:206.

Green, D. E. (1940) Mechanisms of Biological Oxidations, University Press, Cambridge, England.

Green, D. E., Mii, S., Kohout, P. M. and Tisdale, H. (1955) J. Biol. Chem., 217:551.

Green, D. E., Mii, S., Mahler, H. R. and Bock, R. M. (1954) J. Biol. Chem., 206:1.

Green, D. E., Needham, D. M. and Dewan, J. G. (1937) Biochem. J., 31:2327.

Greenstein, J. P., Birnbaum, S. M. and Otey, M. C. (1953) J. Biol. Chem., 204:307.
Gregg, J. H. (1950) J. Exptl. Zool., 114:173.
Gregg, J. R. (1947) Rev. Sci. Instr., 18:514.
Greville, G. D. (1939) Biochem. J., 33:718.
Griffiths, D. E. and Wharton, D. C. (1961) J. Biol. Chem., 236:1850.
Grimm, F. C. and Doherty, D. G. (1961) J. Biol. Chem., 236:1980.
Gunsalus, I. C. and Umbreit, W. W. (1945) J. Bacteriol., 49:347.
Gurin, S. and Hood, D. B. (1939) J. Biol. Chem., 131:211.
Gurin, S. and Hood, D. B. (1941) J. Biol. Chem., 139:775.

Hackett, D. P., Haas, D. W., Griffiths, S. K. and Niederpruem, D. J. (1960) Plant
    Physiol., 35:8.
Hackett, D. P. and Ragland, T. E. (1962) Plant Physiol., 37:656.
Hagihara, B. (1961) Biochim. Biophys. Acta, 46:134.
Handbook of Chemistry and Physics, Chemical Rubber Publishing Co., Cleveland, Ohio.
Handler, P. and Klein, J. R. (1942) J. Biol. Chem., 143:49.
Hanson, J. B. (1959) J. Biol. Chem., 234:1303.
Harman, J. W. and Feigelson, M. (1952) Exptl. Cell Res., 3:47, 58.
Harman, J. W. and Osborne, U. H. (1953) J. Exptl. Med., 98:81.
Hastings, A. B. and Sendroy, J. (1925) J. Biol. Chem., 65:445.
Hatefi, Y., Jurtshuk, P. and Haavik, A. G. (1961) Arch. Biochem. Biophys., 94:148.
Hatefi, Y. and Lester, R. L. (1958) Biochim. Biophys. Acta, 27:83.
Hauschild, A. H. W., Nelson, C. D. and Krotkov, G. (1962) Can. J. Botany, 40:179.
Helferich, B. and Klein, W. (1926) Ann. Chem., 450:219.
Herbain, M. (1951) Bull. Soc. Chim. Biol., 33:1635.
Herbert, E. and Potter, V. R. (1956) J. Biol. Chem., 222:483.
Herbert, E., Potter, V. R. and Takagi, Y. (1955) J. Biol. Chem., 213:923.
Herrmann, H. and Boss, M. B. (1945) J. Cellular Comp. Physiol., 26:131.
Herzenberg, L. A. and Herzenberg, L. A. (1961) Proc. Natl. Acad. Sci., U. S., 47:
    762.
Hevesy, G. (1948) Radioactive Indicators, Interscience Publishers, New York.
Hiatt, A. J. (1962) Plant Physiol., 37:85.
Hillarp, N. A., Lagerstedt, S. and Nilson, B. (1953) Acta Physiol. Scand., 29:251.
Hiller, A., Plazin, J. and Van Slyke, D. D. (1948) J. Biol. Chem., 176:1401.
Hogeboom, G. H. (1949) J. Biol. Chem., 177:847.
Hogeboom, G. H. and Kuff, E. L. (1954) J. Biol. Chem., 210:735.
Hogeboom, G. H. and Schneider, W. C. (1950) J. Biol. Chem., 186:417.
Hogeboom, G. H. and Schneider, W. C. (1952) J. Biol. Chem., 197:611.
Hogeboom, G. H., Schneider, W. C. and Palade, G. E. (1948) J. Biol. Chem., 172:619.
Hogeboom, G. H., Schneider, W. C. and Striebich, M. J. (1952) J. Biol. Chem., 196:
    111.
Hogeboom, G. H., Schneider, W. C. and Striebich, M. J. (1953) Cancer Res., 13:617.
Hokin, L. E. (1955) Biochim. Biophys. Acta, 18:379.
Holter, H. (1943) Compt. Rend. Trav. Lab. Carlsberg (Serie Chim.), 24:400.
Holter, H. (1954) Proc. Roy. Soc. (London), 142B:140.
Holter, H. and Linderstrom-Lang, K. (1951) Physiol. Rev., 31:423.
Holter, H. and Pollock, B. M. (1952) Compt. Rend. Trav. Lab. Carlsberg (Serie Chim.),
    28:221.
Horecker, B. L. and Kornberg, A. (1948) J. Biol. Chem., 175:385.
Horecker, B. L., Smyrniotis, P. Z. and Klenow, H. (1953) J. Biol. Chem., 205:661.
Howard, J. H. and Fraser, W. A. (1941) Org. Syn., 1:475.
Hughes, D. E. (1951) Brit. J. Exptl. Pathol., 32:97.
Hughes, D. E. (1962) J. Microbiol. Biochem. Eng. Technol., 4:405.
Hughes, D. E. and Nyborg, W. L. (1962) Science, 138:108.
Hugo, W. B. (1954) Bacteriol. Rev., 18:87.
Humphreys, T. E., Newcomb, E. H., Bokman, A. H. and Stumpf, P. K. (1954) J.
    Biol. Chem., 210:941.

Hunter, F. E., Jr. and Ford, L. (1955) J. Biol. Chem., 216:357.
Hurlbert, R. B., Schmitz, H., Brumm, A. F. and Potter, V. R. (1954) J. Biol. Chem., 209:23.
Hurwitz, C. and Wilson, P. W. (1940) Ind. Eng. Chem., Anal. Ed., 12:31.
Hurwitz, J., Weissbach, A., Horecker, B. L. and Smyrniotis, P. Z. (1956) J. Biol. Chem., 218:769.

International Critical Tables (1928) National Research Council, Vol. III, McGraw-Hill Book Co., New York.

Jackson, K. L., Walker, E. L. and Pace, N. (1953) Science, 118:136.
Jackson, P. C., Hendricks, S. B. and Vasa, B. M. (1962) Plant Physiol., 37:8.
Jackson, W. T. (1962) Plant Physiol., 37:513.
Jagendorf, A. T. and Avron, M. (1958) J. Biol. Chem., 231:277.
James, W. O. and Cragg, J. M. (1943) New Phytologist, 42:28.
James, W. O. and Das, V. S. R. (1957) New Phytologist, 56:325.
Johnson, M. J. (1941) J. Biol. Chem., 137:575.
Jongbloed, J. (1938) Z. Biol., 98:497.

Kalckar, H. M. (1941) Chem. Rev., 28:71.
Kalckar, H. M. (1947) J. Biol. Chem., 167:429.
Kamen, M. D. (1957) Isotopic Tracers in Biology, Third Edition, Academic Press, New York.
Kaplan, N. O. and Lipmann, F. (1948) J. Biol. Chem., 174:37.
Kaufman, S. and Alivisatos, S. G. A. (1955) J. Biol. Chem., 216:141.
Keilin, D. (1929) Proc. Roy. Soc. (London), 104B:206.
Keilin, D. and Hartree, E. F. (1937) Proc. Roy. Soc. (London), 122B:298.
Keilin, D. and Hartree, E. F. (1938) Proc. Roy. Soc. (London), 125B:171.
Keilin, D. and Hartree, E. F. (1943) Nature, 152:626.
Keilin, D. and Hartree, E. F. (1945) Biochem. J., 39:289.
Keilin, D. and Hartree, E. F. (1947) Biochem. J., 41:500.
Keilin, D. and Hartree, E. F. (1949) Nature, 164:254.
Keilin, D. and Hartree, E. F. (1958) Biochim. Biophys. Acta, 27:173.
Kennedy, E. P. and Lehninger, A. L. (1949) J. Biol. Chem., 179:957.
Keulemans, A. I. M. (1959) Gas Chromatography, Reinhold Publishing Co., New York.
Kielley, R. K. (1955) J. Biol. Chem., 216:405.
Kielley, R. K. and Schneider, W. C. (1950) J. Biol. Chem., 185:869.
Kielley, W. W. and Kielley, R. K. (1951) J. Biol. Chem., 191:485.
Kielley, W. W. and Kielley, R. K. (1953) J. Biol. Chem., 200:213.
Kieselbach, R. (1960) Anal. Chem., 32:1749.
Kimura, T. and Singer, T. P. (1961) In Methods in Enzymology, Colowick, S. P. and Kaplan, N. O., editors, Academic Press, New York, Vol. 5, pp. 562-570.
King, T. E. (1961) J. Biol. Chem., 236:2342.
King, T. E. and Howard, R. L. (1962a) J. Biol. Chem., 237:1686.
King, T. E. and Howard, R. L. (1962b) Biochim. Biophys. Acta, 59:489.
Klein, J. R. and Handler, P. (1941) J. Biol. Chem., 139:103.
Kleinzeller, A. (1940) Biochem. J., 34:1241.
Knight, S. G. (1948) J. Bacteriol., 55:401.
Koepsell, H. J. and Johnson, M. J. (1942) J. Biol. Chem., 145:379.
Koepsell, H. J. and Sharpe, E. S. (1952) Arch. Biochem. Biophys., 38:443.
Kok, B. (1948) Enzymologia, 13:1.
Kok, B. (1955) Biochim. Biophys. Acta, 16:35.
Kok, B. (1960) In Encyclopedia of Plant Physiology, Springer-Verlag, Berlin, Vol. 5, part 1, pp. 526-683.
Kok, B., Veltkamp, G. W. and Gelderman, W. P. (1953) Biochim. Biophys. Acta, 11:7.
Kornberg, A. and Pricer, W. E., Jr. (1951) J. Biol. Chem., 189:123.

Koski, V. M. (1950) Arch. Biochem. Biophys., 29:339.

Krampitz, L. O. and Werkman, C. H. (1941) Biochem. J., 35:595.

Kratz, W. A. and Myers, J. (1955) Plant Physiol., 30:275.

Krebs, H. A. (1935a) Biochem. J., 29:1620.

Krebs, H. A. (1935b) Biochem. J., 29:1951.

Krebs, H. A. (1937) Biochem. J., 31:2095.

Krebs, H. A. (1942a) Biochem. J., 36:303.

Krebs, H. A. (1942b) Biochem. J., 36:758.

Krebs, H. A. (1948) Biochem. J., 43:51.

Krebs, H. A. (1951a) Biochem. J., 48:240.

Krebs, H. A. (1951b) Biochem. J., 48:349.

Krebs, H. A. and Eggleston, L. V. (1940) Biochem. J.; 34:442.

Krebs, H. A. and Eggleston, L. V. (1945) Biochem. J., 39:408.

Krebs, H. A. and Eggleston, L. V. (1948a) Biochem. J., 42:294.

Krebs, H. A. and Eggleston, L. V. (1948b) Biochem. J., 43:17.

Krebs, H. A. and Henseleit, K. (1932) Z. Physiol. Chem., 210:33.

Krebs, H. A., Smyth, D. H. and Evans, E. A. (1940) Biochem. J., 34:1041.

Kuby, S. A., Noda, L. and Lardy, H. A. (1954a) J. Biol. Chem., 209:191.

Kuby, S. A., Noda, L. and Lardy, H. A. (1954b) J. Biol. Chem., 210:65.

Kuff, E. L. and Dalton, A. J. (1959) In Subcellular Particles, Hayashi, T., editor, Ronald Press, New York, p. 114.

Kuff, E. L. and Schneider, W. C. (1954) J. Biol. Chem., 206:677.

Laird, A. K., Nygaard, O., Ris, H. and Barton, A. D. (1953) Exptl. Cell Res., 5:147.

Lamanna, C. and Mallette, M. F. (1954) J. Bacteriol., 67:503.

Lang, K. and Siebert, G. (1952) Biochem. Z., 322:360.

Lardy, H. A. (1960), ed., Biochemical Preparations, Vol. 7; John Wiley and Sons, New York.

Lardy, H. A. and Fischer, H. O. L. (1946) J. Biol. Chem., 164:513.

Lardy, H. A., Gilson, W. E., Hipple, J. and Burris, R. H. (1948) Anal. Chem., 20:1100.

Lardy, H. A. and Wellman, H. (1952) J. Biol. Chem., 195:215.

Laser, H. (1942) Biochem. J., 36:319.

Laser, H. (1955) Biochem. J., 61:122.

Laties, G. G. (1949) J. Biol. Chem., 177:969.

Laties, G. G. (1957) Surv. Biol. Progr., 63:215.

Laties, G. G. (1962) Plant Physiol., 37:679.

Latimer, P. and Eubanks, C. A. H. (1962) Arch. Biochem. Biophys., 98:274.

Lazarow, A. (1942) Anat. Record, 84:31.

Lazarow, A. (1949) J. Lab. Clin. Med., 34:1702.

Lazarow, A. (1951) J. Lab. Clin. Med., 38:767.

Lee, S. B., Burris, R. H. and Wilson, P. W. (1942) Proc. Soc. Exptl. Biol. Med., 50:96.

Lee, S. B., Wilson, J. B. and Wilson, P. W. (1942) J. Biol. Chem., 144:273.

Leech, R. M. (1963) Biochim. Biophys. Acta, 71:253.

Lehninger, A. L. (1951) J. Biol. Chem., 190:345.

Lehninger, A. L., Ul Hassan, M. and Sudduth, H. C. (1954) J. Biol. Chem., 210:911.

LePage, G. A. (1948) J. Biol. Chem., 176:1009.

LePage, G. A. (1950) Cancer Res., 10:77.

LePage, G. A. and Schneider, W. C. (1948) J. Biol. Chem., 176:1021.

Levin, O. (1962) In Methods in Enzymology, Colowick, S. P. and Kaplan, N. O., eds., Academic Press, New York, Vol. 5, p. 27.

Lewin, R. A. (1962) Physiology and Biochemistry of Algae, Academic Press, New York.

Lieberman, M. and Biale, J. B. (1956) Plant Physiol., 31:425.

Lindberg, O. and Ernster, L. (1954) Nature, 173:1038.

Linderstrøm-Lang, K. (1938) Harvey Lectures, 34:214

Linderstrøm-Lang, K. (1943) Compt. Rend. Trav. Lab. Carlsberg (Serie Chim.), 24:334.

Lineweaver, H. and Burk, D. (1934) J. Am. Chem. Soc., 56:658.

Linnane, A. W. and Ziegler, D. M. (1958) Biochim. Biophys. Acta, 29:630.

Lipmann, F. (1941) Advan. Enzymol., 1:99.

Lipmann, F., Behrens, O. K., Kabat, E. A. and Burk, D. (1940) Science, 91:21.

Lipmann, F., Hotchkiss, R. D. and Dubos, R. J. (1941) J. Biol. Chem., 141:163.

Litt, M., Monty, K. J. and Dounce, A. L. (1952) Cancer Res., 12:279.

Loomis, W. F. (1949) Science, 109:491.

Lorenzen, H. (1957) Flora, 144:483.

Lowry, O. H., Rosebrough, N. J., Farr, A. L. and Randall, R. J. (1951) J. Biol. Chem., 193:265.

Lu, G. D. (1939) Biochem. J., 33:249.

Lund, H. A., Vatter, A. E., and Hanson, J. B. (1958) J. Biophys. Biochem. Cytol., 4:87.

Lundegårdh, H. (1952) Arkiv Kemi, 5:97.

Machlis, L. (1944) Am. J. Botany, 31:183.

MacInnes, D. A. and Belcher, D. (1933) J. Am. Chem. Soc., 55:2630.

Mackler, B. and Green, D. E. (1956) Biochim. Biophys. Acta, 21:1.

MacLeod, J. and Summerson, W. H. (1940) Science, 91:201.

McClendon, J. H. and Blinks, L. R. (1952) Nature, 170:577.

McGilvery, R. W. and Cohen, P. P. (1948) J. Biol. Chem., 174:813.

McIlwain, H. (1948) J. Gen. Microbiol., 2:288.

McIlwain, H. and Buddle, H. L. (1953) Biochem. J., 53:412.

Malachowski, R. and Maslowski, M. (1928) Chem. Ber., 61B:2521.

Maley, G. F. and Lardy, H. A. (1953) J. Biol. Chem., 204:435.

Maley, G. F. and Lardy, H. A. (1954) J. Biol. Chem., 210:903.

Malley, E. D., Conway, E. J. and Fitzgerald, O. (1943) Biochem. J., 37:278.

Mann, P. J. G. and Quastel, J. H. (1941) Biochem. J., 35:502.

Mann, T. (1943) Nature, 151:619.

Manning, G. B. and Campbell, L. L. (1961) J. Biol. Chem., 236:2952.

Manning, W. M., Stauffer, J. F., Duggar, B. M. and Daniels, F. (1938) J. Am. Chem. Soc., 60:266.

Marcus, A. and Velasco, J. (1960) J. Biol. Chem., 235:563.

Margoliash, E. (1954) Biochem. J., 56:529, 535.

Marmur, J. and Hotchkiss, R. D. (1955) J. Biol. Chem., 214:383.

Marsh, P. B. and Goddard, D. R. (1939) Am. J. Botany, 26:724.

Martin, A. J. P. and Synge, R. L. M. (1941) Biochem. J., 35:1358.

Martin, E. M. and Morton, R. K. (1956) Biochem. J., 62:696.

Martius, C. and Lynen, F. (1950) Advan. Enzymol., 10:167.

Massey, V. (1960) Biochim. Biophys. Acta, 37:314.

Maxwell, E. S. and Topper, Y. J. (1961) J. Biol. Chem., 236:1032.

Maxwell, R. E. (1949) Science, 110:403.

Mayer, S. W. and Tompkins, E. R. (1947) J. Am. Chem. Soc., 69:2866.

Mazia, D. (1957-8) Harvey Lectures, Academic Press, New York, p. 130.

Mazia, D. and Dan, K. (1952) Proc. Natl. Acad. Sci., U. S., 38:826.

Mead, J. F. and Howton, D. R. (1950) Anal. Chem., 22:1204.

Mehler, A. H. (1954) Science, 120:1043.

Meister, A. (1961), ed., Biochemical Preparations, Vol. 8; John Wiley and Sons, New York.

Meites, L. and Meites, T. (1948) Anal. Chem., 20:984.

Meyer, F., Mackal, R. P., Tao, M. and Evans, E. A., Jr. (1961) J. Biol. Chem., 236:1111.

Meyer, F. R. and Ronge, G. (1939) Angew. Chem., 52:637.

Meyerhof, O. (1941) Biol. Symp., 5:141.

Meyerhof, O. (1942) In Symposium on Respiratory Enzymes, Univ. Wisconsin Press, Madison, p. 1.

Meyerhof, O. and Schulz, W. (1938) Biochem. Z., 297:60.

Michaelis, L. and Rona, P. (1930) Prakticum der physikalischen Chemie, Fourth Edition, Springer, Berlin.

Miflin, B. J. and Hageman, R. H. (1963) Plant Physiol., 38:66.

Millerd, A. (1953) Arch. Biochem. Biophys., 42:149.

Millerd, A. and Bonner, J. (1953) J. Histochem. Cytochem., 1:254.

Millerd, A., Bonner, J., Axelrod, B. and Bandurski, R. (1951) Proc. Natl. Acad. Sci., U. S., 37:855.

Milner, H. W., Lawrence, N. S. and French, C. S. (1950) Science, 111:633.

Minakami, S., Ringler, R. L. and Singer, T. P. (1962) J. Biol. Chem., 237:569.

Mirsky, A. E. and Ris, H. (1947) J. Gen. Physiol., 31:1, 7.

Moore, S., Dimler, R. J. and Link, K. P. (1941) Ind. Eng. Chem., Anal. Ed., 13:160.

Moore, W. E. and Duggar, B. M. (1949) In Photosynthesis in Plants, Franck, J. and Loomis, W. E., eds., Iowa State College Press, Ames, Iowa, p. 239.

Morell, D. B. (1952) Biochem. J., 51:666.

Morton, R. K. (1950) Nature, 166:1092.

Morton, R. K. (1954) Biochem. J., 57:231.

Morton, R. K. (1955) In Methods in Enzymology, Colowick, S. P. and Kaplan, N. O., eds., Academic Press, New York, Vol. 1, p. 25.

Moses, V. and Syrett, P. J. (1955) J. Bacteriol., 70:201.

Muntwyler, E., Seifter, S. and Harkness, D. M. (1950) J. Biol. Chem., 184:181.

Münzer, E. and Neumann, W. (1917) Biochem. Z., 81:319.

Myers, J. and Clark, L. B. (1944) J. Gen. Physiol., 28:103.

Myers, J. and Matsen, F. A. (1955) Arch. Biochem. Biophys., 55:373.

Najjar, V. A. and Fisher, J. (1954) J. Biol. Chem., 206:215.

Naora, H. and Takeda, S. (1954) Biochim. Biophys. Acta, 13:360.

Naylor, J., Sander, G. and Skoog, F. (1954) Physiol. Plantarum, 7:25.

Neilands, J. B. (1952a) J. Biol. Chem., 197:701.

Neilands, J. B. (1952b) J. Biol. Chem., 199:373.

Neuberg, C., Faiker, E. and Levite, A. (1917) Biochem. Z., 83:244.

Neuberg, C., Lustig, H. and Rothenberg, M. A. (1943) Arch. Biochem., 3:33.

Neville, D. M. (1960) J. Biophys. Biochem. Cytol., 8:413.

Neville, J. R. (1962) Rev. Sci. Instr., 33:51.

Newcomb, E. H. and Stumpf, P. K. (1953) J. Biol. Chem., 200:233.

Nishimura, M. S., Whittingham, C. P. and Emerson, R. (1951) Symp. Soc. Exptl. Biol., 5:176.

Noll, C. R. and Burris, R. H. (1954) Plant Physiol., 29:261.

Nord, F. F. (1939) Ergeb. Enzymforsch., 8:149.

Nord, F. F., Dammann, E. and Hofstetter, H. (1936) Biochem. Z., 285:241.

Norris, K. H. and Butler, W. L. (1961) IRE Trans. Bio-Med. Electron., 8:153.

Nossal, P. M. (1953) Australian J. Exptl. Biol. Med. Sci., 31:583.

Novikoff, A. B. (1955) Reports Third Internat. Cong. Biochem., Brussels, p. 315.

Novikoff, A. B., Podber, E., Ryan, J. and Noe, E. (1953) J. Histochem. Cytochem., 1:27.

Ochoa, S. (1954) Advan. Enzymol., 15:183.

Ochoa, S. and Mii, S. (1961) J. Biol. Chem., 236:3303.

Ostern, P. (1933) Z. Physiol. Chem., 218:160.

Overman, R. T. and Clark, H. M. (1960) Radioisotope Techniques, McGraw-Hill Book Co., New York.

Palade, G. E. (1952) Anat. Record, 114:427.

Palade, G. E. (1955) J. Biophys. Biochem. Cytol., 1:59.

Palade, G. E. and Porter, K. R. (1954) J. Exptl. Med., 100:641.

Palade, G. E. and Siekevitz, P. (1955) Federation Proc., 14:262.

Paléus, S. and Neilands, J. B. (1950) Acta Chem. Scand., 4:1024.

Pangborn, J., Marr, A. G. and Robrish, S. A. (1962) J. Bacteriol., 84:669.

Pardee, A. B. (1949) J. Biol. Chem., 179:1085.

Pardee, A. B. and Potter, V. R. (1948) J. Biol. Chem., 176:1085.

Pardee, A. B. and Potter, V. R. (1949) J. Biol. Chem., 178:241.

Park, J. T. and Johnson, M. J. (1949) J. Biol. Chem., 181:149.

Park, R. B. and Pon, N. G. (1961) J. Mol. Biol., 3:1.

Park, R. B. and Pon, N. G. (1963) J. Mol. Biol., 6:105.

Peanasky, R. J. and Lardy, H. A. (1958) J. Biol. Chem., 233:365.

Pederson, C. A., Peterson, W. H. and Fred, E. B. (1926) J. Biol. Chem., 68:151.

Penrose, M. and Quastel, J. H. (1930) Proc. Roy. Soc. (London), 107B:168.

Perkins, J. J. (1943) Ind. Eng. Chem., Anal. Ed., 15:61.

Perlman, D., Lardy, H. A. and Johnson, M. J. (1944) Ind. Eng. Chem., Anal. Ed., 16:515.

Peterson, E. A. and Sober, H. A. (1962) In Methods in Enzymology, Colowick, S. P. and Kaplan, N. O., eds., Academic Press, New York, Vol. 5, p. 3.

Pickels, E. G. (1943) J. Gen. Physiol., 26:341

Pierpoint, W. S. (1962) Biochem. J., 82:143.

Plaut, G. W. E. (1955) J. Biol. Chem., 217:235.

Plaut, G. W. E. and Plaut, K. A. (1952) J. Biol. Chem., 199:141.

Plaut, G. W. E. and Sung, S. (1954) J. Biol. Chem., 207:305.

Plesner, P. and Kalckar, H. M. (1956) Methods Biochem. Analy., 3:97.

Ploeser, J. M. and Loring, H. S. (1949) J. Biol. Chem., 178:431.

Pogell, B. M. and McGilvery, R. W. (1954) J. Biol. Chem., 208:149.

Porath, J. (1954) Acta Chem. Scand., 8:1816.

Porath, J. (1960) Biochim. Biophys. Acta, 39:193.

Porath, J. and Flodin, P. (1959) Nature, 183:1657.

Potter, V. R. (1941a) J. Biol. Chem., 137:13.

Potter, V. R. (1941b) J. Biol. Chem., 141:775.

Potter, V. R. (1945a) Arch. Biochem., 6:439.

Potter, V. R. (1945b) J. Cellular Comp. Physiol., 26:87.

Potter, V. R. (1946) J. Biol. Chem., 165:311.

Potter, V. R. (1947) J. Biol. Chem., 169:17.

Potter, V. R. (1951) Cancer Res., 11:565.

Potter, V. R. and Albaum, H. G. (1943) J. Gen. Physiol., 26:443.

Potter, V. R. and Elvehjem, C. A. (1936) J. Biol. Chem., 114:495.

Potter, V. R., LePage, G. A. and Klug, H. L. (1948) J. Biol. Chem., 175:619.

Potter, V. R., Lyle, G. G. and Schneider, W. C. (1951) J. Biol. Chem., 190:293.

Potter, V. R. and Recknagel, R. O. (1951) In Phosphorus Metabolism, McElroy, W. D. and Glass, B., eds., The John Hopkins Press, Baltimore, Maryland, Vol. I, p. 377.

Potter, V. R., Recknagel, R. O. and Hurlbert, R. B. (1951) Federation Proc., 10:646.

Potter, V. R. and Schneider, W. C. (1942) J. Biol. Chem., 142:543.

Potter, V. R. and Siekevitz, P. (1952) In Phosphorus Metabolism, McElroy, W. D. and Glass, B., eds., The John Hopkins Press, Baltimore, Maryland, Vol. II, p. 665.

Potter, V. R., Siekevitz, P. and Simonson, H. C. (1953) J. Biol. Chem., 205:893.

Pratt, R. (1943) Am. J. Botany, 30:626.

Price, C. A. (1962) Biochem. J., 82:61.

Price, C. A. and Thimann, K. V. (1954a) Plant Physiol., 29:113.

Price, C. A. and Thimann, K. V. (1954b) Plant Physiol., 29:495.

Prop, F. J. A. (1950) Exptl. Cell Res., 7:303.

Pucher, G. W., Sherman, C. C. and Vickery, H. B. (1936) J. Biol. Chem., 113:235.

Pucher, G. W., Vickery, H. B. and Leavenworth, C. S. (1934) Ind. Eng. Chem., Anal. Ed., 6:190.

Pucher, G. W., Wakeman, A. J. and Vickery, H. B. (1941) Ind. Eng. Chem., Anal. Ed., 13:244.

Pullman, M. E. and Racker, E. (1956) Science, 123:1105.

Purington, H. J. and Schuck, C. (1943) J. Biol. Chem., 148:237.

Quastel, J. H. and Wheatley, A. H. M. (1931) Biochem. J., 25:629.
Quastel, J. H. and Wheatley, A. H. M. (1933) Biochem. J., 27:1753.

Randolph, M. L. and Ryan, R. R. (1950) Science, 112:528.
Rapoport, S. (1937) Biochem. Z., 289:406.
Recknagel, R. O. (1950) J. Cellular Comp. Physiol., 35:111.
Recknagel, R. O. and V. R. Potter (1951) J. Biol. Chem., 191:263.
Reif, A. E., Potter, V. R. and LePage, G. A. (1953) Cancer Res., 13:807.
Reiner, J. M. (1959) Enzyme Systems, Burgess Publishing Co., Minneapolis, Minn.
Repaske, R. (1962) J. Biol. Chem., 237:1351.
Reynolds, D. and Evans, W. L. (1942) Org. Syn., 22:56.
Richardson, H. B., Shorr, E. and Loebel, R. O. (1930) J. Biol. Chem., 86:551.
Riggs, A. (1951) J. Gen. Physiol., 35:23.
Riggs, B. C. (1945) J. Biol. Chem., 161:381.
Riley, V., Hobby, G. and Burk, D. (1953) In Pigment Cell Growth, Gordon, M., ed.,
    Academic Press, New York, p. 231.
Ringler, R. L. and Singer, T. P. (1961) In Methods in Enzymology, Colowick, S. P.
    and Kaplan, N. O., eds., Academic Press, New York, Vol. 5, p. 423.
Robbie, W. A. (1946) J. Cellular Comp. Physiol., 27:181.
Robbie, W. A. (1948) In Methods in Medical Research, Yearbook Publishers, Chicago,
    Vol. 1, p. 307.
Robbie, W. A. and Leinfelder, P. J. (1945) J. Ind. Hyg. Toxicol., 27:269.
Robertson, W. B. (1942) Science, 96:93.
Robinson, J. R. (1949) Biochem. J., 45:68.
Rosenberg, L. L. and Arnon, D. I. (1955) J. Biol. Chem., 217:361.
Rotherham, J., Schottelius, D. D., Irvin, J. L. and Irvin, E. M. (1956) J. Biol. Chem.,
    223:817.
Roughton, F. J. W. (1941) J. Biol. Chem., 141:129.

Sacktor, B. (1953) J. Gen. Physiol., 36:371.
Sanadi, D. R., Gibson, D. M., Ayengar, P. and Jacob, M. (1956) J. Biol. Chem.,
    218:505.
Schales, O. (1944) Arch. Biochem., 3:475.
Schatz, A. (1952) J. Gen. Microbiol., 6:329.
Schlenk, F. and Fisher, A. (1947) Arch. Biochem., 12:69.
Schmitz, H., Potter, V. R. and Hurlbert, R. B. (1954) Cancer Res., 14:58.
Schneider, W. C. (1946a) J. Biol. Chem., 165:585.
Schneider, W. C. (1946b) J. Biol. Chem., 166:595.
Schneider, W. C. (1947) Cold Spring Harbor Symp. Quant. Biol., 12:169.
Schneider, W. C. (1948) J. Biol. Chem., 176:259.
Schneider, W. C. (1949) In Respiratory Enzymes, Lardy, H. A., ed., Burgess Pub-
    lishing Co., Minneapolis, Minn., p. 273.
Schneider, W. C. (1953) J. Histochem. Cytochem., 1:212.
Schneider, W. C., Claude, A. and Hogeboom, G. H. (1948) J. Biol. Chem., 172:451.
Schneider, W. C. and Hogeboom, G. H. (1950a) J. Biol. Chem., 183:123.
Schneider, W. C. and Hogeboom, G. H. (1950b) J. Nat. Cancer Inst., 10:969.
Schneider, W. C. and Hogeboom, G. H. (1951) Cancer Res., 11:1.
Schneider, W. C. and Hogeboom, G. H. (1952a) J. Biol. Chem., 195:161.
Schneider, W. C. and Hogeboom, G. H. (1952b) J. Biol. Chem., 198:155.
Schneider, W. C. and Kuff, E. L. (1954) Am. J. Anat., 94:209.
Schneider, W. C. and Petermann, M. L. (1950) Cancer Res., 10:751.
Schneider, W. C. and Potter, V. R. (1943) J. Biol. Chem., 149:217.
Schneider, W. C. and Potter, V. R. (1949) J. Biol. Chem., 177:893.
Scholander, P. F. (1942a) Rev. Sci. Instr., 13:32.
Scholander, P. F. (1942b) Science, 95:177.
Scholander, P. F. (1949) Rev. Sci. Instr., 20:885.

Scholander, P. F., Claff, C. L., Andrews, J. R., Wallach, D. F., Cooper, O. and
    Orski, B. (1952) J. Gen. Physiol., 35:375.
Scholander, P. F. and Iverson, O. (1958) Scand. J. Clin. Lab. Invest., 10:429.
Scholander, P. F., Niemeyer, H. and Claff, C. L. (1950) Science, 112:437.
Schramm, M. and Danon, D. (1961) Biochim. Biophys. Acta, 50:102.
Seevers, M. H. and Shideman, F. E. (1941) Science, 94:351.
Seligson, D. (1959) Clin. Chem., 5:329.
Semeniuk, G. (1944) Iowa State J. Sci., 18:325.
Shedlovsky, T. and MacInnes, D. A. (1935) J. Am. Chem. Soc., 57:1705, 1683.
Shemin, D. (1957), ed., Biochemical Preparations, Vol. 5; John Wiley and Sons, New
    York.
Sher, I. H. and Mallette, M. F. (1953) J. Biol. Chem., 200:257.
Shibata, K., Benson, A. A. and Calvin, M. (1954) Biochim. Biophys. Acta, 15:461.
Siegel, J. M., Montgomery, G. A. and Bock, R. M. (1959) Arch. Biochem. Biophys.,
    82:288.
Siekevitz, P. and Palade, G. E. (1958) J. Biophys. Biochem. Cytol., 4:203, 309.
Siekevitz, P. and Potter, V. R. (1953a) J. Biol. Chem., 201:1.
Siekevitz, P. and Potter, V. R. (1953b) Federation Proc., 12:267.
Siekevitz, P. and Potter, V. R. (1953c) Cancer Res., 13:513.
Siekevitz, P. and Potter, V. R. (1955) J. Biol. Chem., 215:221.
Sjöstrand, F. S. (1953) Nature, 171:30.
Sjöstrand, F. S. and Rhodin, J. (1953) Exptl. Cell Res., 4:426.
Slater, E. C. (1949) Biochem. J., 45:1.
Smellie, R. M. S., McIndoe, W. M., Logan, R., Davidson, J. N. and Dawson, I. M.
    (1953) Biochem. J., 54:280.
Smillie, R. M. (1962) Plant Physiol., 37:716.
Smillie, R. M. (1963) Can. J. Botany, 41:123.
Smith, A. L. and Hansen, M. (1962) Biochem. Biophys. Res. Commun., 8:33.
Smith, G. M. (1951) Manual of Phycology, Chronica Botanica Co., Waltham, Mass.
Smith, L. and Stotz, E. (1954) J. Biol. Chem., 209:819.
Smyrniotis, P. Z. and Horecker, B. L. (1956) J. Biol. Chem., 218:745.
Snell, E. E. (1953), ed., Biochemical Preparations, Vol. 3; John Wiley and Sons, New
    York.
Sorof, S. and Cohen, P. P. (1951) Exptl. Cell Res., 2:299.
Sorokin, C. and Myers, J. (1957) J. Gen. Physiol., 40:579.
Stadie, W. C. and Hawes, E. R. (1928) J. Biol. Chem., 77:241.
Stadie, W. C. and Riggs, B. C. (1944) J. Biol. Chem., 154:687.
Stafford, H. (1951) Physiol. Plantarum, 4:696.
Stafford, H. A. and Magaldi, A. (1954) Plant Physiol., 29:504.
Stephenson, M. (1928) Biochem. J., 22:605.
Stern, J. R. and Del Campillo, A. (1956) J. Biol. Chem., 218:985.
Stern, J. R., Ochoa, S. and Lynen, F. (1952) J. Biol. Chem., 198:313.
Steward, F. C. (1932) Protoplasma, 15:497.
Steward, F. C., Stout, P. R. and Preston, C. (1940) Plant Physiol., 15:409.
Stickland, L. H. (1929) Biochem. J., 23:1187.
Stocking, C. R. (1956) Science, 123:1032.
Stocking, C. R. (1959) Plant Physiol., 34:56.
Stoesz, P. A. and LePage, G. A. (1949) J. Biol. Chem., 180:587.
Stone, H. W. and Skavinski, E. H. (1945) Ind. Eng. Chem., Anal. Ed., 17:495.
Straub, F. B. (1936) Z. Physiol. Chem., 244:117.
Straub, F. B. (1941) Enzymologia, 9:148.
Straub, F. B. (1942) Z. Physiol. Chem., 275:63.
Straus, W. (1954) J. Biol. Chem., 207:745.
Straus, W. (1956) J. Biophys. Biochem. Cytol., 2:513.
Straus, W. (1957) J. Biophys. Biochem. Cytol., 3:933, 1037.
Striebich, M. J., Shelton, E. and Schneider, W. C. (1953) Cancer Res., 13:279.

Stumpf, P. K. (1955) Plant Physiol., 30:55.

Stumpf, P. K., Green, D. E. and Smith, F. W., Jr. (1946) J. Bacteriol., 51:487.

Stumpf, P. K. and James, A. T. (1963) Biochim. Biophys. Acta, 70:20.

Summerson, W. H. (1939) J. Biol. Chem., 131:579.

Sumner, J. B. and Somers, G. F. (1947) Chemistry and Methods of Enzymes, Second Edition, Academic Press, New York.

Swingle, K. F., Axelrod, A. E. and Elvehjem, C. A. (1942) J. Biol. Chem., 145:581.

Tagawa, K. and Arnon, D. I. (1962) Nature, 195:537.

Talalay, P. and Marcus, P. I. (1956) J. Biol. Chem., 218:675.

Tam, R. K. and Wilson, P. W. (1941) J. Bacteriol., 41:529.

Tamaoki, T., Hildebrandt, A. C., Burris, R. H., Riker, A. J. and Hagihara, B. (1960) Plant Physiol., 35:942.

Tamiya, H., Iwamura, T., Shibata, K., Hase, E. and Nihei, T. (1953) Biochim. Biophys. Acta, 12:23.

Theorell, H. (1936) Biochem. Z., 285:207.

Theorell, H. and Akesson, A. (1941) J. Am. Chem. Soc., 63:1804, 1812, 1818.

Thimann, K. V., Yocum, C. S. and Hackett, D. P. (1954) Arch. Biochem. Biophys., 53:239.

Throneberry, G. O. (1961) Plant Physiol., 36:302.

Throneberry, G. O. (1962) Plant Physiol., 37:781.

Tissières, A. and Burris, R. H. (1956) Biochim. Biophys. Acta, 20:436.

Tobias, J. M. (1943) Physiol. Rev., 23:51.

Tso, P., Bonner, J. and Vinograd, J. (1956) J. Biophys. Biochem. Cytol., 2:451.

Turner, J. S. (1938) New Phytologist, 37:232.

Umbreit, W. W. and Gunsalus, I. C. (1945) J. Biol. Chem., 159:333.

Umbreit, W. W., Vogel, H. R. and Vogler, K. G. (1942) J. Bacteriol., 43:141.

Utter, M. F. and Kurahashi, K. (1954) J. Biol. Chem., 207:787.

Van Niel, C. B. (1943) Ann. Rev. Biochem., 12:551.

Vestling, C. S. (1958), ed., Biochemical Preparations, Vol. 6; John Wiley and Sons, New York.

Vincent, W. S. (1952) Proc. Natl. Acad. Sci., U. S., 38:139.

Vogler, K. G. (1942) J. Gen. Physiol., 26:103.

Vogler, K. G., LePage, G. A. and Umbreit, W. W. (1942) J. Gen. Physiol., 26:89.

Vogler, K. G. and Umbreit, W. W. (1941) Soil Sci., 51:331.

Wang, C. H., Doyle, W. P. and Ramsey, J. C. (1962) Plant Physiol., 37:1.

Warburg, E. J. (1922) Biochem. J., 16:153.

Warburg, O. (1919) Biochem. Z., 100:230.

Warburg, O. (1923) Biochem. Z., 142:317.

Warburg, O. (1924) Biochem. Z., 152:51.

Warburg, O. (1925) Biochem. Z., 164:481.

Warburg, O. (1926) Über den Stoffwechsel der Tumoren, Springer, Berlin. (English translation by F. Dickens, 1930, Constable, London).

Warburg, O. (1962) New Methods In Cell Physiology, Interscience Press, New York.

Warburg, O., Burk, D., Schocken, V. and Hendricks, S. B. (1950) Biochim. Biophys. Acta, 4:335.

Warburg, O., Burk, D., Schocken, V., Korzenovsky, M. and Hendricks, S. B. (1949) Arch. Biochem., 23:330.

Warburg, O. and Christian, W. (1936) Biochem. Z., 287:291.

Warburg, O. and Christian, W. (1938) Biochem. Z., 298:150.

Warburg, O. and Christian, W. (1941) Biochem. Z., 310:384.

Warburg, O., Kubowitz, F. and Christian, W. (1930) Biochem. Z., 227:252.

Warburg, O., Kubowitz, F. and Christian, W. (1931) Biochem. Z., 242:170.

Warburg, O. and Negelein, E. (1922a) Z. Physik. Chem., 102:236.

Warburg, O. and Negelein, E. (1922b) Z. Physiol. Chem., 102:336.

Warner, R. C. (1942) J. Biol. Chem., 142:705, 725, 741.

Watanabe, M. I. and Williams, C. M. (1951) J. Gen. Physiol., 34:675.

Webster, G. C. (1957) J. Biol. Chem., 229:535.

Weibull, C. (1953) J. Bacteriol., 66:688.

Weil-Malherbe, H. (1937) Biochem. J., 31:299.

Wellner, D. and Meister, A. (1960) J. Biol. Chem., 235:2013.

Wells, G. P. (1938) J. Exptl. Biol., 15:161.

Werch, S. C. (1941) J. Lab. Clin. Med., 26:878.

Werkman, C. H. and Wood, H. G. (1940) Die Methoden der Fermentforschung, G.
    Thieme, Leipzig, pp. 1191-1214.

Westerfeld, W. W. (1955), ed., Biochemical Preparations, Vol. 4; John Wiley and
    Sons, New York.

Westerkamp, H. (1933) Biochem. Z., 263:239.

Whatley, F. R., Allen, M. B. and Arnon, D. I. (1959) Biochim. Biophys. Acta, 32:32.

Whatley, F. R., Allen, M. B., Rosenberg, L. L., Capindale, J. B. and Arnon, D. I.
    (1956) Biochim. Biophys. Acta, 20:462.

Whatley, F. R., Allen, M. B., Trebst, A. V. and Arnon, D. I. (1960) Plant Physiol.,
    35:188.

White, P. R. (1963) The Cultivation of Animal and Plant Cells, Second Edition, Ronald
    Press Co., New York.

Wiggert, W. P., Silverman, M., Utter, M. F. and Werkman, C. H. (1940) Iowa State
    J. Sci., 14:179.

Wilbur, K. M. and Anderson, N. G. (1951) Exptl. Cell Res., 2:47.

Williams, C. H., Jr. and Kamin, H. (1962) J. Biol. Chem., 237:587.

Williamson, B. and Craig, L. C. (1947) J. Biol. Chem., 168:687.

Wilson, M. E., Stowell, R. E., Yokoyama, H. O. and Tsuboi, K. K. (1953) Cancer
    Res., 13:86.

Wilson, P. W. (1939) In Respiratory Enzymes, Lardy, H. A., ed.; Burgess Publishing
    Co., Minneapolis, Minn.; Chapter X.

Wilson, T. H. and Wiseman, G. (1954) J. Physiol., 123:116.

Winnick, T. (1941) J. Biol. Chem., 141:115.

Winnick, T. (1942) J. Biol. Chem., 142:451, 461.

Winterstein, H. (1912) Biochem. Z., 46:440.

Winterstein, H. (1913) Z. Biol. Tech. Meth., 3:246.

Wolff, J. B. and Kaplan, N. O. (1956) J. Biol. Chem., 218:849.

Wollish, E. G., Schmall, M. and Hawrylyshyn, M. (1961) Anal. Chem., 33:1138.

Wood, H. G., Brewer, C. R., Mickelson, M. N. and Werkman, C. H. (1940)
    Enzymologia, 8:314.

Wood, W. A. (1960) Federation Proc., 19:29.

Woodruff, H. B. and Foster, J. W. (1943) Arch. Biochem., 2:301.

Woods, D. D. and Clifton, C. E. (1937) Biochem. J., 31:1774.

Woodward, G. E. (1935) J. Biol. Chem., 109:1.

Wróblewski, F., Ruegsegger, P. and LaDue, J. S. (1956) Science, 123:1122.

Yudkin, J. (1933) Biochem. J., 27:1849.

Zbinovsky, V. and Burris, R. H. (1954) Anal. Chem., 26:208.

Zelitch, I. (1955) J. Biol. Chem., 216:553.

Zeller, E. A. and Maritz, A. (1944) Helv. Chim. Acta, 27:1888.

Zeller, E. A. and Maritz, A. (1945) Helv. Physiol. Pharmacol. Acta, 3:C6, C48.

Ziegler, D. M., Linnane, A. W., Green, D. E., Dass, C. M. S. and Ris, H. (1958)
    Biochim. Biophys. Acta, 28:524.

INDEX